P9-DXI-248

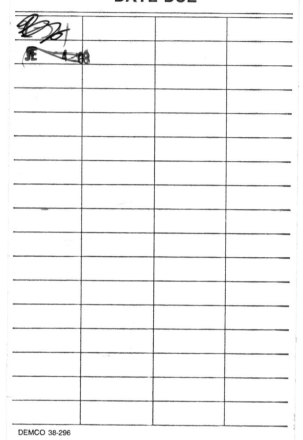

DATE DUE

PIONEERS OF RADAR

PIONEERS
OF RADAR

Colin Latham
and
Anne Stobbs

In 1935 a simple demonstration of the reflection of radio waves from an aircraft led to the formation of the Telecommunications Research Establishment. In this book some of those involved recall their memories of what it was like to be pioneers in the exciting and rapidly evolving new science of radar during the Second World War.

SUTTON PUBLISHING

First published in 1999 by
Sutton Publishing Limited · Phoenix Mill
Thrupp · Stroud · Gloucestershire · GL5 2BU

Copyright © Colin Latham and Anne Stobbs, 1999

Colin Latham and Anne Stobbs have asserted the moral right to be identified as the authors of this work.

British Library Cataloguing in Publication Data
A catalogue record for this book is available from the British Library

ISBN 0-7509-2120-X

Endpapers. *Front*: East Coast CH transmitter towers; *back*: the Countermeasures Group at Malvern.

 ALAN SUTTON™ and SUTTON™ are the
trade marks of Sutton Publishing Limited

Typeset in 10/12pt Bembo Mono.
Typesetting and origination by
Sutton Publishing Limited.
Printed in Great Britain by
WBC Ltd, Bridgend.

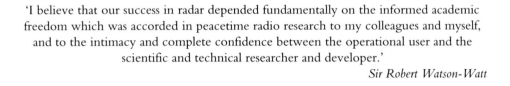

'I believe that our success in radar depended fundamentally on the informed academic freedom which was accorded in peacetime radio research to my colleagues and myself, and to the intimacy and complete confidence between the operational user and the scientific and technical researcher and developer.'

Sir Robert Watson-Watt

HM King George VI standing in front of a centrimetric radar dish at TRE Malvern with F.C. Williams (centre) and P.I. Dee. (Photograph by Douglas Fisher)

Contents

List of Contributors

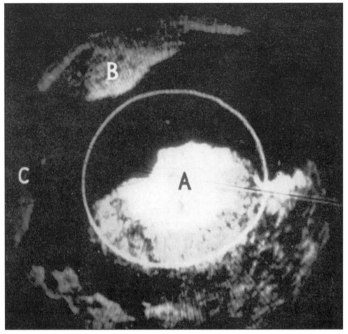

A comparison of the kind of image seen in the PPI screen of the H₂S radar set (above), and an actual map of the region (below).

Foreword
Sir Bernard Lovell, OBE, LL.D, D.Sc., FRS

On one occasion during the desperate days of the Second World War a senior Air Chief Marshal was taken by A.P. Rowe to see the progress on a radar system urgently needed by the RAF. On returning to Rowe's office (then in the former classical sixth form of Malvern College) he complained 'The trouble with your lot, Rowe, is that not one of your Assistant III's will turn a screw unless he is closely informed about the strategic situation in the Far East.'

This epitomised the remarkable collaboration between the operational commands and the scientists that was so fundamental to the immense success of TRE in those days. At that time we believed that radar was a British discovery. Historical research in the postwar years revealed that this was not the case and that German scientists had

demonstrated various forms of radar before the war. It was the vision of Sir Henry Tizard and his Committee who realised the possibilities and the urgency of the application to the defence of Britain that led to the mammoth development of the CH radar chain, to our survival in the 1940 Battle of Britain and all that followed by day and night.

This vision and the belief in ultimate success persisted throughout the darkest days as the German armies swept across Belgium and France. In the summer of 1940 the political and operational demands led to the cancellation of all leave so that a total effort could be deployed on installing and using the equipment which actually existed. It is a great tribute to Rowe and his deputy W.B. Lewis that they resisted

the total application of this demand and that a small group working on the cliff site at Worth Matravers was allowed to continue with the development of centimetric techniques which, at that time, seemed entirely futuristic. Their faith was justified and within a few years these centimetric systems became a vital component in the operation of the three armed services.

Some years after the war, I was asked to lecture on airborne radar to the Aeronautical Research Council. During question time someone asked why it was possible to carry through developments from the laboratory to operational use with such great speed. My response was that no one ever asked how much it would cost. The question was always 'Can you do it and when can we have it?'

TRE evolved from the small pre-war group at Orfordness through the Bawdsey Research Group and the Air Ministry Research Establishment to the TRE of most of the memories in this book. The contributions are a cross section of all the technical and scientific grades who so brilliantly translated the visions to operational realities and no one who was there will be able to read this book without nostalgic feelings that survive the cauldron of those days.

What this Book is About

This book tells how one loosely integrated team of mainly young scientists and engineers played a vital part in enabling Britain to outwit the onslaught of the Nazi bombers in the early years of the Second World War; and how they fought the radar war within a war, providing solutions to each new threat posed by the enemy. They were civilians working strictly under the Official Secrets Act for the whole of their wartime service. But ordinary civilians they were not: nor was the team they made up anything other than extraordinary in its combined brain power, its informality of working arrangements, its continual need for improvisation and its outright dedication to the changing needs of the RAF at home and overseas.

This team was known successively by several transitory titles – BRS (Bawdsey Research Station), AMRE (Air Ministry Research Establishment) and MAPRE (Ministry of Aircraft Production Research Establishment) – until in November 1940 it acquired and retained the name by which it became best known throughout the war: TRE – Telecommunications Research Establishment. It worked under the Directorate of Communications with links to the Air Ministry and the RAF.

The team began as a close-knit group of pre-war scientists already well established in electronics and parallel scientific disciplines and was augmented from 1938/9 by a growing army of young university science graduates. Many had read electrical engineering, physics or mathematics, but others – such as biologists – unexpectedly entered an entirely new field of work and found themselves called upon to fight the war exclusively with their brains, ingenuity and craftsmanship.

To that generation this was a rare privilege and a huge challenge; and the responsibility it placed upon individuals helped to foster the outright dedication with which they tackled the problems put before them. Their dedication was demonstrated by a willingness to work long hours at speed whenever needed, often up high radar masts in freezing gales or crouched in aircraft on radar trials.

The idea of producing this book in celebration of what they achieved arose primarily from an initiative promoted by one of their number: Dr W.H. Penley CB, CBE. In about 1990 he contacted as many as possible of those still alive requesting them to record their recollections of radar development from the mid-1930s onwards, with particular reference to the period 1940–2, when TRE was located near Swanage. The fruits of this initiative were to become part of two new projects: The Purbeck Radar

Museum Trust and CHiDE (Centre for the History of Defence Electronics).[1] The latter was started by a few enthusiasts at Bournemouth University in order to feed historical information on to the Internet and thus to put it on public record in perpetuity and make it accessible to students and historians at any time.

As a result of research for our previous book,[2] we two became 'Friends of CHiDE' and when the idea arose of making his initiative the basis for another book Dr Penley thought only for a few moments before inviting us to go ahead with it. That we have done, subsequently inviting further contributions from others involved both with TRE and with related wartime service or scientific work. So the book now consists largely of Dr Penley's collection of reminiscences for CHiDE, written mainly in the kind of scientific terms scientists use to each other (since all understand them); and partly of contributions written directly for this book and accordingly rather more with the lay reader in mind. Together these carry the TRE story through to its 1942–5 work at Malvern, where it came to be situated having left Worth Matravers. We are very grateful indeed to all who have allowed us to use their contributions here.

There is also a third vital component to this historical record. Throughout those wartime years of TRE there was a clear need for photographic records of the work that was being carried out, in technical detail. From this there has survived a personal photographic archive kept for over half a century by Douglas Fisher (one of TRE's own photographers) now safely stored at his studios in Suffolk and destined for CHiDE. Douglas has generously made his archive available to us and has spent much time locating and printing what we needed for this book. Included too are historical pictures we already possessed, derived from Marconi Radar Systems Ltd with their kind permission to publish, and also our contributors' own personal photographs, for which we are very grateful.

Our job as joint editors and supplementary contributors has been to assemble this mass of information, together with notes where appropriate, for publication in a form that we hope will interest the expert and non-expert alike and illustrate vividly those highly pressured early days of radar development. Our aim has been to catch history on the wing – before it is too late. The TRE boffins amply earned whatever illumination of their long-ago efforts this book may accord them.

Throughout this book we have added explanatory comments and notes which are indicated by the use of smaller type or square brackets thus [ ].

C.L., A.S.

[1] Centre for the History of Defence Electronics, School of Conservation Sciences, Bournemouth University, Studland House, 12 Christchurch Road, Bournemouth, Dorset, BH1 3NA, UK. All the original manuscripts which form part of this book are held, with others, by CHiDE whose intention it is to preserve them and provide access to interested researchers by various means, including a CD-Rom and the Internet. Anyone wishing to take advantage of these media is invited to contact them on http://chide.bournemouth.ac.uk.
[2] *Radar: A Wartime Miracle*, Sutton Publishing, 1996.

Preface
Anne Stobbs

To anyone reading these fascinating stories told by the brilliant men who worked on radar more than fifty years ago, a picture emerges not only of their wonderful technical achievements but of what they themselves were like. Some of them, when they started to work for TRE, were mature, married men with children; some came straight from university; but they all seem to have had characteristics in common: qualities such as resourcefulness and initiative shine through every one of their stories.

We are given a clear picture of these young men, some of whom were moved four times in the course of their TRE careers: from Orfordness to Bawdsey, Bawdsey to Dundee, Dundee to Worth Matravers and Worth to Malvern. This would have been quite an upheaval, especially for a married man with a family. And yet it is clear that none of them was in the least fazed by all this; they piled into their much-loved cars or on to a train or ferry complete with their push-bikes and reported for duty where they'd been told to. They pedalled around strange towns looking for digs, found their way to the place where they were to work, and simply got on with it. Resourcefulness and initiative.

They were not exactly head-hunted; such an expression didn't exist in those days. But many of them seem to have been selected and co-opted in a strange sort of way by someone who was already working for TRE himself and who knew they were likely to be valuable members of the team. The work being so secret, they were asked if they would join something without having any idea what it was. Bewildered, they presented themselves for interview and if they revealed the necessary expertise, they were then offered the job and told roughly what it was. The pay they received was hardly magnificent but it wasn't too bad for those days.

I see them so clearly – bursting with enthusiasm, caught up in the incredible atmosphere of TRE, where each and every one of them was encouraged to give free rein to his ideas, to his imagination, to his intelligence. Thoughts were freely expressed, bounced around among each other, never scoffed at or repressed. Radar developed during the war at an unbelievable speed in great leaps and bounds, which it would never have done if the staff had been afraid of airing their thoughts.

It couldn't have been easy for these young men in their off-duty hours, going to pubs or dances dressed in grey flannel trousers or corduroys and tweed jackets. Unlike some ladies during the First World War, those of the second were not in the habit of presenting white feathers to a passing stranger if he wasn't in uniform; nevertheless a girl at a dance might well have asked him why he was not, and the poor chap couldn't even tell her! (It would be interesting to know how some of them answered these awkward questions.) Little could she dream – how could she? – that he was quietly boffining away, winning the war for her. I personally have absolutely no reservations in saying that this is precisely what he was doing. Without the boffins – no radar. Without radar – no victory. As simple as that.

So take off your hat to them as you read the fascinating reminiscences of their days with TRE, all written by men and women now in their seventies, eighties and even their nineties. Some have died since they wrote their pieces. It is a reflection upon their brilliant minds, and also upon how this unique episode in their lives impinged upon their minds, that they were able to remember so clearly and describe so eloquently what they were doing for this country all those many years ago. We hope the reader will feel gratitude not only for what they did, but for how well they have remembered it all.

1

Introduction

Colin Latham

HOW INSPIRED TEAMWORK HELPED TO SAVE THE COUNTRY

The mood of the country in the 1930s was one of anticipating war and a sombre expectation that when it came we should be bombed heavily from the first day. Those then of middle age retained vivid memories of the First World War with its terrible losses of men in France and at sea, not to mention the numerically slight but highly significant civilian casualties caused by the German bombing at home. They received with alarm the reports of the German Air Force in action in the Spanish civil war, the persecution of the Jews in Germany and Hitler's inexorable rise to power. Grown-ups were not alone in their misgivings; teenagers and young adults heard so much about the recent war from their elders that to many it seemed as if a dark cloud of inevitable war hung over their futures. Most people concentrated on their jobs, hobbies, studies and pastimes and dismissed such unhappy thoughts of war from their minds. That is easy to understand but what is surprising is that this comfortable attitude of pretending it could not happen was shared by many in official government circles whose responsibility was the defence of the country. Fortunately, however, just a few influential individuals saw the futility of our defences and sought an effective early warning system. As a result, radar became a reality.

Ask the man in the street for the leading name in radar and the answer is likely to be Watson-Watt,[1] who by his outstanding drive, enthusiasm and dedication provided this country with radar defence at the time of its greatest need. Nobody will deny the significance of his work, but he was not alone in it: effective teamwork at all levels was the key to success. In this book we attempt to show how he was prompted and assisted by others, some of whom later became highly distinguished in their own fields of science and engineering.

Our aim is to give an insight into TRE's vital contribution to the war effort; but it was not the sole radar research and development unit stemming from Watson-Watt's pioneering team. The scientists of the 'army cell' at Bawdsey became established within

---

[1] Robert Alexander Watson Watt, b. 1892, adopted the hyphen when knighted in 1942 and became Sir Robert Watson-Watt, FRS. In quoting his name, the hyphen may be omitted or included according to context.

ADEE[2] at Christchurch under Sir John Cockcroft, where they continued to specialise in radar equipment for the Army. And the Admiralty, which had ignored the notion of radar made by one of its own staff in 1928, nevertheless noted with interest the progress at Bawdsey and decided to initiate specialised radar developments for naval applications at HM Signal School, Portsmouth.

TWO SIGNIFICANT TEAM EFFORTS

Throughout the history of the radar teams – from Orfordness through to Malvern – a variety of tasks was undertaken. They ranged from initial concepts – when the scientific basis would be analysed – right through to the support of manufacturing units in their production problems and the practical trials of prototype equipment. These activities were maintained at high levels of stress, initially as a result of the pending crisis and later because of the urgent demands of wartime. Throughout, tension was heightened by the limited availability of resources.

THE MOST DEMANDING CHALLENGE

Robert Watson-Watt.

Arnold Wilkins.

The ability to make progress in the absence of any previous experience or known work is perhaps the most severe test of technical judgement, perseverance and initiative. At such an early stage the field is wide open and many options for experimental work may appear possible, some more attractive than others. To forecast which will turn out to be fruitful or which will lead to a dead end is not easy. In the course of wartime radar development many such options arose, but two, airborne radar and the use of centimetric wavelengths, were of paramount importance.

However, before considering those challenges it is worth noting that the very first radar pioneers at Orfordness, led by Watson-Watt and Arnold Wilkins, had previously accumulated some years of relevant experience at Slough working on the detection of distant thunderstorms by radio. They were conversant with radio direction-finding systems using directional aerials with cathode ray tube displays and were not unfamiliar with pulse techniques for ionospheric measurements. While they had to develop entirely new equipment for the purpose of radar, the direction to be followed was reasonably evident: they were able to press ahead along a fairly obvious path, unlike those who tackled the novel problems of airborne and centimetric radar.

AIRBORNE RADAR

When work started, the equipment then currently under development for CH was unrestrained in terms of physical size and weight; it comprised high aerial towers as

---

well as massive transmitters and receivers needing accommodation in buildings. It must therefore have seemed quite unrealistic – with CH radar still firmly in the experimental stage – to promote the idea of an airborne radar system!

However, responsibility for this seemingly impossible requirement was given to Dr 'Taffy' Bowen, who had joined Watson-Watt's staff in 1935 after working part-time on cathode ray direction finders at Slough during his post-graduate student days. There was no precedent for airborne radar: Bowen and his small team had to start from scratch but realised at once that with the limited space available for aerials in an aircraft the wavelength would have to be considerably shorter than that of CH (about 12 m). Less than a metre would have been ideal but the valve technology did not then permit useful transmitter power to be generated at such short wavelengths.

Dr E.G. 'Taffy' Bowen.

After extensive trials with experimental transmitters a compromise of 1.5 m was adopted: just about short enough for manageable aerials, yet low enough in radio frequency to ensure reasonably adequate transmitter power. This decision, and the achievements of Bowen's team in making 1.5 m radar work well, were to have long-lasting effects. That wavelength was used not only for the first generation of airborne radars but was adopted for numerous ground-based applications (e.g. CD, CHL, GCI,

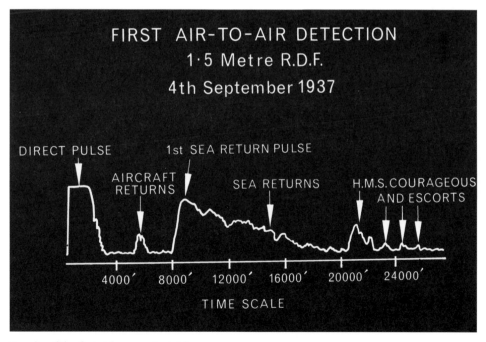

Results of the first airborne radar trials.

LW, SLC).[3] On one occasion when a party of influential VIPs visiting Bawdsey had been disappointed by temporarily poor CH performance, the day was saved by an impromptu and convincing demonstration of a working 1.5 m radar.

Despite the problems of inadequate electrical power supplies in aircraft and the need to use radio components unsuited to high altitudes, work on experimental 1.5 m airborne radars was forced along. Flying with the RAF, Bowen and his scientists demonstrated the locating of ships on the sea, enjoyed crude navigation by 'seeing' coastlines below cloud and detected other aircraft in flight. Overland flights gave indications of the positions of towns and, by using radar to measure the aircraft's height above ground, the feasibility of using terrain-mapping as an aid to navigation was demonstrated. These flights – portents of great things to come – were made as early as 1937/8. Following various experimental models and early production sets of dubious reliability the improved MkIV AI (Air Interception) radar went into RAF service in the autumn of 1940. Meanwhile, a variant of AI, the 1.5 m ASV (Air to Surface Vessel) radar, was widely used by Coastal Command to detect enemy shipping and for convoy control.

Although welcome and effective, 1.5 m airborne radar was not entirely free from drawbacks. In the AI role its maximum range was limited to a distance roughly equal to the aircraft's altitude because of strong ground returns, a characteristic only overcome later when centimetric wavelengths became available; and 1.5 m ASV became less effective after the enemy found it possible to detect the approach of aircraft carrying it. Again, a shift to the less easily detected centimetric wavelengths provided the solution. Nevertheless, 1.5 m airborne radar fulfilled a most vital and immediate need both in the air and over the sea and firmly set the scene for the future.

The seemingly impossible had been achieved by Bowen's dedicated team, working closely with the RAF. The production figures for AI MkIV sets ran into several thousands, while for ASV over 20,000 were made by factories at home, in Canada, the USA and Australia. Meanwhile, large quantities of other pulsed 1.5 m equipments, including Rebecca/Eureka and Lucero, were also manufactured.

THE CENTIMETRE BREAKTHROUGH

It is often said, rightly, that the invention of the cavity magnetron in 1940, the first really effective generator of high power microwaves (wavelength about 10 cm), was a turning point in the evolution of radar. It certainly made a major impact during the war and now, near the end of the century, almost all radars, civil or military, ground-based or airborne, work at wavelengths of less than a metre. Although some experimental centimetric work had been in progress with a relatively low-powered klystron transmitter, it was the availabilty of the magnetron that made centimetric radar a practical proposition. But when the magnetron appeared there was far more to be done than merely plugging in a new type of valve. All the radio frequency parts of the equipment had to be suitably redesigned.

---

[3] CD: Coastal Defence. CHL: Chain Home, Low. GCI: Ground Controlled Interception. LW: Light Warning. SLC: Searchlight Control.

Waveguides (hollow metal pipes, usually rectangular in section) replaced conventional cables or transmission lines and new waveguide-like components were required for most parts of the radio frequency system (e.g. rotating joints, T-R switches, couplings, bends, impedance-matching sections) as well as the aerials and the front end of the receiver. Also, the magnetron had to be supplied with carefully tailored high-voltage pulses which, in turn, entailed new pulse modulator designs. Some of these new techniques were more in the province of the physicist than the conventional radio engineer and many problems owed their solution to the close collaboration between the scientists of TRE and the research staff of approved civilian firms such as EMI and GEC. Once again, teamwork was the key to success.

Not only were new ground-based microwave radars developed (with advantages in low-level coverage and heightfinding accuracy) but, perhaps even more importantly, new designs for AI and ASV. The more precisely shaped radiation patterns resulting from microwave aerials placed new demands on the design of mechanical scanning arrangements, the solutions to which demanded much ingenuity. Experimental work with 10 cm airborne radars demonstrated an ability to detect ground features such as coastlines and towns, as had the earlier work at 1.5 m; but now, because of the shorter wavelength, with such fine detail that it offered real promise as an operational navigational aid to bombers. Thus H_2S was born, becoming one of the most sophisticated of the airborne radar designs.

However, despite the clear advantages of centimetric wavelengths for many applications there remained some for which 1.5 m technology continued to be entirely satisfactory: 1.5 m Rebecca/Eureka, Lucero and BABS went into service with the airborne forces and the special agent support groups throughout the war in Europe and in the Far East.

To sum up, the following three examples of the application of airborne radar indicate how greatly it contributed to the war effort:

i.   AI MkIV (1.5 m) permitted effective night interceptions of German bombers by ground-controlled fighters from early 1941 until superseded by the introduction of the later centimetric Mks. (As available, from 1942 onwards.)

ii.   ASV MkII (1.5 m) in Coastal Command aircraft helped to limit the menace of U-Boats in the Atlantic from the end of 1940; and from early 1943 the introduction of MkIII (centimetric) led to their eventual defeat.

iii. H_2S provided an effective blind-bombing aid for targets beyond the range of UK ground-based systems.

2

Background to the Formation of TRE

Dr W.H. Penley, CB, CBE

[This section has been derived from Dr W.H. Penley's lectures. Departures from the original text have been limited to those appropriate for a written presentation and with regard to the content of other sections of this book.]

Radar has become a household word; nowadays it has many applications – speed traps for motorists – weather forecasting – air traffic control – collision warning at sea – space travel – defence against ballistic missiles – smart weapons and many more. Much of the basic work was done just before and during the Second World War and many far-reaching developments were carried out by the staff of TRE during their two-year stay in the Swanage area from May 1940. The developments in that period played a critical role in avoiding our defeat and then continued to swing the balance of war in our favour, through its various stages, until the Allies were ultimately successful. Subsequently this work also led directly to most of the present uses we now take for granted.

Dr W.H. Penley.

In these days when we hear much about computers, lasers, smart bombs and so many more electronically operated devices, it requires a positive effort to realise what things were like in the 1930s before the Second World War. We now know that the basic ideas for radar had been put forward earlier in several other countries and had been the subject of a proposal to the Admiralty for a patent in 1928; also there had been some work by the Army Signals Experimental Establishment in 1931. Nevertheless, by 1934 nothing had been done in Britain to develop the ideas for military use and, of course, what was being done in other countries had been kept secret.

In 1922 A.P. Rowe joined the small RAF laboratory at Imperial College, London, and trained as a meteorologist. A few years later, the head of the laboratory Dr H.E. Wimperis left to become the first Director of Scientific Research at the Air Ministry, with Rowe as his Personal Assistant.

ALL DONE BY MIRRORS
Rowe has recalled that there was a continuing attitude of 'no war for at least ten years', and a general view that 'the bomber will always get through', which had been enunciated by Stanley Baldwin.

Professor Lindemann (later Lord Cherwell) was pressing strongly for the development of balloon barrages and aerial mines to combat the bombers, and work was going ahead to improve searchlights and listening devices. Rowe visited a site on the Romney Marshes to see a tremendous concrete acoustic mirror 200 ft long and 25 ft high, arranged with sensitive microphones at its focus to pick up sounds from aircraft approaching over the sea, together with 30 ft diameter steerable mirrors to determine direction. His visit was in preparation for a demonstration to Air Marshal Dowding who was to inspect it. While walking round the site with the director, Dr Tucker, a milk cart came rattling through. Tucker stopped the milkman and said, 'You won't be here this afternoon will you?' as the noise completely wrecked the operation of his equipment! These devices eventually achieved about 15 miles detection ranges but no positional data and so were hopelessly ineffective, even when working.

During 1934 a large-scale exercise had been held to test the defences of Great Britain. Mock raids were carried out on London, with the Air Ministry, the Houses of Parliament and Buckingham Palace especially targeted. Even with targets and routes of the bombers known in advance, well over half of them reached their targets with little or no opposition. In the opinion of the umpires the Houses of Parliament, the Air Ministry and other key establishments were eliminated!

Even though the Directorate was excluded from research into radio and armaments, Rowe was so concerned about the situation that he collected together all the files he

One of the pre-war south coast sound mirrors.

could find on the subject of air defence. There were fifty-three, and what he read appalled him so much that he wrote a minute to Wimperis saying that if we became involved in a major war within the next ten years, we would lose it unless something new could be discovered to change the situation. He suggested to Wimperis that a committee of the best advisers possible should be set up to review the whole situation and see if any new initiatives could be found.

THE TIZARD COMMITTEE

Wimperis agreed, and on 12 November 1934 wrote an historic minute to the Secretary of State and all the senior people in the Air Ministry, on the lines suggested by Rowe. It was quickly agreed to set up a committee under the chairmanship of Sir Henry Tizard, as Wimperis had recommended.

Wimperis had already consulted Professor A.V. Hill about the possible effects of radio transmissions on the human body and the energy levels needed to cause physiological damage, and had been given some estimated energy levels that Hill judged would be necessary. With this information he wrote to Robert Watson-Watt, then Superintendent of the National Physical Laboratory Radio Research Station at Slough, to ask his views on the possibility of developing a radio 'death ray' having enough energy to melt metal or incapacitate an aircraft pilot.

The idea of using rays to kill or disable people or machines was very popular at that time, and many submissions were made by crackpot inventors to say that they had 'black boxes' which would do whatever was required. Their bluff was called by offering £1,000 to anyone who could kill a sheep at 100 yds with such a device, with no questions asked about the insides of the box. The mortality of sheep remained unaffected.

Watson-Watt passed the query to one of his senior scientific staff, A.F. Wilkins, who reported that there was no possibility of achieving significant destructive effects over long distances with foreseeable radio techniques. However, he indicated that there ought to be enough energy reflected from an aircraft to enable it to be detected at useful ranges.

This paper was presented to the first meeting of the Committee on 28 January 1935, and on 6 February Rowe asked Watson-Watt to provide quantitative estimates of the possibility of detecting aircraft as distinct from their destruction. Further calculations by Wilkins gave favourable results and Watson-Watt wrote his famous memorandum in which he proposed 'by the extension of known means' a system of radio-location using a pulse/echo technique. This was presented to the Committee in draft form on 12 February and after its very favourable reception Wimperis, on 15 February, proposed to Air Marshal Dowding, who was Air Member for Supply and Research, that £10,000 should be expended to investigate this new method of detection. Dowding was very interested but asked for a simple practical demonstration to show feasibility before committing scarce funds to the project.

THE DAVENTRY DEMONSTRATION

For this demonstration Watson-Watt and Wilkins decided to make use of transmissions from the powerful BBC short-wave station at Daventry, which broadcast 10 kW on a wavelength of 49 m in a beam about 30 degrees wide and inclined up at about

10 degrees. The plan was to fly a Heyford bomber up and down this beam and attempt to measure the amount of power reflected from it at various ranges. Radio receiving equipment was quickly installed in a van and this was positioned, late on 25 February, in a field south of Weedon about 7 miles away from the transmitter. The receiving aerial was arranged so that signals coming from the direction of the transmitter could be reduced to a suitably low level which would not saturate the receiver, while retaining good sensitivity for signals from the direction of the bomber. The strength of the combined signal after detection by the receiver was to be shown on a cathode ray tube.

Next morning, on 26 February, Watson-Watt and A.P. Rowe joined Wilkins, and the Heyford bomber was flown at heights of 6,000 ft and down to 1,000 ft along the beam. The results were immediate and conclusive: 'beats' between the direct and reflected signals were detected up to distances of over 8 miles and this confirmed the predictions Wilkins had made. Watson-Watt was so impressed by the results that he turned to Rowe and said: 'Britain has become an island again!'

Dowding was now convinced that urgent action should be taken to exploit this achievement. It was designated MOST SECRET and he obtained the £10,000 requested for the urgent investigation of these ideas. Watson-Watt was authorised to form a small team from his NPL staff at Datchet and chose A.F. Wilkins and E.G. Bowen as his senior assistants. They decided that it was essential to carry out their detection experiments over the sea, from where intruders would come; and on 1 March Watson-Watt visited and approved a site at Orfordness in Suffolk. Design work started, using the experience the team had built up in the Radio Research Labs, particularly in investigating radio interference from thunderstorms.

ORFORDNESS

Unlike the experiment with the BBC transmitter which sent out radio waves continuously, it was decided that transmission should be in short bursts so that the time taken for each pulse to travel to the target, be reflected, and return to a receiver, would indicate the distance to the target. A cathode ray tube was to be used to display both the transmitted and received pulses and to show the time delay between them. Radio waves travel at a little over 186,000 miles per second, so taking about 10¾ millionths of a second to go and return over each mile of distance.

Design and construction of equipment was quickly put in hand and the small team of Wilkins, Bowen and a few others moved to the hastily provided accommodation at Orfordness on 13 May 1935. Detection ranges of 17 miles, quickly achieved, were soon increased to 30 and then, by July, 40 miles. The aerials were mounted on three pairs of 75 ft wooden lattice masts; one pair was sited near the building used for transmitter work and the other four masts were set at the corners of a rectangle within which the receiver building was situated. It was decided to refer to this activity as 'Radio Direction Finding' or 'RDF'. This was already a well-known technique, so if referred to by accident in public, should not excite interest.

Experiments were initially carried out at a wavelength of 50 m as this, at the time, was expected to give the best reflections from aircraft. As interference between this work and commercial radio traffic was severe, 25 m was tried and then 12 m – new transmitters, receivers and aerials being required for each of these wavelengths. To enable our defending fighters to be directed to the best position to engage the enemy, it was essential to get positional information. So, in addition to achieving the best possible ranges of detection, bearing and height were also needed.

For height-finding, it was necessary to make a calculation from the range and the angle of elevation of a target. It was decided to attempt to measure the phase difference between signals received by aerials placed at different heights. Equipment was set up and an apparently successful demonstration was given on 21 September 1935. However, when the effects of the reflections of the signals from the ground were considered carefully, it became clear that a comparison of the signal strengths received by the aerials, rather than the phase difference, would be a much more satisfactory method, and this was subsequently used.

To achieve the longer detection ranges needed (over 100 miles) it was calculated that much greater transmitter power[1] would be needed, together with higher aerials. It was judged that to avoid saturation problems[2] it would be necessary to site each receiver several miles away from a transmitter. The scheme envisaged, therefore, was to place receivers on each side of a transmitter, about 15 miles away, and to calculate the map position of a target by using the time differences between receiving the reflected and direct signals at each receiver. [Simpler methods were soon evolved.]

THE START OF THE RADAR CHAIN

On this basis, in September 1935, Watson-Watt submitted proposals for a chain of stations to be erected round the coast to provide warning of attack and positional information which would enable defensive fighters to be 'scrambled' and be told where to engage the attackers, thus avoiding the need to maintain standing patrols. In this historic report, he discussed the effects of height of target, height of aerials, wavelength of the transmissions, power transmitted and receiver sensitivity on the detection ranges possible. He concluded that using a wavelength of about 10 m and aerial heights of under 500 ft he could meet the RAF's requirements.

He proposed that a full-scale station to demonstrate this should be built at once, to be followed, if successful, by a group of stations to cover the Thames Estuary and then by a

---

[1] Transmitter power: the illumination of a target by radio waves follows the 'inverse square law' applicable to light, so that if the distance from the source to target is doubled the intensity falls to a quarter of its previous level. (And at three times the distance to a ninth etc.) In radar, the same law applies in both directions – from the transmitter to target and from target back to the receiver. Thus, if a given radar target doubles its range, the power of its echo signal, as received, is a quarter of a quarter (one-sixteenth) of its previous level. Or, to put it another way, if we try to double the detection range of a radar by simply raising transmitter power, an increase of sixteen times is needed.

[2] Saturation: a receiver is saturated when the signal applied is grossly in excess of that which it can handle without damage, distortion or temporary paralysis. Even if it escapes permanent damage from such excessive input, critical circuit potentials may be upset and require time to settle before normal sensitivity is restored. In radar, the necessarily sensitive receiver, unless suitably protected, is at risk of saturation from the close proximity of the transmitter. At worst, damage results; at best, temporary paralysis making it unable to respond to short or medium range echoes arriving soon after the transmitter pulse.

final chain covering the south and east coasts. Agreement to go ahead was obtained and expansion of the team and facilities put in hand. The first stations were to be in groups of three; the sites were surveyed by Wilkins, approved by Watson-Watt and construction started. Four receiving 240 ft wooden towers were to be provided with another similar for transmitting.

Research and design work now needed to be stepped up. To provide extra space and a suitable site for the separation of the transmitter and receiver equipments, Bawdsey Manor, about 10 miles down the coast from Orfordness, was acquired.[3] A 250 ft guyed lattice mast was erected there and receiver aerials installed in February 1936. Early in March, ranges of 75 miles were obtained which Watson-Watt was able to report to a meeting on the 13th set up to consider whether to proceed with the giant acoustic mirror project. (The project was cancelled.) Two further 250 ft guyed masts were erected at Orfordness to support a six element transmitter array, and performance was further improved.

In May 1936 Bawdsey Manor became the centre of the work, and soon a solution was found to the receiver saturation problem so that transmitters and receivers could be operated in reasonably close proximity. Watson-Watt devised a method for measuring the target bearing using a pair of crossed dipoles for the receiver aerials, and Wilkins showed that two pairs of crossed dipoles, mounted at different heights, could also be used for height-finding. So now complete stations could be built on one site and the confusions of attempting to find the map positions of many targets by complex range calculations were avoided.

Sites for the first group of stations in the south east had been chosen on the original basis of separated transmitters and receivers, and work had already started. To save time, it was decided to use these sites for the new station design, even though it might have been possible to find a better disposition. Industry was now playing a major role in the design and the construction work for these operational stations, under the overall supervision of the staff at Bawdsey.

BIGGIN HILL AND THE FIRST INTERCEPTIONS

Tizard was confident that positional information would become available much sooner than was generally thought. He convinced the RAF that an experimental study of fighter control and interception techniques should start immediately. A study group was therefore set up at Biggin Hill and arrangements made for trials to start as soon as there was a fully operating RDF station.

[3] Thanks to Arnold Wilkins's careful reconnaissance, Bawdsey Manor, with its extensive grounds on the coast adjacent to the mouth of the River Deben, was approved by Watson-Watt as an ideal site for radar development; and with remarkable speed the Air Ministry negotiated its purchase for £24,000. It became Bawdsey Research Station (BRS) until the outbreak of war when the research team left, but continued throughout the war (and beyond) as a leading RAF radar station. It housed several operational radars (CH, CHL and, later, various centimetric sets) besides acting as a trial site for experimental equipment. Early radar operators were trained there before the schools at Cranwell and Yatesbury were set up.

During 1936–7, through the remarkable foresight of Sir Henry Tizard and Air Marshal Sir Hugh Dowding, a series of novel experimental flights had been conducted from RAF Biggin Hill, Kent, despite strong opposition from some high-ranking officials and RAF officers. Although radar had not become operational by then, it was thought that no time should be lost in practising mock interceptions by means of directions radioed from ground to air. A system of ground-based radio direction-finding known as 'Pipsqueak' (relying upon airborne radio transmitters) was developed and used, and the preparation and refinement of operating procedures for interception proved valuable in expediting the use of genuine radar data as soon as it became available.

Bawdsey was the first station to become operational and plans were made to test the new interception procedures which had been worked out theoretically. To avoid any possibility of complicity, conscious or otherwise, it was decided to intercept a completely unsuspecting aircraft rather than use another RAF aircraft as the target. Bawdsey had been plotting civil airliners flying into Croydon and so, on the trial day, a KLM flight was selected and a perfect interception made. Our fighters continued on course to counter the impression that they had come out to meet it. To avoid suspicion, no further interceptions of civil aircraft were made. On the strength of these results Watson-Watt was able to persuade the Government to earmark £10 million for a coastal chain of stations – an unheard of sum in those days.

FILTER ROOMS

Soon after this successful demonstration, the stations at Canewdon and Dover were completed. This revealed that the sites were sufficiently close to give considerable overlap in their cover, and because of the relatively low accuracy of the bearing data compared with the range measurements, the reports from adjacent stations on the same aircraft could be mistaken for different ones. It was clear that if this information were fed straight to a central situation map, considerable confusion might result. It was therefore found necessary to introduce a preliminary map on which all information received (from the Observer Corps and the fighter 'Pipsqueak' system as well as from RDF) was plotted and assessed by experienced observers. They had to produce a weighted average and as far as possible determine the nature of each plot – i.e. friendly, hostile, number of aircraft etc.

This intermediate step was carried out in a 'Filter Room' and the results were passed to the General Situation Map in Fighter Command so that the AOC could decide the action to be taken. Each squadron then had to be given precise instructions by a Controller watching the plot. Clearly not everyone concerned could be sitting round the General Situation Map at HQ Fighter Command, so the relevant data had to be relayed back to lower levels of command. From there the flight orders were transmitted, initially by telephone, but once airborne, by radio.

Much work was done to determine the most effective form for these maps and the display of other essential information. A large flat table map marked with grid squares, on which plotters placed and moved blocks to represent groups of aircraft, was usually in the centre of the Operations Room. Other maps and displays giving more general information and specific data on fighter readiness were on the walls. This could all be viewed from a balcony by senior officers and the aircraft Controllers.

In 1936 Fighter Command was created with Air Marshal Dowding as the first AOC. He therefore remained directly responsible for the Biggin Hill studies and for the RAF training unit which had been set up at Bawdsey. He took a very direct interest in these developments and because of his close involvement in RDF (radar) he had a major bearing on our success in the Battle of Britain in 1940.

THE NEED FOR SHORTER WAVELENGTHS
In his memorandum, Watson-Watt had explained the propagational effects which would reduce the detection ranges possible for targets at lower heights. He had indicated that the use of shorter wavelengths would improve matters if adequate transmitter power and receiver sensitivity could be obtained.

A wavelength of 26 m had been chosen for the initial development, as the power available below this wavelength tailed off very quickly. However, he realised that even though his proposal to use wavelengths between 10 and 15 m for the main development might satisfy the RAF's initial requirement to obtain warning ranges of over 100 miles, there remained many other promising and important applications, especially naval and military, for which shorter wavelengths were essential. Some experiments were therefore carried out at wavelengths down to 50 cm and suggestions were made for the use of beamed aerials rather than the 'floodlighting' provided by the initial chain proposals. The concept of having an 'RDF Lighthouse' with a continuously rotating beam to pick up targets and our own aircraft was put forward by E.G. Bowen but its immediate realisation was then beyond technical ability.

Meanwhile, Tizard had become convinced from the Biggin Hill trials that even though effective interception should be obtainable by day against the mass raids expected if hostilities commenced with Germany, the relatively crude positional data which could be obtained from the CH stations would not provide the accuracy necessary to direct our fighters in poor visibility or at night. He therefore pressed for the development of RDF equipment which could be fitted into fighters to enable each fighter to find and engage a target when placed within a few miles of it.

AIRBORNE RADAR
In September 1936 a small group led by E.G. Bowen, who had been investigating shorter wavelengths, started working on the development of airborne RDF. This investigation was called RDF2 to distinguish it from the ground-based equipment programme which was then called RDF1. Initial trials used a wavelength of 6 m with a large transmitter on the ground and a receiver and the necessarily large aerial in the aircraft. (This arrangement was called RDF 1a). A range of 10 miles was obtained but it was clear that much shorter wavelengths were needed to reduce the aerial and equipment size and that, if possible, the transmitter should be in the aircraft rather than on the ground.

The experimental work was continued on higher frequencies for airborne use and a crude equipment working on 1 m wavelength with both transmitter and receiver installed in an Anson was tested in the summer of 1937. Aircraft and ships were detected

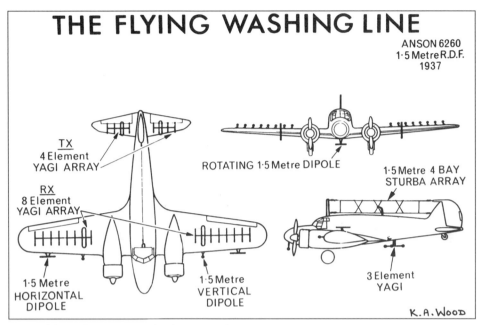

Some of the early experimental airborne aerial arrays.

'Faithful Annie'. One of the Avro Anson aircraft used as 'flying laboratories' for early experimental airborne radar work. (Photograph of a painting by Anthony Cowland G.Av.A)

with this equipment, and in demonstrations that autumn, HMS *Rodney* and HMS *Courageous* were located at ranges of over 5 miles. Development of equipment for both of these functions, by then called AI (Air Interception) and ASV (Air to Surface Vessel) respectively, went ahead with priority given to AI. A wavelength of 1.5 m was chosen, as considerably higher transmitter power and reasonable receiver sensitivity could be obtained.

THE START OF ARMY RADAR
The small Army team sent to Bawdsey towards the end of 1936 had been put to work with various members of the resident team on the most pressing problems of the day, as part of the learning process and to encourage a free and easy exchange of ideas. This policy was quickly to prove most fortunate. The Bawdsey Research Station staff now had to concentrate on the development of the main Chain Stations with their associated reporting and command system and also on the development of equipment for aircraft use, with all the major new problems involved. The Army team therefore concentrated on equipment to aid anti-aircraft guns, for searchlight control and for coastal defence by the detection of ships.

By the end of 1937 P.E. Pollard had a prototype anti-aircraft gun ranging equipment working which, after further development, went into service in 1939. W.A.S. Butement was placed in charge of a Coastal Defence sub-section and after seeing tests of Bowen's AI equipment on the roof at Bawdsey, decided to use this as the basis of his CD set. He was able to use a lot of the techniques developed for the AI equipment but was not restricted to the small size of the aerials allowable on aircraft. Instead of Yagi type aerials (like present-day television aerials) he opted to use large broadside arrays, about 24 ft wide and 10 ft high which would give much sharper beams and higher gain (i.e. more power in a particular direction).

THE START OF NAVAL RADAR
At HM Signals School, Portsmouth, it was decided that the floodlighting system being used for the CH stations would give serious blind spots in cover, and that to operate over the full 360 degrees beamed rotating aerials at masthead level were required. Experiments were carried out at various wavelengths during 1936–7 and finally a wavelength of about 7 m was chosen as this was judged to be the longest for which useful aerials could be made for fitting at the masthead. Two were required, for transmitter and receiver, and these had to be rotated in step. The first installation was in HMS *Sheffield* by August 1938 and the second in HMS *Rodney* by October. Meanwhile work was also in hand to develop equipment for locating surface vessels and for improving range-finding for the main guns.

THE RADAR CHAIN EXPANDS
By the end of 1937 the international situation was deteriorating rapidly. Plans to extend the Chain were hastily made and a final design for the main stations prepared. It was intended to operate on four wavebands as a safeguard against enemy jamming or accidental interference. Four 360 ft steel towers were to be used

In this picture of the CH 360 ft steel transmitting mast at Worth Matravers one can just make out the original design of aerial array strung between the platforms. This design was superseded on all CH stations by much larger curtain arrays strung between adjacent towers. After Southbourne had taken over Worth Matravers's place in the Chain, this tower was used for the Loran navaid.

A group of four 240 ft wooden CH receiver towers, typical of the East Coast Chain (often only two receiver towers on West Coast CH stations).

at each station for the transmitting aerials and four 240 ft wooden towers for the receivers.[4] Progress in erecting these stations was disappointingly slow, especially for the steel towers, and as the situation in Europe continued to worsen, stations were put into operation with just wooden towers. In some areas emergency cover was provided by using mobile stations with portable 70 ft towers which had been designed for use overseas.

Though remarkable progress had been made, by 1938 it became clear to Tizard and Watson-Watt that in the event of war there would be a tremendous demand for effort to cope with the vast range of scientific and technical problems that were arising. Watson-Watt moved to London to deal more effectively with policy matters and in May A.P Rowe took over from him at Bawdsey. In addition to the limited amount of recruiting that was under way for Bawdsey, a list was prepared of suitable people who

---

[4] Later, it became necessary to improve the transmitting aerials but it was felt that the plan for four frequencies was excessive. A pair of larger transmitting aerials, known as curtain arrays, were slung between adjacent towers rather than being mounted on individual towers and each station was limited to two frequencies. Two curtain arrays could be supported by three towers, the central one being common to both; thus some CH stations had only three transmitting towers while others retained the four.

CHL aerial on a gantry. This is the common T&R form established throughout most of the
Second World War.

were at universities. Tizard approached Sir John Cockcroft[5] to see whether some of the eminent researchers in the Cavendish Laboratory at Cambridge might be persuaded to help. He told him a little about RDF, and explained that in the event of war, 'nursemaids' would be needed to make the equipment work well and keep it going.

In August 1938 the RAF carried out an exercise to test the air defences. This clearly showed the need for better low cover, as Watson-Watt had originally predicted, but no specific requirement was stated until June 1939 when the RAF asked for equipments based on the 1.5 m coastal defence set being developed by Butement. The Army team was therefore expanded to provide twenty-four CHL (Chain Home Low) equipments for the RAF in addition to their CD programme. The CHL stations were to consist of broadside aerials 28 ft wide by 10 ft high on searchlight turntables mounted over huts in pairs of 20 ft high wooden gantries for separate transmitters and receivers. The aerials were turned by human muscle-power from servicemen known as 'binders'; using crude bicycle chain drives, they had to keep aerials in step to within 2 degrees. After detecting a target they had to inch the receiver aerials round to point straight at the target so that the direction could be read off and, with range given on a CRT, enable the map position to be plotted.

During this development Wilkins and Larnder tried to establish the RAF's requirements. It was agreed that the need was to detect aircraft flying at 500 ft at least 50 miles away. The original CD set achieved about 35 miles but Wilkins calculated that, with improved transmitters becoming available, 50 miles could be achieved if the aerials were sited 200 ft above sea level. The RAF wanted the CHLs to be placed at CH stations, but many of these were inland or on low sites, so mounting the CHL aerials on towers was proposed.

GERMAN INTEREST IN OUR RADAR SYSTEM AND THE START OF WAR

Towards the end of 1938, after Munich, Cockcroft visited Bawdsey where he was told what had already been done on RDF and was shown the experimental and development work going on. In the spring of 1939 he took a group of the leaders of the Cavendish Laboratory to Bawdsey, and the senior 'old hands' – Wilkins, Bowen, Larnder, Whelpton and Williams – gave them a comprehensive exposition on the situation. Shortly after this the team was asked to consider ways of jamming or confusing RDF systems and it was agreed that Dr W.B. Lewis should join Bawdsey straight away to take charge of the research.[6] Arrangements were also made for parties of

---

5 Sir John Cockcroft, KCB, OM, CBE, MA, Ph.D, FRS (1897–1967), an artillery officer in the First World War, became a most highly accomplished and well-known scientist, making his mark between the wars with work on research into nuclear physics ('atom-splitting') at the Cavendish Laboratory, Cambridge. After going with the Tizard Mission to America, he became head of ADRDE (Air Defence Research and Development Establishment) at Christchurch, responsible for development of Army radar. He shared the Nobel prize with Dr E.T. S. Walton in 1951.

6 The plan was to devise anti-jamming devices and procedures for CH, to counter any future enemy generated interference.

physicists, totalling eighty, to be introduced to RDF by spending a month on Chain stations, starting on 1 September.

Concern that the Germans might be aware of the work going on at Bawdsey was heightened by a visit on 2 August from the LZ 130 *Graf Zeppelin* which hovered out at sea nearby before continuing its spying up the east coast to Scotland.

It was (correctly) thought to be trying to monitor the RDF transmissions, and it was assumed that if the Germans knew Bawdsey's function they would make it one of their earliest bombing targets. In the few days before the declaration of war, therefore, most of the staff were evacuated to the Teachers' Training College in Dundee. Bowen had been given the task of providing a squadron of AI equipments before the end of 1939 and the first MkI was delivered to the RAF in August. To carry out the installation, Bowen's airborne equipment team went to Scone near Perth – a grass airfield without runways – and later to St Athan, a maintenance aerodrome in South Wales where they were bombed by a JU88. It was very fortunate for Lovell and Hodgkin (later Sir Bernard and Sir Alan) that the bomb didn't go off. The equipment was flight-tested in December. The Army team moved to a site, very suitable for the work on CD, at Steamer Point near ADEE Christchurch, Dorset, where radar development for the Army expanded and continued.

On 14 November, six weeks after war was declared, U-boat U-47 sank HMS *Royal Oak* in Scapa Flow. Admiral Sir James Somerville, who had seen at Bawdsey a demonstration of Butement's CD set tracking a surfaced submarine, asked for three of these equipments to be made immediately to help protect that vital area. Cockcroft was asked to undertake this task. He drove a lorry to Bawdsey and collected equipment which had been left in the stores there; took it to Cambridge and mobilised a team from the Cavendish to do the design and construction. These sets were called CDUs (U for U-boat).

After a short time Cockcroft and his team moved to Christchurch to do the work. The first station was operating on site early in December and the other two before the end of February 1940. Performance on submarines was up to 25 miles, and on aircraft up to 70 miles. They detected low-flying aircraft at much greater ranges than the CH stations.

Early in this period the first magnetic mines had appeared on the east coast and were causing many wrecks. Cockcroft was asked to provide two stations for the Thames estuary. The first of the CHLs was erected at Foreness Point and was operating by 1 December 1939. There Cockcroft saw Wg Cdr Pretty (Sir Walter) control the first interception of a low-flying mine-laying aircraft. As a result it was agreed at a meeting on 19 December that the use of single stations for this task was better than tracking target and fighter with separate equipments. This had a profound influence on the development of Ground Controlled Interception (GCI) techniques.

Air Ministry now required many more CHL stations and instructed the BRS team at Dundee – now renamed the Air Ministry Research Establishment (AMRE) – to take over the task from the Army team. For the AMRE team Dundee was most unsuitable; the work had been disrupted and the distance from London prevented the close contacts with the RAF which had been so important. However, three scientists completed the installation of an experimental CHL on the 200 ft platform of the 360 ft steel tower of the CH station at Douglas Wood, near Dundee, and showed that it gave good detection of low-flying aircraft as had been predicted. Another team under R.A. Smith was able to design and test changes to the CH transmitter aerials and achieve a valuable increase in the range of detection possible.

The staff were greatly relieved to hear they were to move to a new site under construction near the CH Station being set up at Worth Matravers, near Swanage. Most of those in Dundee packed up and moved to Worth on 8 May 1940 and were joined by many of Bowen's aircraft equipment team. Quite a significant number from both teams moved to HQ at Leighton Buzzard or joined the RAF, to help deal with all the new technical tasks and problems arising.

3

Photographic Records of Wartime Radars

CH – (CHAIN HOME) AMES TYPE 1 – THE FIRST OPERATIONAL RADAR SYSTEM

Following the successful Daventry Experiment of 1935 by Arnold Wilkins, a scientist on Watson-Watt's staff at the government-run Radio Research Laboratory, development of the CH (Chain, Home) system began in earnest. By the autumn of 1938 five stations, each giving ranges, bearings and heights of aircraft, guarded the Thames Estuary. Prime Minister Chamberlain's epic flight to Adolph Hitler was tracked. Those five early stations, in Suffolk, Essex and Kent, formed the beginning of the east coast Chain that by the summer of 1939 had been increased to twenty, stretching from Ventnor, IOW, to north-east Scotland. With the outbreak of war the chain was extended west from Ventnor until some fifty CH stations encircled the UK.

The Daventry Experiment of 26 February 1935 captured by artist Roy Huxley. (Reproduced by kind permission of Marconi Radar.)

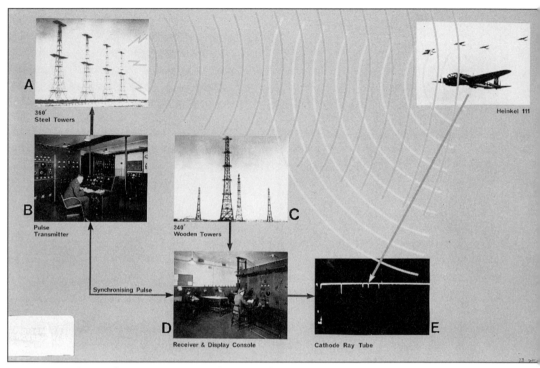

How CH works. Transmitting aerials on 360 ft steel towers (A) are fed with 25 pulses of radio-frequency energy per second, generated by a transmitter (B). Each pulse lasts for some 10–20 microseconds with power in excess of some 600 kW. The transmitted radio signals spread over a wide area and are reflected by aircraft within range. The reflected signal again spreads, but a small fraction may be picked up by the receiving aerials mounted on 240 ft wooden towers (C). The receiving aerials are static but have elements facing in different directions and are coupled via a radiogoniometer1 to a sensitive receiver (D) to find the direction from which echoes are coming. The radar operator observes a display (E), calibrated in miles (0–200 left to right), from which the ranges of echoes are read. By switching in aerials mounted at different heights above ground the angle of elevation of the echo signal is assessed and when combined (automatically by an electrical calculator) with the measured range, the aircraft's height is calculated. CH gave accurate range measurements but bearing and height data could sometimes be in error as a result of external causes. Fortunately, with the close siting of stations most raids were seen by more than one at any time; thus by feeding the plots of stations within a given area into a common Filter Room, composite plots with minimum error could be achieved. (e.g. south-east stations reported to the Filter Room at Stanmore).

¹ Radiogoniometer: literally a device for measuring the angle of arrival of radio signals (the 'gon' coming from the Greek for angle, as in hexagon). It consists of a small rotating pick-up coil that provides the input to a radio receiver, set within fixed coils that are fed from remotely mounted aerials pointing in different directions. On the same shaft is a dial calibrated in degrees of azimuth so that an operator, by rotating the coil and observing the strength of the signal, may determine the direction (bearing) from which it is coming. Such methods were in use for radio direction-finding long before radar.

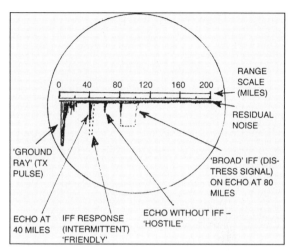

A WAAF radar operator in the observer position seated in front of a CH receiver. While concentrating on the cathode ray tube display, her left hand constantly adjusts the knob of the goniometer.

The form of a CH Display. Echoes are shown as downwards deflections. The direction of each could be found by setting the gonio to the position of minimum signal. ('D/F'ing to min.' in operators' jargon – an operation requiring practice and skill for quick and accurate results). Push-button control of remote aerial relays enabled alternative aerials to be selected when the gonio provided readings which, after automatic calculation, were interpreted as target height.

The ranges and bearings of echoes from CH stations were converted into a national grid reference before transmission to a Filter Room. Each confirmed echo (i.e. a persistent response clearly forming a track) would be identified as friendly or hostile and given an identification number (F or H). High air activity required great concentration from the observer to keep track of all responses and maintain a watch for new ones. Time on the tube was normally limited to one hour before changing to another operator's task such as recording or telling plots by telephone.

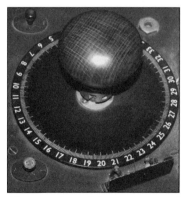

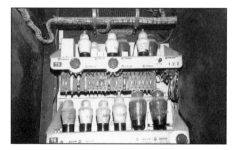

Close-up view of the gonio control knob constantly in use throughout the war on all CH operations.

Rear view of part of the pulse timing units of a CH receiver. The types of valve and form of construction typify the styles of radio set construction in the mid-1930s. Nevertheless, the novel circuits presaged a new era of pulse techniques.

CHL – CHAIN HOME, LOW (CHL) AMES TYPE 2

While CH was a huge step toward effective early-warning it was not a perfect solution. The wavelength of 10–12 m on which the CH stations operated meant it would only be possible to produce narrow beams of radiation with aerials of impractically huge dimensions. Consequently, in the horizontal plane it was more of a 'floodlight' than a 'searchlight' system; and in the vertical plane much of the transmitter power illuminated the ground from which it was then reflected upwards. The result was a radiation pattern permitting the detection of aircraft at normal flight levels but lacking the much-needed low cover and wasting power at altitudes higher than any aircraft could reach.

Long-range early-warning radars need high power transmitters and sensitive receivers. Both, in the mid-1930s, were hard to achieve at wavelengths below about 10 m. Spurred on by the need for early-warning – with whatever shortcomings – the early workers sensibly opted for the shortest wavelength at which reliable transmitter power and receiver sensitivity was assured. However, 1.5 m soon became a practical wavelength and was adopted for CHL, with its lower-looking capability, to supplement CH.

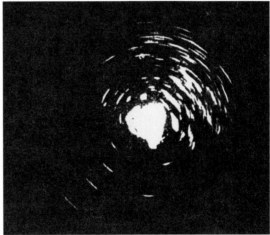

CHL demanded solutions to the problems of (1) aerial design for a well-defined beam from an array of reasonable size; (2) common aerial for transmitter (T) and receiver (R); (3) reliable means of coupling aerial rotating at about 3 rpm to stationary T&R. (4) Plan Position Indicator (PPI) with radial trace synchronised to rotation of aerial. Left: typical wartime CHL aerials, mounted on 185 ft tower (or similar) when situated on flat terrain or on 20 ft gantry if clifftop or hill available (both shown). Right: photograph of typical wartime CHL PPI. Arcs at south are aircraft echoes: those to north-east are mixture of aircraft and permanent echoes. Width of arcs indicates aerial beamwidth of about 10 degrees. PPI was normally overlaid with grid squares or range rings (not shown). CHL radiated peak power of about 150 kW. Pulse duration and repetition rate adjustable – typically 3–5 microseconds and 250–400 pulses per second.

GCI – AMES TYPES 7, 8, 15 – FOR GROUND CONTROLLED INTERCEPTION

In the Battle of Britain, fought mainly in daylight, plots from the early-warning chain directed our fighters to within visual range of intruders. But for the night attacks that followed, a faster and more accurate ground control of radar-equipped nightfighters was essential. It was achieved by dedicated GCI radars reporting not to the general Filter Rooms but to Fighter Command. A GCI controller, by observing a PPI, was able to send instructions by two-way radiotelephone to his allocated nightfighter until an interception was achieved. GCI stations varied in size and facilities from highly mobile (Type 15) through transportable (Type 8) to large fixed installations ('Happidromes' – Type 7). In the latter, multiple PPI displays permitted simultaneous control of several interceptions.

GCI radar equipment worked on a similar wavelength to CHL (about 1.5 m) from which much of the basic equipment was derived. The main difference was in the aerial and associated receiving and display arrangements. By suitable division of the aerial into sections at different heights above ground, height-finding became possible in addition to the range and bearing information provided by a standard CHL. Valuable features of the British GCI system were that both intruder and interceptor were displayed on the same screen and heightfinding was common to both aircraft. Thus errors of absolute position were of secondary importance: relative position counted most in achieving interception. Following the introduction of centimetric radars some GCI stations achieved improved height accuracy and target discrimination by using additional Type 13 (10 cm) heightfinders.

Left: Common T&R aerial of mobile GCI (Type 15). Right: Interior of typical mobile GCI vehicle. The left-hand display (similar to the range tube of CHL) has additional facilities for estimation of target heights. PPI is on the right.

AMES TYPE 7 – THE 'HAPPIDROME' OR FINAL GCI STATION

A common T&R aerial array mounted above the underground turning gear together with transmitter, radar receiver and associated equipment. The main radar displays and operations rooms are housed in a separate remote protected building (in distance to the right).

The Chief Controller's room. The console in foreground displays IFF; the other is normal PPI for radar responses.

The Reporting Room (as seen from the overlooking Chief Controller's room). Two WAAFs in the foreground are supervisors. The large and small plotting tables show the general and local situations respectively.

AIRBORNE RADAR – AI, ASV, H₂S, IFF, BEACONS, GEE

As described elsewhere, the earliest work before the war used the then shortest practical wavelength of 1.5 m, resulting in the development of AI (Air Interception) to MkIV and ASV (Air to Surface Vessel) to MkII. Both were used operationally with success until they were eventually superseded by improved sets working on centimetric wavelengths. The basic advantage of cm waves for AI is illustrated, right.

F is a nightfighter flying at, say, 10,000 ft. With a 1.5 m radar its necessarily rudimentary aerials will produce a vertical polar diagram of the form shown — — —. The radar will see a bomber at about 1.5 miles range (B1) but not at about 2 miles (B2) because its echo will be lost in the clutter of ground echoes. If, however, the fighter has a 10 cm radar, aerials having much more directivity can be made compact enough to be accommodated in the airframe, producing the narrower beam shown -------. It is now possible to see a bomber at B2 free from ground clutter and to fly at lower altitudes without limiting radar range by ground clutter.

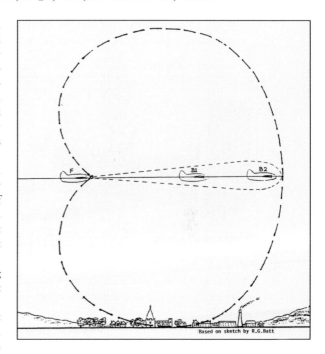

Based on sketch by R.G.Batt

Below left: typical 1.5 m dipoles on an aircraft wing. Right: 10 cm scanner in the nose of a Beaufighter.

Dipoles on both wings (Rx) and centrally (Tx) imposed drag.

The common T&R scanner was covered in flight by a streamlined nose-cone transparent to radio waves.

Being larger than nightfighters, long-range Coastal Command aircraft were better equipped to carry complex 1.5 m aerials and so sideways-looking ASV arrays were employed to achieve maximum ranges. Even so, advantage was soon taken of centimetric waves which were less detectable by the enemy.

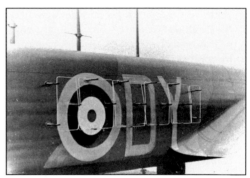

Long-range ASV sideways-looking 1.5 m aerials on Whitley aircraft.

Early AI work had indicated the possibility of ground-mapping by radar, a technique fully exploited by H_2S when microwaves became available. An adaptation of H_2S formed the basis of the microwave versions of ASV.

All Allied aircraft carried IFF transponders to prove their identity by giving pulse-coded replies to interrogating pulses from ground-based radars. This technology soon spread to the development of coded beacon systems such as Rebecca (airborne) and Eureka (ground) to guide aircraft to specific locations. General navigation was transformed by the use of airborne GEE sets displaying the time intervals between the reception of pulses from fixed ground stations.

Lancaster with H_2S.

Standard airborne IFF transponder.

4

The Reminiscences

Dr E.H. Putley on A.P. Rowe (1898–1976), Superintendent of TRE

'Rowe believed in being master in his own house.'

[A.P. Rowe is mentioned frequently in this book, somewhat naturally since he was 'the Boss'. By all accounts he was a man of complex character and everyone who worked under him at TRE remembered him well for the rest of their lives.

The following is an extract from an Appreciation by Dr Ernest Putley written for an exhibition held in Malvern Public Library in March 1998, to mark the centenary of A.P. Rowe's birth.]

A.P. 'Jimmy' Rowe, Chief Superintendent of TRE, 12 March 1942.

Albert Percival Rowe was born in Launceston, Cornwall in 1898. After attending one of the Royal Naval Dockyard schools, he entered the Imperial College of Science and Technology in London in 1918. He graduated with first class honours in physics in 1921 and took a postgraduate diploma in air navigation in 1922.

As far back as 1934, Rowe had become preoccupied with the problem of Britain's air defence in a future war, and on his own initiative he made a study of the Air Ministry's plans for air defence. His conclusion, which he placed before his Chief at the Air Ministry H.E. Wimperis, was that unless new methods of air defence could be quickly found we would lose the next war. This led Wimperis, with the agreement of the Air Minister, to set up the Committee for the Scientific Study of Air Defence (chaired by Sir Henry Tizard and better known as the Tizard Committee). It was to this Committee that Watson-Watt suggested the possibility of radar. Rowe was Secretary of the Tizard Committee until he replaced Watson-Watt as head of the research team (which was to become TRE) set up to develop radar.

The first task of TRE was to build the Home Chain to give early warning of approaching attackers. The second was to design small radars to fit in fighter aircraft to enable them (with help from the ground) to find night intruders. The latter task, of developing this, the first airborne radar in the world, was given to E.G. 'Taffy' Bowen, who brilliantly succeeded. In his account of the work, Bowen criticises Rowe bitterly for failing to give him adequate support with the result that at the end of 1940 the airborne radar was not ready when the Blitz began and the RAF were unable to cope with these attacks until about May 1941.

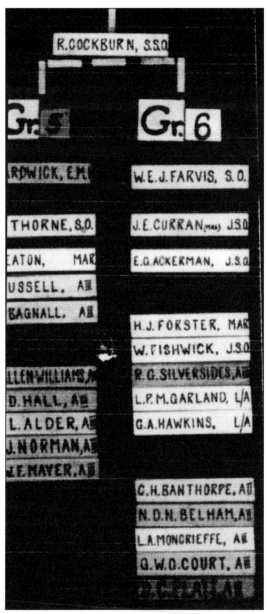

A tiny portion of the extensive wall chart in A.P. Rowe's office that showed the organisation and grouping of TRE staff.

This undoubtedly was the situation, but was Rowe to blame? I think the answer is no. The requirement for airborne radar was based on the supposition that daylight attackers would be defeated. If, however, the daylight raiders were successful, there would be no requirement for airborne radar. Therefore, in 1938 and 1939, the overriding priority was to get the Home Chain completed and working efficiently. To achieve this took up the bulk of TRE's resources. Even then it was a close thing. Final touches to the CHs were still being added in 1940 and the CHL chain was made up of a variety of experimental models, mostly lacking common T&R, continuously rotatable aerials, power turning or the PPI. These features did not become generally available until the end of 1941.

There was another matter which must have upset both Bowen and Arnold Wilkins, the leading members of Watson-Watt's original team. As war became imminent, TRE was strengthened by a group of senior university scientists, the most prominent being W.B. Lewis, Sir John Cockcroft and J.A. Ratcliffe. Rowe immediately appointed Lewis his deputy and Ratcliffe to a comparable position. Rowe has said that he did this in what he considered to be the best interests of the Establishment, regardless of personal feelings. To their great credit, neither Bowen nor Wilkins ever complained publicly about this; but they both left

TRE shortly afterwards – Bowen to become a founder member of the MIT[1] Radiation Lab and Wilkins to join Fighter Command.

The invention of the cavity magnetron has been described as the most significant discovery of the war. It opened up the centimetric waveband, making possible applications that otherwise would not have been feasible. This probably would not have happened but for the activities of TRE led by A.P. Rowe. This is a fact not widely appreciated. Rowe revealed his belief in the importance of centimetres not only by assigning a strong team to it but also by ensuring that they were able to work undisturbed. At that time (midsummer 1940) he was afraid some people would regard centimetre work as too long-term when the country was under imminent threat of invasion. So when ACM Dowding paid a visit, Rowe made sure he didn't see it.

Why was Rowe so effective at the head of TRE? He always seemed to know exactly what he wanted and more often than not he was right. He had the ability to persuade everyone most of the time that he was right, but when he failed he still persisted regardless. He has said that on occasions all the TRE Divisional Leaders disagreed with him, but he still pressed on. Similarly he did not always receive Headquarters backing for his plans. A good example was the development of Oboe.

Lord Cherwell thought it wouldn't work, while Prof. Rankine at Bomber Command ORS[2] said the perpetrators should be sacked. Yet it turned out to be the most precise bombing aid of the war. Almost the same fate befell H_2S which the Americans initially derided. But when they found the skies over Europe to be not quite as clear as over Arizona, they clamoured for it in their daytime bombers.

Rowe believed in being master in his own house. He believed that to be effective a Research Establishment had to be free to determine its programme. Whilst it must maintain close contact with its customers, it must decide for itself how best to meet their requirements.

Rowe undoubtedly succeeded in his task. But by the end of the war he was completely worn out and in very poor health. This is why he left TRE so quickly, and was found a job in Australia which it was felt would be less stressful. But his health recovered and he became the first Scientific Advisor to the Australian Government and later Vice-Chancellor of Adelaide University. On his retirement, he returned to England.

People with such a strong sense of mission as Jimmy Rowe tend to be rather difficult to live with. Both at TRE and at Adelaide University there were those who fell out with him.

But at TRE, with due respect to Rowe's eminent successors, there was a feeling of loss, almost a malaise, which was widely felt after he left.

[1] Massachusetts Institute of Technology.
[2] Operational Research Section.

Arnold ('Skip') Wilkins, OBE, M.Sc. (d. 1985)

[These are extracts from his contribution to *Bawdsey – Birth of the Beam*, by kind permission of the author Gordon Kinsey.]

During August or September, 1935, it became apparent that the accommodation at Orfordness would soon become inadequate and that extra space would have to be found. . . . I told Watson Watt that I could show him the ideal place but that it might not be for sale. He decided nevertheless to see it and and we set off immediately. I remember the journey well because we were riding in a 15 h.p. Daimler car which he had recently bought. As we drove along I said, 'I see these cars have a fluid flywheel which permits one to go into reverse at 60 m.p.h. and all that happens is that the car rapidly decelerates and then moves off backwards.' 'That's interesting,' said Watson Watt, 'shall we try it?'. And he did there and then, and it behaved just as I had said!

When we arrived at Bawdsey Ferry Watson Watt was so charmed with the Manor that he requested the Air Ministry to find out whether the owner would be willing to sell it. To our delight Sir Cuthbert [Quilter] seemed quite ready to do this. The Air Ministry bought the whole estate for £24,000.

The main result [of the RAF Air Exercises of 1937 with the first five CH stations] was that a decision was made to extend the Chain to cover the whole coastline from the Isle of Wight to the Tay. I was again asked to find suitable sites for all the stations required. The sites selected for this extension of the Chain were: to the north, High Street, Darsham, Suffolk; Stoke Holy Cross, Norfolk; West Beckham, Norfolk; Stenigot, Lincolnshire; Staxton Wold, Yorkshire; Danby Beacon, Yorkshire; Ottercops, Northumberland; Drove Hill, Berwick; Douglas Wood, Angus; and to the south, Rye, Sussex; Pevensey and Poling, both in Sussex; and Ventnor, I.O.W.

Allocation of frequencies for these stations was made by myself with help from E.W. Seward. In these days of strictly controlled frequency allocations it is amazing to look upon the way we carried out this task. We decided what the frequencies should be in the band upwards from 22.4 MHz and we gave no heed to foreign users of frequencies in this band who might be interfered with, deciding only to avoid the television and amateur bands at home. We spaced the frequencies round the Chain so as to minimise mutual interference.

When we started work on RDF in 1935, Watson Watt gave us until the summer of 1938 to have operational equipment, as this was when he expected war with Germany to break out. He was not a long way out.

It has been said of Arnold Wilkins that he often allowed others to take the credit for his work. After his calculations and Daventry demonstration of 1935 which identified him with the very birth of radar, he continued to take the lead in setting up the CH system, solving many tricky basic problems, until joining Watson-Watt at the Air Ministry. From 1942–4 he was in charge of the Operational Research section of Fighter Command and in south-east Asia in 1945. After the war he returned to the Radio Research Station becoming deputy Director.

Dr E.G. (Taffy) Bowen, CBE, FRS (d. 1991)

[The following extracts are taken from Dr Bowen's book, *Radar Days*, by kind permission of IOP Publishing Ltd.]

I first met Watson Watt in 1933 while I was a student at King's College in London. He had the reputation of being a very relaxed and pleasant administrator who kept closely in touch with the technical work of the Station.[1] He was much loved by the staff and with his deputy, Jimmy Herd, headed an extraordinarily powerful group of people who were at the forefront of radio research.

I remember a very relaxed interview with Watson Watt and Jimmy Herd during which the main item discussed was whether, as a Welshman, I could survive with two Scotsmen as bosses. They challenged me to sing the Welsh national anthem as the price for entry into the system. . . . I joined the staff as a Junior Scientific Officer at £256 per annum. I was still unaware that the Station harboured a great secret but I realised something very unusual was in the wind when I was introduced to the provisions of the Official Secrets Act. This task was solemnly performed by Jimmy Herd in which he explained the penalty for the slightest deviation from the most meticulous standards of security – literally to be 'hanged by the neck until life was extinct'. He enlarged on this with enormous gusto and only after I had agreed to the provisions and signed on the dotted line was I told of the secret of radar.

[The following extract describes the very beginning of the team that eventually became TRE.]

The radar group left Slough for Orfordness on a delightful spring morning, 13 May 1935. The party consisted of only four people, Wilkins, Bainbridge-Bell and myself of the scientific staff, and George Willis who had been been Bainbridge-Bell's technical assistant for many years. Wilkins and I went in his Armstrong Siddeley and the others in B–B's MG. The convoy was completed by two large RAF vehicles loaded with our equipment and we arrived at Orford that evening without incident. After the mild spring weather at Slough the contrast was alarming and it was some time before the impression that we had arrived at an Arctic waste faded away. We spent the next few days like slaves, humping the equipment off the wharf at Orford on to a powered craft under contract to the Air Ministry which carried it to another wharf on the far side of the river. We then transported it across a rough track to the reconditioned huts on the chassis of a Model T Ford and an ancient fire-engine which must have remained from World War I.

[After describing work at Orford, Bowen tells of the move to Bawdsey.]

The move to Bawdsey began in March 1936 and gradually we took over the Manor and the estate. The establishment was called Bawdsey Research Station with Watson-

---

[1] The Radio Research Station, Slough, where Bowen was attached during his Ph.D. research and subsequently interviewed for a permanent staff position.

Watt as the first Superintendent. Up to that time the staff had been employed by the National Physical Laboratory, but on 1 August 1936 they were transferred to the Air Ministry. Watson-Watt took up residence in a palatial flat overlooking the water and at his suggestion bachelor quarters and a Mess were established in the Manor for the single members of staff. Those who were married – and there were not many – lived in Felixstowe and came to work by ferry across the River Deben.

[Dr Bowen, who successfully led the initial development of airborne radar, comments on the background and problems.]

In the early part of 1936, when the success of the air-warning chain against day bombers was assured, the much more difficult question of intercepting night bombers came up again. . . . At night, the range at which an enemy aircraft could be seen and identified was about 1,000 feet, and it was clearly beyond the capability of a ground system to place a fighter as close as that. What was required was a radar small enough to be installed in a night fighter, which would enable the pilot on his own initiative to close from a range of 4 or 5 miles down to the required minimum of 500 or 1,000 feet. In the light of many discussions I had with Tizard in later years, it became quite clear that he was probably the one man who, in the mid-1930s, correctly foresaw how the situation would develop and what should be done about it.

No one was very optimistic about being able to make such a miniature radar at that time. The existing transmitter at Orfordness was a whole room full of equipment weighing many tons. The aerial masts were 75 ft high, soon to be 240 ft. The receiver was a large rack bristling with valves, knobs and indicators requiring the attention of a highly skilled operator. Miniaturisation of the kind common in the 1950s was still unknown and the marvels of solid state technology were not even dreamed about. To achieve reasonable antenna size, the wavelength would have to be reduced to one or two metres. This was at a time when the shortest wavelength for which components were available was 5 m. In addition, to achieve a minimum range of 1,000 feet the pulse width had to be reduced to near one microsecond. The reduction from 200 to 20 microseconds which had already been achieved had not been difficult but going down to 1 microsecond was strictly unknown territory.

Dr 'Taffy' Bowen moved to Australia after the war where he became a prominent figure in the field of radiophysics. His many achievements included leadership of the giant Anglo Australian radio telescope project at Parkes, New South Wales.

Professor R. Hanbury Brown, AC, FAA, FRS

[In 1935 the young Hanbury Brown was persuaded by none other than the Rector of Imperial College, London, Sir Henry Tizard, to put off his Ph.D. studies in favour of joining the Radio Research Station at Slough. The following extracts are from *Boffin* by Professor R. Hanbury Brown, AC, FAA, FRS, by kind permission of IOP Publishing Ltd.]

The interview at the Air Ministry was conducted by someone I had met before, Robert Watson Watt. As usual he talked a lot, but didn't tell me anything about the job.

A fortnight later I got the first piece of paperwork, a letter offering me a 'probationary' appointment as Assistant Grade III at the princely salary of £214 per year! 'In the first instance', so the letter said, the job would be at the Radio Research Station of the National Physical Laboratory in Slough. What I would be expected to do, it didn't say.

[Almost immediately after joining Slough, Hanbury Brown was told to report to Bawdsey.]

Poorer by one week's rent which I had paid in advance for my digs in Slough, I borrowed my sister's Austin 7 and drove up to Bawdsey on the 15th of August 1936, two weeks before my twentieth birthday. It was a long drive and like most people, especially if they are used to working in London, I found the Suffolk countryside alien. Indeed by the time I had reached the gates of the Manor I felt like someone from another planet, and as I drove up the long drive under its dark overhanging trees I wondered anxiously what on earth could be going on in such a remote place – it must, I felt, be something sinister. However all my worries were forgotten when I emerged from the trees and saw the great Manor House in the evening sunlight.

No one who worked at Bawdsey in those days will ever forget the place. The Manor was a fairy castle on a distant shore and had the quality of a dream – and that of course was what it was, a late Victorian dream.

Watson Watt was a delightful person to meet and the best salesman I have ever met. Nowadays he would, I suppose, be called charismatic. When he was in good form words bubbled out of him like a fountain – usually very long words in convoluted sentences.

[Of the notorious day when the radar demonstration to VIPs went wrong:]

A line of three operators, Wilkins, Dewhurst and myself, sat silently in front of our cathode-ray tubes; silently because there was nothing to report. Watson-Watt hovered about anxiously, giving a running commentary on this non-event.

[On the general working conditions:]

When in 1936 the early work on radar was transferred from the Radio Research Board to the Air Ministry the work at Bawdsey and Orford came under the official system of issuing 'stores', a system which was designed for a large military force in peacetime and which was peculiarly unsuited to a small research establishment in a hurry. . . . To accept this ridiculous system was very hard for young men on whom the urgency of the work had been impressed. We realised that no commercial research laboratory would have tolerated such a system, but we were caught between the irresistible force of the urgency of radar and the immoveable object of Air Ministry procedure.

What was even more remarkable about our group at Orfordness was that there was not a single experienced radio engineer. In the receiver group our boss had some knowledge of radio, but I wouldn't have described him as a radio engineer, while Donald Preist and myself were straight out of college. . . . Fortunately both Donald and

I had been keen radio amateurs and had built our own equipment; without that experience we would have been lost.

We also had very little test gear which, even in those days, one might reasonably expect to find in a modest radio laboratory, let alone one engaged on important work. All we had in the receiver hut was a Cossor double-beam oscilloscope, an Avometer, and a wavemeter which would have been more at home in a science museum. As for books the only one I can remember seeing was the Radio Amateur's handbook.

In his postwar career Professor Hanbury Brown has made significant contributions to the sciences of quantum optics, optical and radio astronomy including his Presidency of the International Astronomical Union. He is a Companion of the Order of Australia, where much of his work was done.

Donald Preist, FIEE, Life Fellow IEEE

'It turned out to be the most thrilling, the most challenging education in a setting so beautiful and so spellbinding.'

My instructor was a kindly man, quite ancient, with great patience. Attired in tweeds, plus-fours and a cap — perfect for grouse shooting — he hardly seemed to belong at Biggin Hill RAF Station, which in 1936 was destined to play a major role in the coming war with Germany. He was trying to teach a young man (me) how to operate a sound locator for detecting enemy aircraft.

A sound locator was a contraption that had two large paraboloidal 'dishes' at the ends of a long horizontal boom. The whole thing was mounted on a central pivot with hand control wheels. The operator had a headset with pipes attached. The right ear was connected to the right dish, the left ear to the left dish. When the thing was pointed at an aircraft, both ears would hear the same sound. A slight deviation from this position would bring about a different sound. Perceiving this, the operator would rotate the thing until the first sound was heard again, and could therefore keep it pointed at the aircraft as it moved across the sky. Any normal person, I was given to understand, could learn how to do this in a day or two.

After two weeks I had shown absolutely no aptitude for it. My tweedy friend regretfully gave up. As a parting shot, he told me to report to the Officers' Mess at 5.30 p.m. where the Commanding Officer wanted to see me. This, to me, was no trivial matter. This was my first paying job. The Great Depression was on. It was not a good day.

The CO, Maj Lamb, turned out to be an affable gentleman with a twinkle in his eye. As we sat at the bar he said: 'Preist (may I call you Don?) — we've been looking into your background. You have an engineering degree with Honours from London University. You have an amateur radio station and have communicated with other hams all over the world. You have interrupted your studies for a Master's degree to help a friend develop an aircraft-to-aircraft radio communication system, which the RAF badly needs.'

'Now Don, listen carefully. We have just the right job for you. Show up here on Monday morning. Be prepared to drive 150 miles. You'll get sealed orders telling you where to go. Be prepared for a long stay. I think you'll love it.'

A mobile sound detector typical of the kind described by Don Preist.

My sealed orders were there on the Monday, as promised. The excitement was almost unbearable. Would I be equal to the job? Why had Lamb been so sure that I would love it? I pointed the Lagonda in the direction of Chelmsford – Colchester – Ipswich and on eastward towards the coast of Suffolk. At last there was a large iron gate, a guardhouse, a uniformed sentry and, beyond, groves of pine trees lining a road which disappeared round a bend. My papers satisfied the guard; on them had been the magic words 'MOST SECRET: OHMS'. James Bond would have felt quite at home but this was long before his time.

After about a mile through the pines there it was – a large imposing edifice of reddish brick two or three stories high; the Red Tower and the White Tower facing me. I drove up to the front door, got out and read the inscription on the wall of the porch: '*Plutot mourir que changer*'. I would reflect upon that motto later.

I was greeted by a young man in walking shorts, a shirt and gym shoes: 'Welcome, number 14' he said, 'you're in time for dinner. Come and have a drink. You can

Dr Bill Penley outside the Red and White towers of Bawdsey Manor, 1997. This background has remained virtually unchanged in over sixty years.

unpack later when I show you your room.' I was inside what was probably the most secret of all the secret British installations: Bawdsey Research Station, the purpose of which was to develop what later became known as radar. This was to be my home from home for three years until war was declared on Germany.

After a week or two, having learned what was going on; what the radar pioneers had done; what the overall picture was, I began to understand just how lucky I was. Lamb had foretold that I would love it. It turned out to be the most thrilling, the most challenging education, in a setting so beautiful and so spellbinding. I see it now as the outstanding experience of my life.

We all knew that war with Germany was coming; the only question was when. We also knew that what we were doing was crucial. Hitler had a large air force under Hermann Goering. We had a very small air force with few pilots and aircraft. Not knowing when the German bombers would arrive, we would have to keep our fighter aircraft aloft all day to make interception possible – standing patrols – and this would wear out the pilots and the planes. We would be easy meat for the Luftwaffe and once they had obtained mastery of the air, an invasion by sea would be unstoppable. Fortunately, we had a weapon in preparation which gave us hope, if only we could get it ready in time. We called it RDF (Radio Direction Finding), later radar.

The detection range using the equipment we had was up to about 100 miles. The German bombers would fly at about 250 miles per hour, so if they were flying towards us, there would be twenty-four minutes' warning, in which time a squadron of Spitfires or Hurricanes could take off, reach the altitude of the bombers, and with guidance by radio from the ground, could position themselves for an interception. Our aircraft and pilots could therefore be resting on the ground until the last possible moment – much better than 'standing patrols'!

Our task at Bawdsey was to develop the technology to make all this possible. Also the appropriate equipment had to be installed at a number of stations around the English coast. We had also to set up a communication system so that the information giving positions of enemy formations could be sent to a central Command Headquarters. The Commander of the defence force could then act accordingly. To do all this required a mountain of work. Time was running out. The sense of urgency at Bawdsey was ever-present.

I was a Technical Assistant Grade 3 on a salary of £214 a year. One of my colleagues was Robert Hanbury Brown who was the same age as me within a few months. Bawdsey Manor itself made a deep impression on us both; in my mind there will always be an indelible image of the sea and its constant presence.

Teething Troubles

We were not there to dream, however. One day in October 1936 there was a demonstration to the visiting dignitaries, including ACM Dowding, C–in–C Fighter Command, and also Sir Henry Tizard who had been a champion of radar from the start. The purpose of the demo was to show how aircraft could be detected at 60–80 miles and tracked. I had the privilege of being present in our control room (in the old stables) during this great event. Three operators were sitting ready at their instruments; the cathode ray tube was lit up, showing the transmitter pulse followed by a horizontal line on which the echoes from the aircraft would eventually appear.

Watson-Watt hovered about. A few underlings including me provided the chorus. By prior arrangement a flight of aircraft had taken off, and at a specified time were positioned some 50 to 80 miles from Bawdsey. They were to fly directly toward us. After about ten minutes there was nothing on the CRT but residual noise. Watches were consulted. Frowns appeared. The chorus shuffled. More time went by. Like stout Cortez's men, we looked at each other with a wild surmise. Something had gone wrong.

Finally an echo appeared on the screen at a few miles. Immediately after, the sound of the aircraft engines could be heard distinctly overhead. The reaction of the brass was immediate and explosive. Stuffy Dowding turned to our Chief Engineer A.F. Wilkins and called him a charlatan. Then they all walked out and went back to London, with the exception of Stuffy who stayed to lunch. He was told that a separate radar in another part of the building was working well. This was demonstrated to Stuffy who went away mollified but not very happy. In the days that followed it took all the persuasive powers of Robert Watson-Watt, our Superintendent – a superb salesman – to prevent the Air Ministry chopping off the funds and closing down the project.

Six months later a first-class demonstration was given, at a higher frequency, with everything properly tuned up. After that there was no looking back. Reflecting on the original fiasco, I was able to throw a little light on what went wrong because of my ham radio experience. I explained to the transmitter people why their method of measuring power output would overestimate it by a factor of ten to thirty times. I also confirmed what everyone had begun to realise: that the frequency we had been using would guarantee perpetual interference from short-wave stations all over the world. All hams knew that. The decision was made to double the frequency: this meant new transmitters, new receivers, new antennas − in fact new everything.

We worked for about six months at Orfordness to bring about this frequency change. There we had a transmitter in the T-Hut and a receiver in the R-Hut. These huts were left over from the First World War; they were a few hundred yards apart connected by telephone. The T people would adjust their equipment for best results and then call us in the R-Hut for comments. We had a monitor with a CRT display showing the wave form of the T pulses very accurately.

There was great concern about the shape of this pulse. Ideally it should approximate to a rectangle, flat on top with steep sides. But for some unknown reason there was always an appendage − quite large − at the end. We called this a 'cob'. No matter how hard they tried, the T people couldn't get rid of it. Attached to the monitor was a telephone headset on which the pulse repetition frequency could be heard. One day I aimlessly pulled the phone plug out of its jack: the cob instantly disappeared!

Back at Bawdsey our T and R development work also took place in separate wooden huts connected by a telephone line. By this time I was one of the T men. It was winter and frequently things were pretty damp inside the hut. I learned then that a bakelite rod about 4 ft long should not be used to touch parts of the equipment 20 kV above ground. The rod was damp. The shock was not fatal but it was not trivial either.

On more than one occasion the R hut would call up and say: 'What are you bastards doing? All our lights have gone out and smoke is coming out of our power sockets!' This would happen immediately after an arc-over inside one of our transmitting valves. We finally caught on, learned about transients and solved the problem.

I spent many days inside this hut developing transmitters of various kinds. They all used silica valves manufactured by the Royal Navy at HM Signal School Portsmouth (at that time we were not allowed to use commercially available valves because of the concern about secrecy). The valves had a cylindrical envelope with about a 6 in diameter and about 6 to 12 in long. The connections to the internal electrodes (filamentary cathode, grid, screen grid, anode) were metal rods passing through the envelope. They stuck out in various directions like a porcupine. It was a real challenge to get these valves to work at frequencies and power levels much higher than their designers intended. I enjoyed this challenge.

Incidentally, the silica envelopes were odd looking − of fused silica, a form of quartz. This stuff was semi-transparent, rough and lumpy looking. The filaments were made of pure tungsten. To emit the copious quantities of electrons needed to give the high pulsed power required, they had to be run very hot. The heat passed through the envelope and heated up the environment which included me. I found it possible to coax 250 kW of pulsed power out of one of these monsters. By combining *four* of them efficiently in a circuit I hit on, we measured 1,000 kW or one megawatt – a record at the time.

This transmitter was shipped, much later, to Netherbutton in the Orkney Islands. The war by then was on, especially the U-boat war, and the Germans had a very remarkable long-range reconnaissance aircraft called a Focke Wulf Condor. It was based in Norway and would take off, fly west over the Atlantic Ocean, locate convoys and radio their position to U-boats, which would then close in with their torpedoes. The megawatt radar enabled our fighter aircraft based in Scotland to intercept and shoot down the Condors. The Germans stopped using the base in Norway and found a new home on the west coast of France, which was far less convenient for them.

Development of CHL

The main radar chain at about 13 m wavelength could not detect low-flying aircraft; circa 1.25 m was thought to be the solution. I was given the job of designing and constructing a transmitter and receiver, connecting each to a Yagi antenna and preparing for tests. Eventually a chain of stations at 1.25 m was set up and given the name of CHL (Chain Home, Low) and my apparatus was the prototype for these. The transmitter used Western Electric type 316A (door-knob) valves made in the USA. I had found out how to combine sixteen of them.

When all was ready we carried the whole thing up to the first level of one of the 120 ft wooden CH receiver towers where there was a fairly large platform. We spent a day looking for aircraft but had no success. Then we pointed it out to sea and to our joy got a good return from the Cork Lightship at about 3 miles; later in the day we also got an excellent signal from the Harwich to Hook of Holland ferry at 7 miles.

When Robert Watson-Watt, our enthusiastic and charismatic Superintendent, heard of this he rushed up the tower, saw it for himself and rushed down again in a manic state bordering on ecstasy. He called up his old friend Max Horton, Superintendent of HM Signal School, Portsmouth, to crow a bit. Apparently the Navy chaps had been trying to detect ships, but had achieved a range of only a few hundred yards!

[Many contributors to this book refer to the Bruneval raid and the part played in it by Don Preist. In the following account, he describes his unique part, as a TRE scientist, in that daring raid on a German radar station on the northern coast of France on Friday 27 February 1942. Some items of equipment were brought away for examination which led to successful jamming of German radars later, but the raid was not achieved without casualties and loss of life among the servicemen. A fuller account of the background and of the part played by radar mechanic Flt Sgt Cox appears in other books; see Bibliography: Colin Latham and Anne Stobbs, *Radar: A Wartime Miracle* and George Millar, *The Bruneval Raid*.]

The Bruneval Raid

One day I got a phone call from the Air Ministry and was told to put on my RAF uniform and report to the headquarters of the First Airborne Division at Netheravon, Wiltshire. I did so and, in something of a daze, found myself welcomed by an affable Army officer, Maj Bromley-Martin, who said I was just in time for lunch. He tipped me off that the CO was Gen Browning – 'Boy Browning, you know – Daphne du

Maurier's husband.' I found myself sitting next to him at lunch. The talk was informal and it was obvious that everyone liked Browning.

After lunch, Bromley-Martin took me upstairs to a room with a table on which was a large aerial photograph. 'This was taken from a great height over the north coast of France,' he said. The detail was amazingly good. He pointed to an object about the size of a pea. 'Do you think', he asked, 'that that could be a mobile radar? Could that round thing be a small antenna dish – attached to a small cubicle, mounted on a rotatable pedestal?'

I stared at the photograph for a long time, using a magnifying glass. Finally I said, 'I think you're right. It could be a radar at a rather high frequency.' 'I'll tell you why we're so interested,' he said. 'The Germans have been shooting down our bombers with ack-ack gunfire over the Ruhr Valley at night when the sky is completely overcast. Their accuracy is amazing. We know they have a radar for gunlaying called a "Würzburg" and this one across the Channel looks like a "Würzburg" only it may be a bit smaller. We intend to make a raid and bring it back here. By taking it apart, we may learn something interesting, like how to jam it. Would you like to come along?'

'I certainly would. When do we start?'

'Come back here in a couple of days and we'll train you in parachute jumping,' he replied. 'This is going to be a raid by paratroops. When they've taken the equipment and neutralised the Germans, they'll move it down the cliffs and the Navy will take it away in their boats.'

'How high are the cliffs?'

'About 300 ft, but they are not steep.'

On my way back to Swanage, my feet were a long way off the ground. This was to be a great adventure – heady stuff. But the following day I got a 'phone call from Bromley-Martin. 'Sorry to disappoint you. Somebody pointed out that you are a radar expert loaded with information, most of it secret. If you fell into enemy hands it could be a bit awkward, possibly very unpleasant for you. So we want to cancel your paratroop training and we'd like you to go with the naval force, make a landing on the beach and make sure the radar gear is brought safely back.'

'Disappointing,' I said, 'but I see your point. I'll be glad to go with the Navy. What do I do next?'

'Report to Combined Operations HQ in London,' he said.

Here I was briefed on the planned raid on Bruneval which was the name of the village close to the mobile radar. First, a detachment of Royal Engineers would be trained in demolishing a piece of delicate equipment without wrecking the contents. I was to advise Brig Gen Schonland who would be in charge. Second, a radio receiver would be prepared and given to me to take along in a landing craft when we crossed the Channel. Third, I was to report to Cowes on the Isle of Wight to take part in exercises in which Commando forces would gain experience in making landings at night on a beach.

Schonland was a most engaging man – a South African, world famous for his researches and his understanding of lightning. Here he was, like so many others, doing a job for which his previous experience was completely irrelevant. He had quickly learned all the important things about modern high explosives including plastics. He showed me how, by wrapping a small piece of plastic explosive, rather like putty, around a long piece of steel bar and then detonating it, the steel would be cut exactly where the plastic was placed. We discussed the probable configuration of the radar equipment at Bruneval. I could make some fairly shrewd guesses about it.

My next temporary home was a house in Cowes taken over by the Government for billeting Service personnel. Here I would spend the nights except when out in boats practising landings. This time of preparation was fascinating for me. There were officers and men from some of the 'crack' regiments of the British Army: the Grenadier Guards, the Coldstream Guards, the Argyll and Sutherland Highlanders – regiments which had distinguished themselves for centuries. The officers and men were mostly regulars and some were dukes, earls and knights; they had tremendous *esprit de corps*. They were all training for the invasion of Europe which was to come: a few would be involved in the Bruneval raid.

We spent a lot of time on board our mother ship – an ex cross-Channel passenger ferry boat which was tied up at a nearby dock. From the davits – normally used for lowering lifeboats – our Assault Landing Craft could be lowered into the water. Each ALC held twenty to thirty men. There was plenty of room on the mother ship, which we used for meetings and relaxation. The bar was well patronised in the evenings since we qualified for duty free alcohol. A gin cost 3*d* and a Drambuie 7*d*.

There was a lot of waiting. What we were waiting for was a combination of moonlight, a calm sea and favourable tides. Our ALCs were unseaworthy unless the sea was fairly calm. Rain would interfere with good visibility.

Then, one day, we got the word: 'Tonight's the night!'

We put on our battledress with extra warm clothing, blackened our faces with burnt cork, then had our briefing about the plan of action. Several flights of two-engined Whitley bombers fitted out for paratroops would leave England and rendezvous at a spot close to the target. The troops included the Sappers (RE) and enough soldiers to take care of the Germans stationed in a house near the radar station: we had 120 paratroops altogether.

Meanwhile our naval party would arrive by sea at the appointed time. We had enough boats to hold all the paratroops as well as our small force (including me) to ensure the safe removal of the radar gear. Positioned 3 miles off the French coast, a few motor gunboats (MGBs) would be ready to cover the withdrawal of the ALCs and one would pick me up as well as the radar gear.

It was a good plan. But as some wise guy once quipped: 'The best-laid plans of mice and men are usually about equal.'

About 20 miles from the French coast we got in the ALCs, were lowered into the water and proceeded under our own steam. It was very cold. I had my little radio receiver, tuned to 550 Mhz – the frequency of the radar. I picked up the signal from the radar with no difficulty. It got louder and softer, rhythmically, because it had a narrow beam and was sweeping automatically through an arc of about 180 degrees. I was not too concerned about our boats being detected because we were very close to the water and had no superstructure.

A mile or so from the French coast we stopped and waited for the show to begin. For a long time nothing happened. It was a worry. We couldn't discuss it between the boats because radio silence was imperative. At last we saw signs of activity ashore. The signal from my receiver disappeared. We moved close in to shore, expecting to land peacefully on the beach, but to our surprise we were fired on from a machine-gun post at the top of the cliff. Evidently this had not been put out of action as planned. We could see the tracer bullets and obviously it was aiming at us. We were sitting ducks, but most of the bullets were going into the water.

Then at last the troops came down the cliffs. I spotted the radar gear and had it put into my boat. Then we tried to move out to sea but our boats were stuck in the sand! Because of the delay, the tide was now ebbing fast and the water was very shallow. A gallant naval lieutenant jumped overboard and managed to attach a line between my boat and another which was able to move, and with a lot of pushing and shoving – still under fire – we got under way at last. (I later learned that the naval chap had deservedly got a decoration.)

At last the machine-gun stopped firing. We sailed away and soon found the MGBs, and by now quite a sea was running. My job was to get the captured equipment on to an MGB and this proved tricky. I climbed aboard an MGB, and told the chaps on the ALC to hand the gear up to me. I leaned over the rail but when I went up the ALC went down, and vice versa. I visualised with horror the consequences. After all the hard work; the preparations and the battle itself, we looked like dropping the stuff in the drink. My arms became as strong as steel.

At last it was all on board the MGB and so was Flt Sgt Cox, the radar mechanic who had actually done the job at the station and removed all the essential parts. Without delay I took him below. I wanted him to tell me exactly what had happened before he forgot the details.

'Please sir,' he said, 'I'm seasick. I want to be sick.' I had visions of Cox, incapacitated for hours, exhausted and in a daze, unable to remember anything much. I had no mercy.

'Sorry old man, come down below and tell me the story. Then you can be sick.' He obeyed, gave me his report very clearly, then went up on deck, leaned over the rail and was very, very sick indeed. He was a brave and extremely capable man.

Dawn came and the daylight grew. The Commander of the MGB – a young man dressed in flannel trousers and a sweater – seemed quite upset.

'Where's the RAF?' he wanted to know. 'They're supposed to be giving us cover. A German bomber could blow us out of the water.' I didn't know quite what to say. But he said: 'You must be cold; come below and we'll have some good Navy rum to celebrate.' And this we did.

Soon after, I found myself on a larger naval vessel talking to my old friend from Netheravon, Bromley-Martin. He told me what had happened.

'The Whitleys took off on time,' he said, 'and arrived over France. Then they got lost. About half the paratroops were dropped in the right place, after a considerable delay, but the other half were dropped about 5 miles to the east. The first lot waited for the others, finally deciding to press on regardless.'

'Fortunately,' I said, 'Cox was among them.'

'Indeed yes,' said he. 'They reached the station and did the job but there weren't enough of them to wipe out that machine-gun post. We were in radio contact with the chaps who landed in the wrong place, but there was no way they could get to Bruneval in time. We told them to make their escape through the route they had all been taught. They had false papers and French money. We wished them goodbye and good luck.'

(I heard much later that they all escaped to Portugal – a neutral country – with the aid of the French Underground, and most of them were able to return to Britain and continue their service.)

'How many men did we lose?' I asked.

'Miraculously, only two that we know of.'

'That fellow with the machine-gun was a poor shot,' I remarked.

Back in London next day, weary but happy, I was taken by Bromley-Martin to the Air Ministry where I was introduced to the Assistant Chief of Air Staff, AM Sir Charles Portal. He was terribly pleased by the success of the raid and said that the news of it would boost morale in Britain no end. 'All the war news has been bad for some time,' he said, 'but here is a great success.' He shook my hand warmly.

Bromley-Martin took me for lunch at his club and told me how lucky we'd been. 'Just before the show started, a flotilla of German E-boats sailed along the coast between us and the shore. These boats are heavily armed. Fortunately for us, they saw nothing.'

That was the end of the Bruneval raid. But not the end of the story. Back at Worth Matravers I had a look at the captured gear and admired the German craftsmanship and

Donald Preist with part of the aerial assembly of the Würzburg radar captured at Bruneval.

technology it revealed. On the whole I thought they were ahead of us. Then it was whisked away to the RAE at Farnborough for further study. I heard later what they did, and this was very significant. They found a weak spot in the design of the receiver and they designed a very clever jammer which was installed in our bombers. For a long time the RAF were able to bomb the Ruhr Valley at night without being troubled by Ack-Ack gunfire. This confirmed the earlier suspicions that the Ruhr Valley radars and the one at Bruneval were similar: now it was clear that their receivers were identical. I was told that the Germans never found out how the jamming was done.

After the war, Donald Preist moved to California and worked in industry developing high-power vacuum tubes. He published some thirty papers and was awarded in 1990 an Engineering EMMY for the joint invention of the 'Klystrode' tube. Since 1992 he has been a consultant to the English Electric Valve Co. He now helps to run a sheep farm in Colorado.

Sir Edward Fennessy CBE, B.Sc., FIEE, FRIN

> *'Not bad mileage for the Group described somewhat dismissively in 1940 as "the Group that flaps but seldom flies".'*

It was very much a blind date. The Air Ministry telegram informed me that I'd been appointed a Technical Officer at the Air Ministry Research Station Bawdsey Manor, to where I was to report immediately. All I knew was that the work I was to be engaged in was Top Secret and exciting. Geoffrey Roberts, an old friend and previous colleague at Standard Telephones and Cables where I worked, in persuading me to apply for this appointment, had told me that much and not a single clue more. Trusting Roberts, I agreed to abandon a promising career with STC and take a newly married wife with me into an unknown future.

So on 28 September 1938, as the storm clouds of the Czech crisis were becoming increasingly ominous, and preparations made for war, I found myself in Charlie Brinkley's rowing boat being ferried across the River Deben towards the towers of Bawdsey Manor. Charlie – with a metal hook where one hand had once been – pulled hard against the tide, unaware that his hook was to bring him immortality in the RAF Equipment List for the item 'Hooks, Earthing, Brinkley'.

Up the drive I walked to the manor, past the cricket field – pride and joy of A.P. Rowe the Superintendent, noting as I entered the manor the inscription above the door in French which translated read: 'Rather die than change'. What a motto for a research team who were to transform air warfare for ever. For as I was soon to learn, far more than the development of Watson Watt's brilliant concept of RDF was taking place at Bawdsey. Working with the RAF, scientists and engineers were creating an entirely new weapon system: a weapon that would enable Fighter Command to win the Battle of Britain and save the country from Nazi conquest.

Eager with curiosity to learn what all the Top Secret mystery was about, I found myself in A.P. Rowe's office, with its sweeping views of the Deben. Introductions done and formalities completed, I was led off by my old colleague Geoffrey Roberts to be briefed in the secret project he had persuaded me to join. By late afternoon, as I was

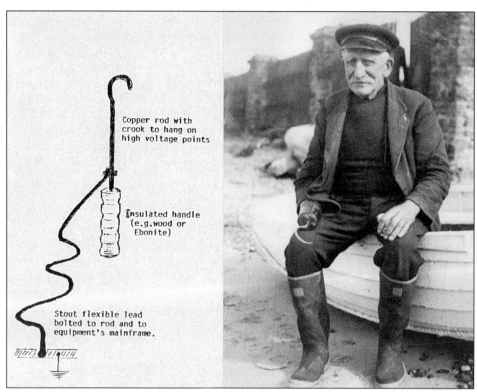

Charlie Brinkley, well-known Bawdsey ferryman. The sketch on the left is of a typical 'Brinkley earthing stick', used for safety during transmitter maintenance and named after Charlie's artificial right hand.

'Plutot mourir que changer' (Rather die than change) – the motto over the main entrance to Bawdsey Manor – could not have been less appropriate for the radar pioneers.

beginning to grasp the technicalities and potential of RDF, Geoffrey announced we were to leave that evening to install an RDF Filter Room at Fighter Command, Bentley Priory. But first he would show me an operational RDF station.

So, late in the evening we set off in his old Fiat car for Canewdon near Southend, one of the five CH stations then operational. Here I met the CO, WO Scarfe, later to become Wing Commander and to play a significant part in the operational use of radar. It was near midnight before the tour of the CH station was complete and Roberts and I departed for Fighter Command at Stanmore, seeking first a very late bed for the night and breakfast from a very surprised wife at my home in Woodford Green. I had left it some eighteen hours earlier for Bawdsey, with no promise as to when we might meet again.

First Filter Room

At Bentley Priory we met the Chief Signals Officer Fighter Command, Wg Cdr Rodney. Roberts explained that our task was to build a Filter Table on which the raw RDF data from the CH stations would be plotted, to enable filtered and derived track information to be passed to the Operations Room. Rodney led us off to meet the C-in-C, the formidable ACM Sir Hugh Dowding, who subjected Roberts to a searching cross-examination. Clearly he approved, to the extent of our being allocated a very dusty cellar for our purposes, deep below Bentley Priory.

Cleaners, carpenters and Post Office engineers were summoned and as Neville Chamberlain flew back from his Munich meeting with Hitler, clutching his famous piece of paper, his plane was tracked by the five CH stations – Dover, Dunkirk, Canewdon, Great Bromley and Bawdsey – and plotted on the first ever radar Filter Table, a table that would play such a major role in the battle that was so soon to come.

It had been a dramatic and stimulating two days. I had now been briefed in the secrets of RDF, later to be known as radar. I had met men with whom I was to serve throughout the coming war and in particular the great Sir Hugh Dowding – a man who had in 1935 foreseen the potential of Watson Watt's proposal to use radio energy to detect aircraft, and was to employ it so effectively in fighting and winning the Battle of Britain.

And so back to Bawdsey and my immediate task of planning the communications network that the rapidly growing East Coast Chain would require; also to develop the one-in-one system to synchronise all CH stations to enable the 'Chapman method'[1] to

---

[1] CH stations found the plan position of a distant target from its range and bearing. Range measurements were accurate and reliable but those of bearing less so. By displaying at a CH station a target echo derived from a transmitter located some miles away, as well as that from its own, it was possible to determine accurately the target's position by range cuts. A procedure for this was invented by Corporal Chapman in the early days of CH but was later little used because it was time-consuming and Filter Rooms could often make range cuts from the plots of two or more stations plotting the same aircraft.

For the Chapman method – and to avoid interference between closely spaced CH stations – it was essential that the pulses (25 per sec.) from the separate transmitters were synchronised. This could be achieved where a common alternating current mains supply existed by locking each to it. But if the supplies were independent – or if more accurate locking was needed – a synchronising signal was sent from a central source by landlines. This was called 'One-in-One' (one synch. waveform in one line).

be used should it be required operationally, and with Roberts, to develop the electrical converter, or fruit machine as it became known. This was a brilliant concept of Roberts's that would enable the rapid conversion of CH data and which, when demonstrated to Dowding, led to his comment 'It will not be long before the scientist replaces the C-in-C Fighter Command by a gadget.'

On 3 August 1939, a massive slow-moving echo was plotted by Bawdsey. At some 30 miles from the coast, it turned north and was tracked all the way to Scotland by the CH stations. It was soon identified as a Zeppelin, confirmed by several visual sightings. This incident produced much interest and concern at Bawdsey, Fighter Command and the Air Ministry. It was (correctly) assumed that it was engaged in radio surveillance of the entire CH system, and the reasonable conclusion was drawn that it would have returned to base with the location of all CH sites, operating frequencies and other vital information. What would be the likely consequences of the Luftwaffe now having this information? It was more than likely that they now had a good appreciation of the defensive potential of the British RDF system. What would be their response?

The two main conclusions were that they would now be likely to develop jammers to which the CH stations would be highly vulnerable, and that the stations would be high priority targets for bombing once war broke out. This resulted in intensification of research at Bawdsey on anti-jamming techniques and the construction by RAF Kidbrooke of mobile CH stations to be used when a CH station was destroyed.

'For Want of a Nail'

When the war started, the devastating bombing we had feared did not come until 12 August 1940, when Dover, Dunkirk, Pevensey, Rye and Ventnor were all bombed, although, with the exception of Ventnor, ineffectively. But why, we asked ourselves, did the Luftwaffe fail to make more effective use of the intelligence gathered by the Zeppelin mission? This remained a mystery until after the war, when I met Gen Martini who had been Chief Signals Officer of the Luftwaffe throughout the war. In the early 1950s Sir Robert Watson-Watt brought the General over to the Farnborough Air Show, and after lunch we discussed the late war and the role radar had played in it.

'Why,' I asked Martini, 'did the Luftwaffe not destroy the CH stations before they launched Eagle Day?' (the Luftwaffe assault planned by Goering to destroy Fighter Command, so leaving the skies clear of the RAF for the invasion of Britain to proceed).

Martini told me an intriguing story. In 1938–9 Luftwaffe intelligence watched the construction by the RAF of large radio installations along the east coast. What was the purpose of these stations with 360 ft towers they asked themselves. Particularly as they did not conform to the Germans' concept of radar installations. But Martini was suspicious, and with some difficulty persuaded Goering to allow the Zeppelin LZ130 to conduct a radio spy mission. A strong technical team under Dr Breuning was put on board for the mission on 3 August, but they returned to base at Frankfurt to report that no radar-type signals were detected. This led to the conclusion that the RAF had not at that time a working radar system – an intelligence blunder that was to have a profound impact on the outcome of the coming Battle of Britain. (The technical reasons for this

The LZ130 *Graf Zeppelin* photographed from an aircraft of RAF Dyce (Scotland) after she had flown past Bawdsey and other East Coast CH stations on her radar spying mission in August 1939. (By permission RAF Museum, Hendon.)

blunder have been fully analysed by Colin Latham and these explain why this crucial mission went so badly wrong.)[2]

Gen Martini was clearly shocked when I told him how we tracked the Zeppelin over the whole of its spy mission up the east coast. For Martini, an alert and intelligent man, knew better than anybody the consequences of the Zeppelin mission's failure. He told me that despite the negative results of the Zeppelin mission, he became convinced in July 1940 that Fighter Command's interception successes were based on the use of radar. Goering, who was dismissive of radar's role in air warfare, reluctantly agreed to the 12 August attacks, but only a week later he forbade any further such attacks as ineffective and a waste of bomber resources. Had Martini been aware that we had a fully operational system in August 1939, I am convinced that he would have taken measures leading to the effective destruction of the CH cover before the Battle of Britain was joined. Perhaps the failure of the Zeppelin mission was the first lost nail that cost Germany a battle and a war.

[2] Colin Latham, 'I SEE THE CAT BUT HE CAN'T SEE ME!', *Marconi Radar News and Views*, July 1992. Briefly, the failure to detect the radars was a result of a combination of several factors including: overloading of the German receivers; harmonics of the CH transmissions; the low repetition rate of CH pulses and their being locked to the UK's electricity grid system; the 'floodlight' CH radiation pattern; effects of the airship's structure; simultaneous German investigative ionospheric transmissions for radio communication in the CH waveband. This article is reproduced in full in another book, M. Bauer and J. Duggan, *LZ10 Graf Zeppelin and the End of Commercial Airship Travel*.

In July of 1939 Rowe called a meeting to announce plans for the evacuation of Bawdsey to Dundee upon the outbreak of war. I protested that the work of the team under Dewhurst, of which I was a member, could not be carried on from such a remote location, as by this time we were deeply involved in building, maintaining and extending the CH stations. Rowe – none too pleased – asked if I thought I knew a better place. I did, and the day Germany invaded Poland we said farewell to Bawdsey and our Dundee-bound colleagues and established Base Maintenance HQ at Carlton Lodge, Leighton Buzzard, close to RAF Central, the hub of RAF communications.

Leighton Buzzard was chosen for three reasons: firstly RAF Central was planned to house a reserve for a Fighter Command Operations and Filter Room should Bentley Priory be destroyed. For this we had installed telephone lines from all CH stations; hence, until required in an emergency, we could use these lines for routine contact with the stations. Furthermore, we would be in short travelling distance to the vital south coast Chain and close to Fighter Command with whom we required frequent contact.

60 Group is Born

In the spring of 1940 the rapidly growing Base Maintenance HQ ceased to be a civilian establishment and became an RAF unit – No. 60 Radar Group Fighter Command, with Air Cdre Gregory as AOC. Joining the RAF (by a somewhat short-cut and unorthodox procedure) I was to serve on the 60 Group staff throughout the war. The Group was immediately deeply involved in maintaining and upgrading the CH and CHL system for the Battle of Britain that was to come in July 1940, and in rapidly extending the CH and CHL coverage round the British Isles. To this commitment was soon added GCI for the night-bomber battle.

In addition to this, at 60 Group from 1942 we planned, constructed and ran the great complex of Gee, Oboe and Gee-H stations for Bomber Command's navigational and blind-bombing needs. Firstly in early 1942, the Eastern Gee Chain was built to provide accurate radar navigation as far as the Ruhr. This was soon followed by the Southern Gee Chain, covering the English Channel and northern France. Later the South-Western and Northern Chains completed the total coverage of Britain, providing accurate navigational service for virtually all allied aircraft operating from Britain. Soon came the remarkable precision bombing aids Oboe and Gee-H, each to play such a major role in the allied bombing offensive.

On the night of the invasion, Gee stations, built in secret and only switched on just before the invasion fleets sailed, provided navigation through the swept channels for the vast armada of vessels to the beaches of Normandy. In the early hours of 6 June specially built Oboe stations provided precision cover for the Pathfinders of 8 Group Bomber Command to attack and mark the German gun positions covering the approach to the beaches, which the heavy Lancasters of Bomber Command then destroyed.

In support of the invasion of Europe, 60 Group was called upon to build, equip, and man a complete mobile wing comprising Gee, Oboe and Gee-H stations – 72 Wing – under the command of Wg Cdr Phillips. The first units landed in France in July 1944. Based at first near Caen [later Mons], 72 Wing rapidly deployed its mobile units with the advancing Allied line, providing navigational and blind-bombing cover for the British and American air forces operating in support of the Allied armies as they advanced through France and into Germany. During the Ardennes offensive, some of these mobiles sited well forward east of Laroche very narrowly escaped capture by a German armoured detachment detailed by FM von Rundstedt for that specific task.

By the end of the war in Europe, units of 72 Wing had penetrated deep into Germany. There were stations built and operated by 60 Group as far afield as Iceland and North Africa, while planning was well advanced – and some stations built – for a series of Gee chains from Britain to the Far East. Their purpose was to provide navigational aid for Transport Command ferrying troops to the Far East – an operational requirement cancelled after the dropping of the atomic bombs on Japan. Not bad mileage for the Group described somewhat dismissively by a joker at Fighter Command in 1940 as 'the Group that flaps but seldom flies'.

The value of 60 Group to Fighter Command was summarised well by its C-in-C AM Robb in his victory message to the Group:'Since its formation in early 1940, No. 60 Group has been the eyes of Fighter Command and it is of interest to record that nearly 5,000 enemy aircraft were destroyed as a result of radar information it supplied. I have no hesitation in saying that without 60 Group and radar, the Battle of Britain, even the war itself, could not have been won.'

At the same time, ACM Sir Arthur Harris, C-in-C Bomber Command, paid his tribute: 'Now that something of the immense part that has been played by radar in winning the war has been made public, it is possible to acknowledge that without the work of No. 60 Group, Bomber Command could not have brought its task to a successful conclusion.'

Offspring as it was of Bawdsey, 60 Group was to work in close partnership with TRE throughout the war. Staffed largely with engineers, it enabled the rapid implementation of TRE's brilliant radar projects as working systems – capable of being effectively operated in the field by the many thousands of young men and women technicians and operators whose contribution to the war and to ultimate victory was so outstanding.

Sir Edward joined the board of Decca Navigator Co. on release from the RAF. In 1950 he formed Decca Radar Co. and was Managing Director until in 1965 he moved to Plessey Electronics Group, of which he was also Managing Director. In 1969 he joined the board of the British Post Office as Managing Director, Telecommunications, becoming Deputy Chairman until his retirement.

Dr J. Rennie Whitehead, FRSC, F.Inst.P, FIEE, FCASI, P.Eng., C.Eng.

'I was interviewed in London by two important-looking men. I learned later that one was C.P. Snow and the other Robert Watson-Watt!'

In my third undergraduate year at the University of Manchester (1938–9), work towards the final degree examination went pretty well and I took the finals in June. I had become deeply involved in Brentano's research on the wave-mechanical theory of photographic action, in the course of which I was able to design instruments – such as an automatic-recording densitometer – which were some years ahead of the technology available in commercial instruments.

By the beginning of 1939 the clouds of war were on the horizon. In the spring, Professor Blacket took me aside in great confidence and revealed that he was advising the Government on military research (he was, in fact, a member of the Committee for the Scientific Survey of Air Defence – the Tizard Committee). He told me he was involved also in the selection of young scientists for a highly secret defence research project. He would not press me, but strongly advised that I agree to be interviewed at the appropriate time. He seemed certain that war was inevitable.

So it was that I found myself at an interview in a building in Grosvenor Square, London, in the summer of 1939, along with a couple of my colleagues and one or two others. I was confronted by two important-looking men at the other side of the desk. One was rather large, portly and somewhat forbidding in appearance; the other was smaller, plump and round-faced and had a clipped Scottish accent. I discovered later that they were respectively C.P. Snow (later Lord Snow – author of many novels and at that time head of the Civil Service Commission) and Robert Watson-Watt (later Sir Robert, who came to be known as the inventor of radar).

The two seemed to take for granted my academic record but surprised me by pursuing in detail my experience in electronics, instrument design and experimental physics. I must have satisfied them, because they told me on the spot that I had a job as a Junior Scientific Officer in the Scientific Civil Service at £240 a year, and that I was to report to Bawdsey Manor in Suffolk on 11 August. They were unable to tell me what kind of work I would be doing, or the purpose of the establishment I was joining. These things would be revealed at Bawdsey after I had signed the Official Secrets Act.

I suppose we rarely recognise the major turning points in our lives at the time. This, for me, was one of them. It was with regret, excitement and a certain amount of apprehension that I left Lancashire and headed for Bawdsey and the secrets of war.

Bawdsey

The embryo research establishment I joined at Bawdsey was called simply the Bawdsey Research Station. The first man I met there was A.B. Jones, the administrator. I recall climbing the stairs of the manor to his office where I signed the Official Secrets Act and then at last learned what this secret establishment was doing. And I was now a part of it, thanks to the insight of Professor Blackett. It was an exciting day.

I found digs in Felixstowe, reached by ferry across the estuary and a bus ride. I was assigned to work with a Professor Oliphant,[1] who was temporarily in charge of the IFF group (Identification Friend or Foe). The idea was that a friendly aircraft could identify

---

[1] It was under Professor Oliphant (later Sir Mark, KBE, FRS), at the University of Birmingham, that centimetric radar became possible in 1940 through the work of his staff including scientists Randall and Boot, who devised the first cavity magnetron.

itself to radar by picking up the radar pulse, amplifying it and sending it back to the originator. By interrupting the retransmission at regular intervals, the echo of a friendly aircraft seen on the screen would flash repeatedly (lengthen the blip) and so could easily be recognised as friendly.

During these first days at Bawdsey I met some of the members of the small original RDF team that had moved there from Orfordness. Notable among them were Arnold 'Skip' Wilkins, Eddie Bowen, R. Hanbury Brown, Donald Preist and a senior technician R.H.A. 'Nick' Carter. Carter was a tall, gangling man of extraordinary integrity, with a tremendous fund of common sense and practical ability. It was an honour to work with Nick Carter and I learned a lot from him.

Several scientists from universities and other sources had already joined the Bawdsey group. Notable among them was Dr W.B. (Ben) Lewis from the Cavendish Laboratory Cambridge, who, though I was unaware of it at the time, was to have a great influence on my future. During the first two weeks at Bawdsey I also met Sidney Jefferson with whom I still correspond fifty years on and 3,500 miles apart, and Harold Larnder, the father of Operational Research who, as we did, later emigrated to Canada to establish the first operational research work in the Defence Research Board of Canada.

Then there was Joe Airey, a remarkable, practical man, small in stature but high in wisdom. Joe was responsible for workshops and transportation at TRE throughout the war. He soon became a friend and ally and I remember him with great affection.

It soon became clear that the Government expected an early attack on Bawdsey and so at the end of August 1939, after I'd been there for only three weeks or so, we packed all the apparatus into crates and, on the night of 1 September, loaded them on a train in some rural station in pitch darkness. I am not sure I ever knew where it was – just that we all stripped to the waist and worked like navvies for the whole of that night, until the train departed for Dundee.

Dundee

My first boss, Professor Oliphant, drove three of us from Felixstowe to Dundee on Saturday 2 September. We stopped over at his home in North Berwick and it was there that we heard Neville Chamberlain on the Sunday morning announce that we were at war with Germany.

I was working very hard on IFF MkII at the time. Work occupied all my waking (and some of my sleeping) hours, except for visiting the Palais two or three evenings a week. Derek Ritson and I used to conduct ground tests on IFF MkII between the roof of the Teachers' Training College and a van parked at Broughty Ferry, along the north bank of the Tay. By this time Oliphant had left and F.C. Williams was in charge of IFF.

To identify itself to radar, every aircraft needed not only a receiver-transmitter (transponder) but a suitable antenna. As we were then dealing with wavelengths of 10 m or so, and as MkII IFF responded directly on the frequency of the radar, the length of the aircraft antenna had to be a [dimensional] compromise. We first used an airfield at Scone near Perth for early antenna experiments on a Fairey Battle aircraft. The Battle was a single-engined two-seater (fore and aft seating) and looked something like an

Dundee Teachers' Training College.

overgrown Hurricane. I personally drilled holes in the tailplane, put bolts through and connected wires which went forward to the mid section of the fuselage to form a sort of triangle. I flew in the Battle to ensure that the IFF transponder was operating correctly and to measure the strength of the irradiating radar pulse at various ranges.

Scone airfield had no runway nor fuelling nor service facilities and we soon moved to Leuchars near St Andrews for our flying. I remember the take-off from Scone in a Hampden bomber one day to do an IFF flight test over the North Sea in conjunction with the radar station at Douglas Wood near Dundee. The pilot was an RAF officer called Jacklin – about nineteen years old but of quite senior rank with competence and leadership to match, both of which were sorely tested on this flight.

The aircraft was low on fuel so he decided to fly it straight to Leuchars to refuel, then carry out the trial. We rumbled over the grass at Scone and took to the air. Within a minute or two the starboard outer engine began to cough and died. The starboard inner was next. We were still below 1,000 ft and we were running out of fuel. Then one of the port engines began to cough. Jacklin ordered us to stand by to bale out. Then he countermanded it saying we were too low and he was going to fly it in. By this time we had lost three engines out of four and Jacklin was braced in his seat, fighting the aircraft into the direction of Leuchars runway. We just cleared the fence at a steep angle, the lower wingtip almost brushing it. Jacklin managed to wrench the aircraft level and bang it down on the runway, just as number four spluttered and died. We had to be towed in and refuelled but within half an hour we were on our way to the test. It transpired that the fuel gauges were faulty and gave too high a reading.

After Christmas 1939 I continued to prototype different types of aircraft for IFF. Our flying was mostly done on aircraft borrowed from operational units but later on we developed a Test Flight Unit of our own, which grew steadily throughout the war to include a large number of military aircraft of all types. Working with operational aircraft and pilots had its own peculiar qualities: when we borrowed a Spitfire, it arrived with a flourish in a low roll and an archetypal fighter pilot stepped out. He refused to let anyone else fly the aircraft or do anything to it without his supervision. So we drilled holes in the tail, stuck bolts through (with the pilot wielding the wrench), and mounted the IFF unit amidships. We were all worried about the shift in balance but there was no time for all the bureaucratic complexity of consulting the designers or bringing in aeronautical engineers. So the pilot, who claimed to know the exact location of the centre of balance, took out the lead ballast, weighed it and with a hacksaw cut off a slice of the lead to correspond with the weight of our 'box'. Then he took the Spitfire up for a test flight and pronounced it perfect.

After lunch he took it up again to show it off to some of the local RAF types as there were no Spitfires at Leuchars. He ended his show of aerobatics with a fierce loop that he only just pulled out of in time. I met him as he climbed out of the cockpit. 'That was a tight one,' he said, 'it must have been 7g the way it felt!' I remarked that the Spitfire evidently felt the same way, pointing to a crease in the stressed skin behind the cockpit. He had almost broken its back. It was a write-off, but not, I think, due to the installation of IFF.

On another occasion, a pilot took me up on a particularly successful test using the coastal CH radar at Douglas Wood, north of Dundee. He decided to make a low pass on the station where there were four wooden 240 ft towers and four 360 ft steel towers in a row. The steel towers had cantilevered platforms like shelves sticking out from each side. We dived towards the towers, banked and went between two of them below the platforms. From my point of view these masses of steel sweeping across my field of vision were spectacular to say the least. But on landing, the pilot was told to report to the Flight Commander who tore him off a strip then dismissed him. As we reached the door he said: 'Oh and by the way, they're putting up a curtain array between those two towers tomorrow'. A curtain array consists of a veritable spiders' web of heavy wire which, had it already been there, would have cut our aircraft to ribbons. Moreover, it would have been impossible to see the array until too late. The pilot was suitably chastened.

Worth Matravers

We worked in huts whose walls were lined with work benches covered in linoleum. Our hut was equipped for the IFF and radar beacon work. It was here at Worth that F.C. Williams did his pioneer work on circuit development inventions that permeated the whole of radar circuitry in Britain and, eventually, on both sides of the Atlantic. In a booklet published in his memory in 1965, I was quoted as writing:

Dr F.C. Williams.

He was most prolific, enthusiastic and unselfish in his creativity. His sole concern was to see the desired electronic function performed elegantly, efficiently and reliably. His ideas were transmitted during informal, usually intense sessions. He was notorious for his tangled breadboard circuits which often drooped over the edge of the bench towards the floor – a unique combination of conceptual elegance and material chaos. It was thus that we saw the birth of a whole range of feedback timing circuits that brought precision into radar circuitry by use of inherently linear, instead of exponential timing waveforms.[2] These circuits carried typical Williams names, created on the spur of the moment in the laboratory: the 'Phantastron' (fantastic!), the Sanatron ('sanitary' was his favourite description of a well-behaved circuit) and the hybrid Sanaphant. I remember improvements and extensions of these circuits such as the cathode-coupled phantastron and the sanatron stepping divider.

During this period the first experiments were made on a separate band IFF system and on the first radar homing beacons. IFF MkII – by then in service – responded directly to the radar signal and sent back an amplified, coded version of it on the same frequency – the radar frequency itself. When many of our own aircraft were doing this, it tended to obscure the hostile aircraft echoes. Moreover, it required a separate receiver-transmitter for each type of radar, and as the types on different frequencies proliferated, it would become impracticable to design IFF sets to respond to all of them. Thus the idea of a separate frequency band for IFF was conceived and pursued by F.C. Williams from 1940 onwards. This was to become my major occupation for the rest of the war: first under Williams then under B.V. Bowden and finally heading the IFF group myself.

In the early days at Worth Matravers, we did our flight tests from a field in Christchurch, which was the first airfield devoted exclusively to TRE work.

I did a lot of flying out of Christchurch. The pilots of the Special Duty Flight were remarkable fliers. They flew anything and everything without instruction; more than once I would climb into an aircraft for an IFF test flight and remark to the pilot 'I'm flying in a (say) Mosquito for the first time' and it was disconcerting to say the least when the pilot replied, 'So am I'!

IFF MkIII was under way and I had the job of developing the airborne transponder. We were always working against the clock. Equipment was no use if it was too late. Research, development, production, testing and installation had to be compressed into the least possible time. That is why, as soon as the outline of the idea for the MkIII was there, I went up to Ferranti Ltd in Moston near Manchester and acted as project officer, design authority, researcher, engineer and everything else concerned with the MkIII transponder.

We chose the frequency band of 157–87 MHz and therefore all radars – on the ground, in the air or at sea – needed to have an IFF transmitter ('Interrogator') and an

---

[2] Some electronic functions (e.g. deflecting the beam of a cathode ray tube for the display of radar signals) require voltages that change at a constant rate – i.e. linear waveforms. Many early circuits, relying on the charge and discharge of capacitors, were inherently non-linear, but Williams, by adapting the known 'Miller effect' elegantly overcame this problem by several novel arrangements that became widely used in radar circuits.

MkIII IFF transponder with the top cover removed; it was fitted to vast numbers of aircraft during the war.

IFF receiver ('Responsor') within this band. In the radars the IFF response was blended, as appropriate for the particular display, with the direct radar echo. Inside the airborne transponder a small motor generator, fed from the aircraft's DC supply, provided the various voltages required for the electronics; it also drove a mechanism coupled to the transponder's tuning condenser so that its frequency was repeatedly swept through the band. This ensured that, for each interrogating radar, the IFF response appeared intermittently: it also avoided possible problems of frequency drift. Preset coding could cause the transponder to miss sweeps in a variety of patterns according to the 'code of the day'. The transponder used a superregenerative receiver which, unlike its predecessors, was automatically stabilised for sensitivity to the incoming signal, thus making the unit extremely reliable.

While the IFF MkIII production was under way at Ferranti, there arose an urgent need for a navigational aid to help the pilots of Fighter and Coastal Command to navigate directly back to their bases. F.C. Williams had the idea of using a transponder beacon on which the AI (Air Interception) and ASV (Air to Surface Vessel) radars could home. I was asked to design and produce about 125 units for this purpose with the utmost despatch. I decided that the only way it could be done quickly was to pirate the components from the production line at Ferranti Ltd. I had been told there was an empty factory in Manchester – a 'shadow' factory belonging to another electronics company A.C. Cossor Ltd – which I could use for the job. I went to Manchester to investigate and found the empty building with a manager and, of all things, an AID (Aeronautical Inspection Directorate) inspector, though what he was there to inspect, we never knew.

The design had formed in my mind on the journey up to Manchester. Coding, to identify each airfield uniquely, was very important, so I first sketched out a coding wheel, much more elaborate than the one in MkIII, but still driven by the generator gearbox. Art Levin (the inspector chap) and I worked continuously for forty-eight hours and by the end of that time we had a fully tested production prototype. We made a components list and cabled London for authority to steal the parts from Ferranti. The Directorate of Defence Production was less than co-operative at first and our headquarters, the Directorate of Communications Development, was also involved in the person of a man called Ball. This enabled me to send a cable to DDP which began 'Reference mine to you on the 15th, Ball's to you on the 16th. . . .' This ended the deadlock. I took the parts across to the Cossor factory in a station wagon. In the meantime, Art Levin had almost literally gone out on the streets to put together a team of girls for the assembly line. This was because Ferranti had only been able to supply the gearbox parts, not the assembled unit. So there we were with girls who had never seen a gearbox or an electronic circuit, being taught to solder and to assemble complex mechanical parts!

However, thirty days after my arrival we had the first 125 radar homing transponder beacons ever made. Again we worked for forty-eight hours continuously to test and adjust every one of them against specification. I drove them down to Swanage, where two of my excellent nineteen-year-old technicians had been occupied in building 125 antennas for them. In an incredibly short space of time, the beacons were distributed and installed at coastal and fighter stations throughout the UK and these beacons successfully brought home our aircraft for two and a half critical years of the war, before being replaced.

While I was away in Manchester, a stray German aircraft had let loose a string of bombs one of which had left metal fragments embedded in the headboard of my bed! Air attacks on TRE and the streets of Swanage were becoming more frequent and TRE's days in Dorset were numbered. This was sad for us, because the laboratory site on St Alban's Head was very attractive. We could walk along the cliffs or down to the Square and Compass pub for a ploughman's lunch and a mild and bitter. During the Battle of Britain we would lie on the grass at lunchtime and watch dogfights overhead.

But German attacks on the area became more and more frequent and even began to coincide with the departure by train of the various Cabinet ministers and commanders-in-chief who had been attending a 'Sunday Soviet'. These were a remarkable phenomenon, brilliantly conceived by A.P. Rowe, which probably had more influence on the outcome of the war than any other single military or civilian activity.

Rowe realised at the outset that in order to give the military the tools they needed, the scientists of TRE and the strategic and tactical decision-makers of the three armed

Participators in a 'Sunday Soviet' at the Telecommunications Research Establishment, Malvern. Sitting, left to right: Air Cdre W.C. Cooper, Air Cdre C.S. Cadell, Air Cdre W.P.G. Pretty, Sir Robert Renwick, Lord Cherwell, AVM Sir Victor Tait, Mr A.P. Rowe, Mr D.W. Fry, Air Cdre C.P. Brown, AVM W.E. Theak, Gp Capt E.C. Passmore, Dr F.C. Williams, Mr C. Holt Smith, Air Cdre M.K. Porter, Dr W.B. Lewis. Standing: AVM O.G.W.G. Lywood, Air Cdre G.P. Chamberlain, Gp Capt J. Shepherd-Smith, Gp Capt G.N. Hancock, Gp Capt C.A. Bell, Prof. D.M. Robinson, Mr C.J. Carter, Sqn Ldr W.H. Thompson, Gp Capt C.C. Morton, Mr J.C. Duckworth, Mr E.H. Cook-Yarborough, Dr R.A. Smith, Mr A.B. Jones, Mr J. Stewart, Dr A.T. Starr, Dr T.C. Keeley, Dr A.H. Cooke, Gp Capt J.A. Macdonald, Mr R.J. Dippy, Dr D.A. Jackson.

forces would have to act with great speed and flexibility. This could never be achieved through bureaucratic channels. So the 'Sunday Soviets' came into being which brought together top military and political figures – the decision-makers – with the TRE scientists. There was no formality at these meetings. The Chiefs of Staff spoke openly of their plans and welcomed suggestions from TRE – even youngsters like us – on how to fight the war. If a suggestion appealed to the top brass, immediate authority was given, on the spot, to proceed with the work. By this means we always knew directly the implications of our work on the conduct of the war and this led to the remarkable speed and enthusiasm with which TRE pursued its task.

The 'Soviets' were, of course, Top Secret and involved absolute trust on both sides. There is no record that that trust was ever betrayed. Most ex-TRE people I am sure would agree that the years in Swanage represented the peak of creativity in radar. Nothing like it had happened before nor since. All the fundamentals of ground and airborne radar and air traffic control were invented during that period. Tribute must always be paid to the early team at Orfordness under 'Skip' Wilkins and Watson-Watt. But the radar war was won by the superhuman efforts of a large, well-motivated, immensely capable, inventive team of scientists in Swanage. The spirit continued later in Malvern, until the end of the war, but it had settled down to a steadier pace by then and most of the work was the development of ideas conceived in Swanage rather than the evolution of new ones.

Dr Whitehead remained with TRE after the war as Head of Physical Electronics, Physics Department, until 1951. He then became Associate Professor of Physics at McGill University,

Montreal until 1955. For ten years he worked in industry in Canada and in 1965 became Principal Science Advisor to the Privy Council. From 1972–5 he was Assistant Secretary to the Ministry of State for Science and Technology. He still works as independent consultant on science management and policy and describes himself as being 'semi-retired'.

Douglas Myhill

> *'Her Ladyship approached me rather crossly and asked where*
> *"the foreman" was. What could I do but point to Butement!'*

I attended an interview at the Royal Engineers and Signals Board in the autumn of 1938. The Board was responsible for Army research, including those elements of ADEE[1] (Biggin Hill) concerned with RDF which were seconded to the Air Ministry Research Establishment at Bawdsey. As a result of the interview (chaired by H.W. Forshaw, the Principal Scientific Officer in charge of the Army 'cell' at Bawdsey) I was sent to Bawdsey in late 1938 as a Laboratory Assistant.

There were two teams: one, headed by P.E. Pollard, was concerned with the development of the anti-aircraft gun-laying equipment (GL) and the other, which I joined, was headed by W.S. Butement and was responsible for the development of the Coast Defence radar (CD). In January of 1931, Pollard and Butement had submitted a proposal for a 'Coast Defence Apparatus'. It was recorded in the Inventions Book of the Royal Engineers Board and was, I believe, the genesis of single-station radar.

My first task at Bawdsey was to assist R.H. Davies on the 18 cm experimental equipment using parabolic reflectors. This was soon abandoned and I was assigned to work with D.R. Chick on the 1.5 m transmitter. The basic design had been finalised using GEC VT58 copper anode triodes and passed to Metropolitan Vickers for pre-production.[2] However, the broadside aerial array was still under development and I well remember climbing the array in a freezing North Sea wind and 'tuning' the dipoles using a neon bulb. The design of the array allowed for the introduction of 'split' which made possible a major advance in the accuracy of angular measurement and continuous following.

When I arrived at the labs, the receiver was still a box on a 'table, airman, 6 ft' with a hand-made Yagi on the roof directed by hand (guess whose hand!). Our bible was the ARRL 'Radio Amateur's Handbook'[3] and the new RCA acorn valves which we were testing were described therein. Apart from Butement, the head of the CD cell, there was A.J. Oxford, the principal developer of the receiver and who, later in 1940 with Chick and Eastwood, developed 'Elsie' (SLC – Searchlight Control). B. Newsam was working on a spiral timebase and I remember dear Bainbridge-Bell, who had written

---

[1] Air Defence Experimental Establishment.
[2] This became the transmitter widely used on CHL and GCI stations.
[3] American Radio Relay League handbook, published in USA but available in UK at 5s. A popular and very valuable source of information for radio hams.

Air Intake Filter
Calibration Chart
Matching Tuner
Wavemeter
Access to PRF and
X shift Control
Grid Tuner
Control Panel
Filament Rheostat
H.T. Voltage Control
Relay Compartment
H.T. Power Supply
Compartment

Lecher Compartment
Oscillator Valve
Compartment
Anode Squegging
Condenser Compartment
Coupling Tuner
Monitor Cathode
Ray Tube
HT Isolating Switch
Panel Keys
Tools Compartment
Monitor CRT & Power
Pack Compartment
HT Supply Compartment

A 1.5 m transmitter as used for CHL and GCI stations.

the definitive book on oscillographs and oscilloscopes and was then in charge of the Test Equipment Labs.

By the middle of 1939 the Tx and Rx were remounted (separately) in cabins on, I think, 4.5 in gun pedestals. With this arrangement we were able to observe echoes from sailing vessels and ships at ranges of about 10 miles. The Naze tower 11 miles away was used as a marker. During the trials it was found possible to obtain the range and bearing of a ship sailing into the river mouth towards Harwich after it had passed out of sight behind the Felixstowe headland. In July 1939 we were able to observe the echoes from the columns of water raised by 9.2 in shells from the Brackenbury battery of Harwich defences striking the water some 5 miles from the set.

Of far greater importance was the realisation that the set was able to detect and track aircraft flying at low levels, which the CH stations could not. The equipment was subsequently designated CD/CHL (Chain Home, Low). A seaplane flying at 500 ft was followed with accurate azimuth up to about 20 miles and then even more successfully using a Sunderland flying boat.

In the meantime, sea trials continued and, as the junior member of the team, it was my lot to crouch in the scuppers of a borrowed MTB (Motor Torpedo Boat) in the middle of the North Sea, working the Wireless Set No. 7 and conveying directions from the team to the skipper. The exercise was not a total success as the stink of diesel oil in the bilges combined with the very rough seas brought on an attack of 'mal de mer'. This made communication with the shore somewhat difficult!

VIP Visits

The work of the Research Establishment had not escaped the notice of our political masters and we were visited by Lord Chatfield (Minister for the Co-ordination of Defence), who seemed only to be interested in the red lights showing on the power units. This visit was followed by that of Winston Churchill in July 1939. At that time Churchill was not in the Government but since 1935 had been a member of the Committee of Imperial Defence on Air Defence Research, with his adviser, Professor Lindemann, a member of the Technical Sub-Committee.

The great day arrived and Churchill climbed into the receiver cabin and, prompted by Butement, looked in the observation telescope. He could not see the aircraft which was flying down the coast. Great consternation! Then it was found that, on that particular day, the azimuth accuracy was so great that the cross-hairs of the telescope actually covered the target aircraft! (At the end of his visit Churchill informed us that, although he was impressed, we were on the wrong track. The Germans, using infra-red, were ahead of us! I fear that he was reflecting the – often erroneous – opinion of the 'Prof'.)

The Army cell's time at Bawdsey was rapidly drawing to a close. At the end of August 1939 our labs were dismantled and on September lst I climbed aboard an enormous Scammell truck next to the driver, loaded with our gear, and set off for Christchurch. We were sad to leave Bawdsey and the somewhat benevolent direction of the Engineer Board. Our practice of pursuing an experiment regardless of time of day and without a thought of overtime pay was restricted when we came within the purview of the Ministry of Supply at Christchurch. The name of the establishment changed from ADEE to ADRDE (Air Defence Research and Development Establishment).

Soon after our arrival we were joined by staff from Biggin Hill and also by Professor John Cockcroft and his team from the Cavendish Labs. Cockcroft later took over as Superintendent. We were housed in a rather dilapidated large house called Bure Homage, which was also our temporary headquarters. We began unpacking on 3 September while listening to Chamberlain's speech announcing a state of war with Germany.

The following day the CD cell set off for Steamer Point in the grounds of Highcliffe Castle overlooking Christchurch Bay, Dorset. We had our first brush with the lady of the manor when manhandling a 15 kW diesel generator through the grounds. Typical of those times, our team leader W.S. Butement was pushing with the rest of us. Her ladyship approached me rather crossly and asked where 'the foreman' was. What could I do but point to Butement!

Disaster struck in the winter of 1939. Chick and I were returning from lunch when we learned that the transmitter hut was on fire. All our notes and personal effects were destroyed and the trials delayed. Security were soon on the scene and by following footmarks in the snow were initially convinced that intruders had scaled the cliffs. This was found to be false and rumour had it that they (like Pooh and Piglet) had been following their own footsteps in the snow.

The spring of 1940 was spent on trials of the VT98 a new version of our VT58 transmitting valve, now with thoriated tungsten filament, and other experiments leading to the development of a common aerial system. At the beginning of June 1940, after lunch at 'Betty's' in Bournemouth, I watched the arrival of some of the survivors of

Dunkirk. They were in bad shape – grey with exhaustion. On a perhaps quixotic impulse, I returned to the labs and – as I was in a 'reserved occupation' – requested permission to enlist. This was granted and I joined the Royal Artillery three weeks later.

After the war, Douglas Myhill became a staff officer (Telecommunications) at AA Command, Uxbridge, before moving to Canada where he worked as a Technical Officer in the Department of National Defence, Ottawa. He became Director of the Electronics Branch before going on to become General Manager of the Canadian Commercial Corporation. Finally he became Director General (Supply) in the Department of Supply and Services.

James R. Atkinson, BA (Cantab) (Maths and Physics), C.Phys., F.Inst.P, F.R.Met.S, FRSE

'Shortly after officers were appointed as station COs, armed guards were posted to the guardhouse for each station. As a result I was shot at twice.'

In my final year at St John's College, Cambridge, 1938, I had become closely acquainted with the late Hugh Carmichael, a Fellow of the College. He was preparing equipment for the Carmichael/Dymond Expedition to Greenland to measure the high-altitude soft component of the cosmic radiation. I helped in the preparation of the equipment and became so interested in cosmic rays that I was determined to join a research team investigating the problem. Hugh Carmichael suggested Uppsala in Sweden as one of the main centres. I went to see my supervisor, the late Sir John Cockcroft who told me that there was a need for a physicist in a research unit of the Air Ministry and that it would be an excellent opportunity to gain research experience.

After two fascinating interviews at the Air Ministry, I found myself reporting to Watson-Watt and A.P. Rowe at Bawdsey in September 1938. The radar project was explained to me and I was told that I would be working under Cyril Fogg in a section of the Chain Station Receiver division headed by Sidney Jefferson. The latter had written in 1937 a comprehensive paper on the different ways in which the Chain stations might be jammed by the Germans if and when the anticipated hostilities might commence. [With Mr Jefferson's permission, an abridged version of his paper is reproduced below.] The part which Fogg and myself were allocated to carry out was the development of afterglow cathode ray tubes to combat possible spark jamming. The aim was to develop a tube in which the afterglow could be filtered out for normal conditions but contain the afterglow characteristic under jamming conditions.

After many trials and tests, GEC Wembley was chosen as the contractors. Under C.C. Paterson, L.C. Jesty was in charge of the tube and screen development and J.W. Ryde was responsible for the colour filter development. After initial satisfactory tests on the Bawdsey Chain station in April 1939, Fogg and I proceeded to make the necessary changes to the Chain stations near Bawdsey. We had found that it was necessary to increase the tube voltage from 2.5 kV for the RF5 Cossor receivers to 5 kV to give the required focus and of course this meant modifications to the time base and vertical signal amplitudes and the power supply.

In the meantime GEC were developing better tubes and filters: a green/blue filter for no jamming, yellow for light interference, and orange for strong jamming. By July 1939 it was thought that a satisfactory system had been developed and it was planned to train a team of RAF technicians to carry out the necessary modifications to the additional Chain stations being constructed as they became operational.

The famous Zeppelin North Sea cruise of August 1939 changed all our provisional plans. Our priority was increased; Cyril Fogg became involved in the development of receivers for a variety of radar equipments to supplement the main Chain defence line. I was told to carry on fitting tubes and filters, modifying receivers and training the operators at the stations between Ventnor in the south and St Abb's Head in the north, with Dover as the highest priority.

When war was declared on 3 September, the Bawdsey staff were moved to 'safety' at Dundee with one or two exceptions, including myself. I was instructed to proceed as quickly as possible to continue testing the tubes and filters being made at Wembley. Bawdsey was no longer available for tube testing, so I modified the RF4 receiver at Cossor, Highbury, and drew the necessary components from 60 Group at Leighton Buzzard.

My fiancée Mona and I had planned to get married in November 1939 but in view of the uncertainties of the immediate future and that I knew that I should badly need help with driving, we were married by special licence on 7 September 1939. Until March 1940, when I was recalled to Dundee to start the 10 cm research with Herbert Skinner, Mona was my unpaid driver, and together we enjoyed some of the incidents that took place on our Chain station tours. An important fact was that Fighter Command would not allow stations to be off the air during daylight, so my work had to be done mainly during the hours of darkness.

Jimmy Atkinson's Austin 12. (Photograph: J.A. Atkinson.)

Our car — a 1928 Austin tourer — became well known particularly at Dover in about May 1939, when I was explaining to the lads there that we would be modifying their receiver for fitting the afterglow tubes, and gave them the reasons why. The steep hill to the radar site was being used by the Army to test small tractor-driven machines. I remarked that my Austin could easily manage the hill as it had a very low bottom gear. I was bet 10s by the day shift team that I couldn't manage it. We agreed on a time the following day and before they went on duty they were all watching at the top of the slope and I duly ascended. We met in a local pub in the evening, and the CO of the station — a warrant officer — duly handed over the ten bob.

I should add that at that time, the CO of radar stations was usually a flight sergeant or a warrant officer. I was told the reason for this was to play down the significance of the Chain stations. In 1944, when I was in the Officers' Mess near Inverness on other duties, one of the officers asked me how YH3586 (the Austin) was doing! When I knew him first in 1939 I was very impressed with his knowledge and capabilities and was not surprised to find that he was now a wing commander.

We Tour the Chain

On 4 September 1939, Mona and I set off on our tour of the Chain together with frequent calls at 60 Group Headquarters at Leighton Buzzard, at Highbury and at GEC Wembley. Subsistence claims were paid monthly but of course only for myself. As a result, at the beginning of each month we were usually able to afford a hotel, which would let me have a key because of returning very late in the evenings. (Towards the end of the month, a bed and breakfast establishment had to suffice.)

Occasionally I was allowed to put a station off the air late in the afternoon, but sometimes my work was interrupted by Fighter Command demanding that the station went back on the air. Mona used to wait patiently for me in the car outside the guardhouse. She spent the time knitting, reading or writing letters (without of course saying where we were). On some occasions she would be invited to have a cup of tea in the guardhouse; but at Canewdon she was told she was not to get out of the car for any reason, and on no account to cast her eyes up to the top of the 240 ft wooden towers. With no technical background, I doubt if the size of the dipoles would have made any impression on her.

Right from the start of the war, security was very strict to the extent that nobody could enter a Chain station without permission from Fighter Command, who would then inform the station concerned of their identity and ETA. This led to an embarrassing situation on a certain station (which I won't name), because one evening, when I was modifying the equipment, the RAF personnel on duty at the entrance guardroom rang the CO (then a flight sergeant) to say that a cavalcade of high-ranking officers had demanded entry and were making their way to the receiver hut. After a loud knock on the door, the flight sergeant was confronted by an air commodore accompanied by his staff. The commodore stated that he was AOC of the local Group HQ and as the station was in his area, he had come to inspect it. The flight sergeant clearly stated that as he had not received any prior notice of the visit he could not allow entry. During the ensuing heated argument, I had to move across the back of the room to collect a tool and the AOC demanded to know what a 'blankety blank' civilian was doing on his property. Eventually the flight sergeant firmly closed the door and locked it and then asked me if, in the event of any enquiry, I would be prepared to state what I had heard and seen. As I knew the duty officer at Stanmore, when I'd finished my work and reported the station back on the air, I gave him my account of what had happened. I understood later that the flight sergeant did not hear any more about the incident; whether the air commodore did or not – who knows?

Shortly after, officers were appointed as station COs and armed guards were posted to the guardhouse for each station. As a result I was shot at twice. (Fortunately, it being dark at the time, I am here to describe the events.) In the first case I had parked the car on the only firm ground available, which was at some distance from the guardhouse. On approaching the guardhouse, a shot rang out *followed* by the appropriate challenge. On the second occasion an enterprising CO had rigged up a line carrying tin cans between the receiver hut and the guardhouse. This was set up after the night shift had gone off duty. Unfortunately he must have forgotten that I was still working and when I was leaving I ran into the line. Again a shot rang out *followed* by the usual challenge 'Halt – who goes there?'

There was one incident which led to a cool – and fortunately brief – spell concerning my relations with Stanmore. I had the bright idea during one of my visits to Bawdsey to check the efficiency of the afterglow tubes and colour filters with real spark jamming – simulators did not exist then. I managed to borrow from Ipswich Hospital a disused diathermy spark machine, which we tried at the hospital and it seemed just what was needed. We put it up the mast at Bawdsey and I agreed with the operators there and at other nearby Chain stations that I would switch it on for five minutes at 6 p.m. We also agreed not to tell Stanmore as I thought they might object. It all went very well except that stupidly I had forgotten that 6 p.m. was the time that most people turned on their radios to find out how the war was going. A relatively large number of residents in the area heard none of the news until 6.05 p.m. Eventually the truth came out, and on condition that I tried no further experiments of any sort or at any location, a senior officer told me that I could regard the matter as closed.

In November 1939 I was provided with an assistant to help in the modifications and also in the training before Yatesbury eventually took over. There were many other incidents at some of the stations we visited and both Mona and I still remember them clearly after nearly sixty years. But in March 1940 our life became quite different on receiving the call to report at Dundee.

There I joined an eminent physicist Dr H.W.B. Skinner, and we were given the task of carrying out research into the feasibility of producing equipment at 10 cm wavelength capable of being installed in fighter aircraft. Right through until 1945 I was concerned with the testing and proving of cavity magnetrons at wavelengths of 6 cm, 5 cm, 3 cm and 1 cm. This work included the installation of a 3 cm system in an experimental flying laboratory. The research also included investigations into superrefraction as well as tests of centimetre wavelengths to detect schnorkels.

A Typical Month from J.R. Atkinson's Grand Tour of the Chain, September 1939–April 1940

1 September	Felixstowe to Stenigot
	Stenigot to Staxton Wold
2 September	Staxton Wold to Felixstowe
3 September	Felixstowe to Gt. Bromley
	Gt. Bromley to Canewdon
	Canewdon to Leighton Buzzard
4 September	Leighton Buzzard to Pevensey
5 September	Pevensey to Poling
	Poling to Pevensey
6 September	Pevensey to Rye
	Rye to GEC Wembley
7 September	GEC Wembley to Leighton Buzzard
	Leighton Buzzard to Pevensey
8 September	Pevensey to Rye
	Rye to Dover
9 September	Dover to Dunkirk
	Dunkirk to Pevensey
10 September	Pevensey to Ventnor IOW
11 September	Ventnor to Pevensey
	Pevensey to GEC Wembley
12 September	At GEC Wembley
13 September	GEC Wembley to Dunkirk
14 September	Dunkirk to Dover
15 September	Dover to GEC Wembley
16 September	GEC Wembley to Dover
17 September	At Dover
18 September	Dover to GEC Wembley
19 September	GEC Wembley to Leighton Buzzard
20 September	Leighton Buzzard to Stoke Holy Cross
	Stoke Holy Cross to High Street
	High Street to Bawdsey
21 September	Bawdsey to GEC Wembley
22 September	At GEC Wembley
23 September	At Cossors Highbury
24 September	Wembley to Canewdon
	Canewdon to Great Bromley
25 September	Great Bromley to Bawdsey
26 September	Bawdsey to Wembley
	Wembley to Cossors Hackney
27 September	London to Leighton Buzzard
28 September	Leighton Buzzard to Stoke Holy Cross
29 September	At Stoke Holy Cross

30 September   Stoke Holy Cross to High Street
                        High Street to Stoke Holy Cross
                        Stoke Holy Cross to Bawdsey.

Total Mileage for September 1939: 2,648

[The figures taken from J.R. Atkinson's logbook for that year.]

After the war, J.R. Atkinson joined the University of Glasgow as a senior lecturer and researcher in nuclear physics and subsequently held senior appointments in the UKAEA, the British Ship Research Association and Heriot-Watt University, Edinburgh.

[EXTRACTS FROM AND COMMENTS UPON SIDNEY JEFFERSON'S REPORT: 'GENERAL PERFORMANCE SPECIFICATION FOR RECEIVERS TO MINIMISE EFFECTS OF JAMMING'

Looking back now, from the late 1990s, after a half-century in which countless technical papers have been published on subjects such as the reception of radar signals and the effects of interference, one cannot fail to be impressed with this far-sighted paper. Although undated, most of its recommendations were embodied in the design of the CH receivers, the first types to be used in the UK early warning radar stations. It must therefore have been in existence – in substance if not in final form bearing a TRE reference – as early as 1936–7. (Copies with TRE reference include mention of PPI displays which postdate CH but are directly relevant otherwise.) It clearly presaged many of the radar techniques that were to become standard in later years.

For the purpose of this book – a non-technical survey of life at TRE rather than a guide to engineers – it is felt more appropriate to summarise its scope in general terms, quoting just a few extracts, rather than to reproduce it in full.

In the first part of the paper various likely forms of jamming are envisaged and possible palliatives outlined. It is acknowledged at the outset that while it may not be possible to reject jamming completely the aim is to provide means whereby, in spite of it, the vital radar data may nevertheless be extracted. In the second part more specific recommendations are made for the design of practical radar receiving systems. Combining these two parts, the subjects covered are summarised under appropriate headings.

Radio Frequency

A change in radio frequency 'is the most obvious step to take if jamming is encountered' but 'it is immediately obvious to the enemy and he may therefore get a measure of the effectiveness of his jamming, whereas if no frequency change is made he does not know whether his jamming is effective or whether it is not possible to change operating frequency'.

CH transmitters and receivers were originally designed to work on any of four selectable spot frequencies in the range 20–50 MHz. But final CH installations used only two spot frequencies.

The use of superheterodyne receivers is presupposed and the importance of adequate radio frequency selectivity before the frequency-changer is explained and stressed. (CH receivers used no less than three tuned r.f. stages – an exceptional measure.)

Receiver Bandwidth

The importance of adequate bandwidth for the faithful reception and display of pulses is explained together with guidance for calculating bandwidth in terms of pulse characteristics. (CH receivers had three preset bandwidths, manually selectable by the operator, for optimum results according to the transmitter pulse length being used and the prevailing clutter conditions.)

Filters

'. . . CW signals at frequencies within the acceptance band can easily overload the receiver since the transmitted energy is confined to a very small frequency band. Since the desired signals spread over a wide frequency it is possible to reduce the response of the receiver over a relatively narrow band without seriously distorting the desired signal.' And '. . . cuts of this kind in the response curve are generally best made early in the i.f. amplifier since here sharper cuts are more easily obtained and made moveable in position in the response curve. The ability to move the position of the cut or cuts is most important since the CW interference may come in anywhere in the acceptance band of the receiver.' (CH receivers had two such highly effective tuneable filters known as Intermediate Frequency Rejection Units ['IFRUs']).

Dynamic Range

Although this all-embracing term, commonly used today, is not actually employed in the report its meaning was thoroughly understood. It is in effect referred to under several headings including 'DC Feedback', 'Reduction of Overload', 'Superpositioning of Desired Signals', 'Rapid Recovery from Overload'. The overall aim was to ensure that any reduction in the receiver's essential sensitivity to weak signals by the presence of grossly large ones was kept to a minimum and for as short a time as possible. Also, the extra-strong signals should not cause displacement of the positions at which echoes were displayed on the screen. Guidance on actual magnitudes is given to designers. (In the CH receivers the various design features that ensured satisfactory results included appropriate time constants in decoupling circuits, dc feedback in i.f. stages and adequate bandwidth overall, including video stages.)

Blackout

'By blacking out the CRT by the jamming signal it is often possible to make the desired signal more easily detectable largely by reducing the distraction which the jamming signals might produce.' Methods of generating the blackout waveform are suggested. (CH receivers included an Anti-Jamming Blackout Unit ['AJBO'].)

Irregularity of Pulse Recurrence Period

'This method was first used as a means of resolving decoy echoes which the enemy might transmit in synchronism with the pulse recurrence frequency'. Recommendations for the extent of variation for different conditions are given. (CH receivers included an Intentional Jitter Anti-Jamming Unit ['IJAJ' pronounced 'Idge-Adge'].)

Pulse Width Discrimination

This was not then considered to be a suitable technique when dealing with multiple echoes and was not incorporated at that time. However, often termed 'PLD' (pulse length discrimination), it was adopted in the signal processing systems of some postwar radars.

Integration of Radar Signals

It was recognised that the successive superimposition of radar signals at the pulse repetition rate might render them more obvious to the observer than non-synchronised jamming. Both pre- and post-detection circuit methods of integration together with their pros and cons are discussed as possibilities. However, the method recommended was the use of special slow build-up and long afterglow CRT screens with coloured filters as fitted by J.R. Atkinson.]

Sidney Jefferson.

Sidney Jefferson, an EMI receiver engineer, designed CH receiving equipment at Bawdsey from 1936 and later, as a Senior Scientific Officer, led various groups at TRE. He married Nellie Boyce, one of the first three women radar operators selected personally by Watson-Watt. After the war he joined the United Kingdom Atomic Energy Authority, Harwell, and set up the Grove Research Laboratories near Wantage.

Olive Carlisle, WAAF Technical Officer

When I arrived at Worth Matravers CH station, I was a humble LACW (Leading Aircraft woman), but I had my hour of glory.

I was twiddling the gonio one day when I became aware that an officer and an elderly gentleman had come in and both were looking over my shoulder. The elderly gentleman asked if I would explain what I was doing, and on a nod from the officer, I proceeded to try to teach him in the simplest layman's language. He thanked me kindly and left. The officer came back, patted me on the shoulder and said: 'That was Dr Watson-Watt.'

After the war, Olive Carlisle was a pioneer air stewardess with BAOC and flew on Dakotas to the Middle East and Africa, then on the first passenger flying boat to Johannesburg. Constellation services to Sydney, followed by Argonauts to Hong Kong and Tokyo, Strats to New York, finishing on the ill-fated Comet, gave her plenty of excitement before settling down to domesticity. For six years she was Chairman of Berkshire County Blind Society.

R.V. ('Polly') Perkins, BEM, in Charge of Machine Shop (d. 1991)

'Winston Churchill had a high regard for us and if anything was required urgently he would say "Send it to TRE".'

It was September 1937 when I was directed by the Labour Exchange to proceed to the Air Ministry Research Station, Bawdsey and report to the workshops manager about a possible job. I cycled from Ipswich to Bawdsey ferry and stood there on the shingle beach thinking what a pretty place it was. I could just see the towers of the manor through the trees; then I noticed a motor launch leaving the other side with the RAF flag on the stern. I got on board and as we crossed the boatman – 'Tubby' Marjoram – told me to walk up the drive and look for the stables which were now the workshops and there I would find Mr Airey.

It was a beautiful walk up the drive, lined with trees and shrubs of many kinds blending into a magnificent pattern of colour. I found Mr Airey in the stables and I liked him immediately. He questioned me closely about my experience and then told me I was just the man he was looking for to be in charge of his machine shop. He took me on a tour around the U-shaped building, full of benches occupied by instrument makers. He showed me a brand new Denham lathe and asked me if I could work one; I said yes I could. He offered me the job at 70s a week – riches indeed! I had to be security vetted, but this was quickly done as I had previously served in the RAF, and on the Monday I started work at the highly secret Bawdsey Research Station. Little did I realise that this was the start of a career which would span over thirty-eight years, ending in 1975.

I soon settled down to the work, and my wife and small son and I moved to a rented house in Felixstowe. The scientific staff used to visit the workshops to get jobs done and explain what they wanted: I remember well Dr Bainbridge Bell – a nice old chap with snowy white hair who always wore his trousers at half mast. Then there was Jimmy Rowe, Secretary and Chief Administrator, who eventually became the Superintendent – a job he held for the rest of the war and he was the best and most efficient director I ever knew.

We had our own football team at Bawdsey consisting of a good mixture of scientists, workshop men, administrative staff, RAF and some of the riggers (the chaps who were erecting transmitter towers all round the country). But the happy days at Bawdsey quickly came to an end; a couple of days before war was actually declared we were told to get ready for complete evacuation. Everybody was detailed to stay on at work to start

Joe Airey, Workshops Manager from Bawdsey through to Malvern.

packing; my job was to see that all the machine tools and equipment were packed and loaded on to lorries – no mean feat since we had only ropes and rollers and the machines had to be manhandled up a 4 ft ramp on to the lorries.

We were not told our destination until the very last minute. Then we were issued with travel warrants to Dundee, to report there the following Monday. This journey took about ten hours (par for the course in wartime). On arrival at the university we congregated in the grounds where A.B. Jones, the Senior Administrative Officer, called our names and gave each of us an address for digs. A friend and I made our way to the address given and there we were shown to a huge room with six beds in it: two were for us and the others were occupied by sailors from the submarine base – smashing blokes they were, and later on we had some good times with them over a few pints. We had to be at work at 7.45 a.m. and when we went into the kitchen that first morning for breakfast, we weren't prepared for the sight that met us: the landlady's sister was in one bed and the daughter in another! And there we sat – two healthy, virile blokes munching toast and getting an eyeful of two young ladies in their nighties. The landlady took no notice at all – simply sat there drinking tea and chatting to us.

Finances were difficult while we were at Dundee. Skilled craftsmen got £3 10s a week with £1 1s added for subsistence. It cost us 25s a week for digs and I had to send home at least £2 10s for Ruby and our two children, leaving me just a few bob for incidentals and entertainment. We were not allowed to do any overtime, even though all our jobs were urgent and badly wanted, so we had all our evenings free with little or no money to spend. We'd visit the pictures twice a week at the old 'flea pit' where we could get in for 4d; at least we were out of the cold there.

Eventually I found a flat and sent for the family. Poor Ruby had a dreadful journey, with two young children and all the luggage, travelling to London from Ipswich then on to Dundee; the journey took twelve hours in trains crowded with troops – it must have been a nightmare for her. Alas, her stay would not be for long, as rumours were flying that we would soon be moving again – Dundee University was too small for us and too far from the action. And so, in due course, we were heading down south to a new site in Dorset.

Swanage

On arrival in Swanage I soon found some unfurnished rooms next door to a small grocers. I took the coach each day to Worth Matravers where there was a lovely old pub called the Square and Compass, which before the war had been a favourite haunt of West End actors and film stars, many of whom had left signed photographs on the walls. When I arrived that first day, I found the instrument shops, the machine shop and the stores were all located in a compound of Nissen huts, where my machines had all been installed.

New recruits were arriving daily; Dunkirk was very recent and the war was on with a vengeance – overtime now became a necessity as we were working flat out to win the war. Radar was top priority and no effort was spared to get equipment and to encourage the 'brains' to develop this extraordinary new technique. They were mostly young men fresh from university, full of ideas and many of them are now household names.

As we had only two lathes and a milling machine, it became impossible to keep the instrument makers fully employed on assembly. In due course we acquired three small bench lathes and a 6.5 in Wilson centre lathe, and to operate them we were sent a bunch of 'Dilutees' – men directed from their homes to vital war work. More and more kept coming, including some girls and soon I had twelve working under me. A lot of chassis and other sheet-metal items were required so we set up a sheet-metal section.

While we were at Swanage we had several heads of engineering, one of them Mr Seiger, a tall, dark, handsome chap always smartly dressed. He often walked through the workshop with his wife – a lovely lady who was always beautifully dressed – and his dog, a red setter. He certainly was a character. Later on he set up and ran the workshops near Bournemouth where the prototypes were manufactured.

The war situation was becoming more tense and it was decided to mount a raid on a German radar station on the French coast. It needed a scientist to collar the important items and the man they selected was Mr Preist, a really likeable lad. The raid was a big success and naturally reprisals were feared. There we were, stuck on the cliffs near Swanage just 60 miles from the enemy, with tall masts to advertise our position, and news came through to expect an attack within a few days.

Another for the Swanage–Malvern road! Standard 10 (*c.* 1934) reliable work-horse of the 1930s, owned by one of the ground aerial erection team.

One of the many Pickfords pantechnicons loading up at Worth Matravers for the move to Malvern, May 1942.

So once again we loaded up the lorries with all our machines and accessories in double quick time. A fleet of Pickfords vans arrived and it rained all the time we loaded. It was vital that all the equipment arrived safely, so the whole convoy was heavily guarded all the way to Malvern.

Malvern

We took over the boys' college, although the boys had only just returned from being evacuated. But apparently Churchill gave the order that they'd have to go again so that TRE could carry on with their vital work.

By this time there were over a thousand of us, and once more we congregated outside while A.B. Jones and Arthur Wolleter gave us addresses of requisitioned billets. You can imagine the reception we were given – frigid would be an understatement!

The Ministry of Works (Flying Squad) had built us a workshop on the Junior Turf at the college. With the shortage of fuel there was usually no heating in the workshops and my Denham lathe was parked in the corner of the shop under a galvanised roof; when the wind blew from the north it came through all the gaps and I would have to try and work the lathe wearing my overcoat, hat, scarf and gloves. We moaned a lot but never thought of going on strike, although we did have a spot of labour trouble brought on by two factors. Firstly the money was poor compared to wages in industry, and secondly we had a lot of 'Directed Labour' which meant that married men and others were living in digs and they only got two free passes home a year. This began to bring trouble (what with all the girls working there) and eventually a report of the dissatisfaction reached Jimmy Rowe, who came down to speak to the blokes. As soon as he entered the place with Joe Morley and Air Cdre Gregory, everybody stopped work and assembled at the bottom of the shop. Jimmy started talking and the 'Bolshies' started singing 'Tell me the old old story'. Jimmy was livid; he'd never been treated like this before and he asked me if I could stop them. I told them to give him a chance, and gradually the noise subsided while Mr Rowe told them that a new pay scheme was starting which would give them another £2 per week and that there would be more free passes home.

Ruby and the kids were staying with her mother on the east coast, right in the path of the Doodlebugs, so I was determined to find some suitable accommodation in Malvern. I found a place with a lovely old lady, a Miss Wilson, who was very good to us, especially the children.

Meanwhile work was going on at a tremendous pace; the station was still growing and radar equipment was required for all three Services. Every Sunday in the headmaster's room at the college Jimmy Rowe had what were called 'Sunday Soviets', at which the heads of all the fighting Services met the scientific staff and discussed the progress of the war and the future requirements.

In 1943 we were transferred to a new workshop called the Engineering Unit, which was a wonderful building comprising a large machine shop, two instrument shops, a sheet-metal and fitting shop, heat treatment and toolroom, as well as transformer and wiring shops. On the first floor was a large drawing and design office. Beneath the whole building was a network of underground shelters. I found the machine shop fully equipped with new lathes and milling machines in addition to all my old machines. By then we had over seventy blokes and girls working in the machine shop – most of them Dilutees but also a sprinkling of skilled men who I made up to chargehand status to help me train and supervise all the unskilled staff. The volume of work was enormous but we set to work with bags of enthusiasm; we had a happy shop with the girls and chaps all pulling together and singing songs. It was a treat to hear the whole shop belting out 'Onward Christian Soldiers'. The girls adapted quickly to the work; many had never seen a lathe before yet they turned out to be damn good machinists.

Winston Churchill had a high regard for TRE and if anything was required urgently he would say 'Send it to TRE'. Consequently we were inundated with problems that resulted in fantastic ideas being created and transformed into reality.

Jimmy Rowe knew how to sell our efforts and many famous people came to visit us including Sir Stafford Cripps. Peter Ustinov made a film about our activities and eventually the King and Queen made a visit and presented some medals. I thought the Queen was lovely; she had the most beautiful blue eyes I'd ever seen.

In 1945 the war was going our way at last and Hitler gambled everything on the Doodlebugs and the V2s. TRE was called in to help and Dr Penley was put in charge of

King George VI and Queen Elizabeth (the present Queen Mother) presenting awards to some of the staff at TRE Malvern in July 1944.

the project named 'Rugger Scrum'.[1] A team of draughtsmen was allocated to the job and I was told to get on with it. I told my blokes how important it was so when draughtsmen arrived from the RAE they had the shock of their lives: as soon as they finished a drawing it was whipped away into the machine shop and completed in hours. They'd never seen anything like it having been used to waiting weeks and even months for a job to be completed.

Almost all the jobs were urgent and I was working eighty hours a week (for a weekly wage of £6). New techniques were being developed all the time: one scientist, Dr F.E. Jones, was in charge of a very successful project (Oboe) that involved the machining of small section silver waveguide to extremely fine limits. He used to visit the machine shop regularly and explain to the men what he was trying to achieve. He was extremely popular especially when he came in one day and showed us the results of the first mission in which his equipment was used – they were fantastic (bombing accuracy).

Soon it was VE Day and in no time at all the war was over. In due course TRE was amalgamated with ADRDE (the Army research establishment in Malvern) and became RRE (Royal Radar Establishment), a title that was conferred upon us by the Queen at a special ceremony. Slowly the staff began to leave, many of them to work in atomic energy stations; but I stayed on at Malvern for the rest of my working life, retiring in 1975 with a huge party for over 150 guests including many old colleagues who came from afar to see me off.

Reginald 'Polly' Perkins continued at Malvern after the war and was in charge of the mechanical engineering workshops and later became instructor of mechanical engineering at the College of Electronics at Malvern. His last job was as Safety Officer at RRE Malvern.

Dr George Lonsdale Hutchinson, B.Sc., Ph.D.

'You were either a rigger, a frigger or a boffin.
Sometimes I felt that I was all three.'

During 1939 the Royal Society compiled a central register of university lecturers and research graduates to facilitate postings to the Services or research establishments in the event of war. In August 1939 several of us who were on this register were invited to spend six weeks at various radar stations around the country. I was in a group sent to Darsham, Suffolk, to report at an Air Ministry station called High Street near Darsham on Monday 28 August 1939. The group contained Dr Barlow from University College, London, Drs W. Cochrane and Wynne Williams from Imperial College, S. Humphreys-Owen from Birkbeck, R.A. Smith from Cambridge and myself and Joe Aharoni from King's London. Remuneration would be at the rate of 5 guineas a week, which I thought gave it rather a gentlemanly touch.

---

[1] 'Rugger Scrum' was a crash programme for defence against the V1 flying bomb. The equipment consisted of a 3 cm tracking radar feeding a predictor which in turn controlled a twin-barrelled automatic Bofors gun.

At High Street we went through the security indoctrination and then set about learning how the Chain Home (CH) stations worked. Soon the MB1 transmitter on the station went unserviceable and in the receiver block the operators stared at a blank tube. A couple of regulars came up from Bawdsey to sort things out but High Street was actually off the air when war was declared on 3 September.

Early in October I was called to the Admiralty for interview and by the 19th I had been accepted as a Junior Scientific Officer to work at AMRE Dundee to where Bawdsey had been evacuated. I reported to Dundee Training College for Teachers in Park Place the first week in November.

Initially I worked with a New Zealander, Mr Banwell, and Dr R.A. Smith was section leader on a project to make a scaled-down version of a CH aerial system to study redesigns and to look into the effects of the terrain. Since valve oscillators at that time were unlikely to work satisfactorily at less than 20 cm wavelength, it can be seen that with CH at 10 m, the best scaling factor we were likely to achieve was about 50, and therefore 'model' mast heights of at least 6 ft would be required.

The aerial work was part of J.A. Ratcliffe's division at Dundee and I remember him asking me if I thought there was a chance of centimetric magnetrons being operated in aircraft. I had worked on split anode magnetrons in 1938–9 and had no reservations in saying that I thought there was little chance.[1] Within a year breadboard centimetric radars using cavity magnetrons were being tested at TRE so I was hopelessly wrong in my forecast.

In a laboratory near us, Wynne Williams was working on what I imagine was to be an improved 'fruit machine' – the CH calculator. Later on Wynne Williams moved to the Enigma team at Bletchley Park.

By the end of 1939 a number of us were sent out to the CH stations as scientific observers, checking on performance in range and height-finding, on the ability to judge numbers of aircraft in formations and so on. I was sent to Ottercops in Northumberland, but early in 1940 I was at Ventnor IOW. This station on St Boniface Down was at about 700 ft so that normal CH height-finding was impossible.[2] It was thought that some approximate height-finding might be possible by observing variations in signal strength as a target aircraft passed in and out of the beams. I reported on tests to the Research Establishment, with a copy direct to Watson-Watt in London.

By the beginning of April 1940 I was loaned to the newly formed 60 Group RAF, which, based at Leighton Buzzard, was responsible for the installation, maintenance and operation of the RAF radar chain. At first my work concerned the installation of the permanent gear in CH stations, some of which had started the war with temporary equipment. I worked in Proctor Wilson's section directly under Fennessy (now

---

[1] Although the split anode magnetron was well known in research laboratories during the 1930s, it had never become established as a reliable high-power microwave generator. But when, in February 1940, resonant cavities were formed in the anode of the valve itself – rather than using external tuned circuits – the performance was transformed. The cavity magnetron was the key to microwave radar.

[2] CH height-finding depended on ground reflections for which a surrounding area of smooth and level ground was required.

Sir Edward) and Seward. It was then that I first heard of the categories of workers: you were either a 'rigger', a 'frigger' or a 'boffin'. Sometimes I felt that I was all three! Often I co-opted a rigger to work with me and I remember one, when we were coming down from the top 360 ft platform of the steel tower, challenging me to a race – I'd go down the ladders and he'd go down the steelwork. He won hands down and was there to welcome me when I stepped off the bottom ladder.

After a brief spell calibrating Netherbutton on the Orkneys, I was off to Ventnor again. I left there on 12 August and the ferry was bombed at Ryde. We were landed at Clarence Pier, Southsea, since the normal Portsmouth Harbour ferry pier was out of action, and as we walked to Portsmouth station, machine-gun bullets spattered all around us. Enemy aircraft were trying to shoot down the barrage balloons and the bullets had to come down somewhere. The following morning when I got to work at 60 Group, a fast car was ready with a senior RAF officer aboard to take me straight back to Ventnor: the CH station had been badly bombed while I was making my way across the Solent the day before. The RAF officer was coming to comfort the troops and I was to report on the damage, what could be repaired easily and so on.

Shortly after, I became involved in the siting of radar stations. This was a complicated business in those early days of CH: new sites had to be selected so that ground reflections produced the required beams in the vertical plane, and of course the azimuthal coverage had to meet Air Ministry requirements. Then we had to find good access; proximity to telephone lines; low-value agricultural land, and a layout that lent itself easily to good camouflage. Responsibility for site selection rested with AMRE but it was thought that with 60 Group's interest in the installation and operation of the stations, they should be represented on the siting party (by me). The immediate task was to locate standby sites around the south-east corner of the coast, so that in the event of the CH's being knocked out, mobile units could be deployed.

So off we went to scour the country around Poling, Pevensey, Rye, Dover (Swingate) and Dunkirk, accompanied by the Research Establishment member and Post Office engineers. The AMRE member was Bernard Ewing who had been with the forces in France picking sites for mobile radar stations. Our siting team had the job also of naming any new site – choosing a name that referred to some local feature and was also distinctive over the phone. Selecting a standby site for Dunkirk, Ewing took a schoolboy delight in naming it after the nearby farm – Cutballs. But he was overruled by the Air Ministry and it was finally christened Blean Wood.

From this time on, most of my time at 60 Group was involved in siting and layout of new CH and GCI stations. I covered Northern Ireland and the Scilly Isles and Cornwall, Wales including Anglesey, the Isle of Man and Scotland, including the Hebrides, the Orkneys and Shetlands. Bernard Ewing, having been given a nominal commission in the RAF, was also sent to Iceland and the Faroes to select sites. His trip to the Faroes almost ended in disaster when he became unwell and the naval surgeon diagnosed appendicitis and said he'd have to operate in the morning. Bernard asked if there was any alternative and the surgeon said he had known that drinking gin was sometimes an effective cure. Bernard welcomed this opportunity and drank gin with enthusiasm. By morning he was cured, apart from a hangover, and held a belief thereafter that alcohol would cure anything.

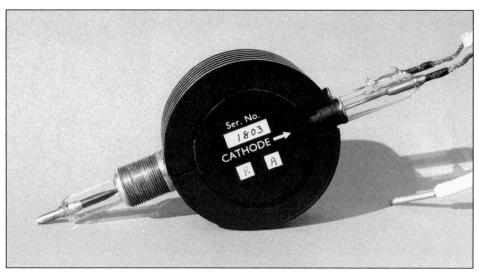

A typical wartime air-cooled magnetron. The output probe is on the left and the heater and cathode connections on the right.

By the end of 1942 most of the ground radar cover was sited and the advances into microwaves meant that a radar site could be selected purely to provide the type of coverage required.[3] I started manoeuvres to return to TRE, which by then (January 1943) had moved to Malvern. At first I worked on AI under Dr W.E. Burcham. There was a requirement to generate a larger drive pulse from the modulator of AI MkVIII and although this could be done in theory, retaining the same polarity, there was not enough space in the modulator to house the equipment required.

At the same time, trials of the American SCR720 – a centimetric AI with a helical scan – were under way at the Night Fighter Interception Unit at Ford, and a TRE representative was required. Since it was unlikely that any new R and D would produce equipment in time to influence the war, I was not unhappy to transfer to these trials of the American-built AI, which became known as AI MkX. In the end it was decided to go ahead with this equipment which was to be fitted in several Mosquito squadrons. Early production models of the AI MkX were flown out of America in June. In parallel the USAAF had installed this equipment in the Black Widow night fighter. Back at TRE we were preparing for an installation of it at our flying unit at Defford, in a Wellington 'Flying Classroom' in which a few operators at a time could learn how to operate the equipment in the air. A servicing manual for AI MkX was written and a first draft produced by Publications Branch at Malvern.

---

[3] By comparison with earlier radars working at longer wavelengths, e.g. 1.5 m, the microwave sets did not cause significant ground reflections. Thus the character of the terrain was no longer important.

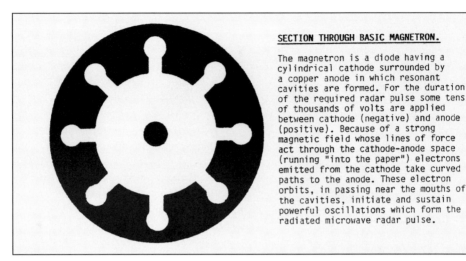

SECTION THROUGH BASIC MAGNETRON.

The magnetron is a diode having a cylindrical cathode surrounded by a copper anode in which resonant cavities are formed. For the duration of the required radar pulse some tens of thousands of volts are applied between cathode (negative) and anode (positive). Because of a strong magnetic field whose lines of force act through the cathode-anode space (running "into the paper") electrons emitted from the cathode take curved paths to the anode. These electron orbits, in passing near the mouths of the cavities, initiate and sustain powerful oscillations which form the radiated microwave radar pulse.

A diagram showing the internal arrangement of cavities and cathode in a typical magnetron.

By now I was in the Post Design Section (PDS) at TRE and back under J.A. Ratcliffe. By late 1943 I went to West Malling airfield to help 85 Squadron to convert from AI MkVIII to MkX. I spent most of my time in the radar section, getting the bench set going and also doing some test flying in the early installations. The CO of the station was Wg Cdr John Cunningham who, with his operator Jimmy Rawnsley, were both very well known in the airborne night fighter world.

I stayed at West Malling through Christmas and most of January 1944 when I became involved with the other squadrons converting to AI MkX. Later on I participated in a programme to try and reduce ground returns by spraying aluminium under the noses of the Mosquitos. I often wondered if this was worth the effort, but D-Day was approaching and everything had to be on the top line.

Dr Hutchinson remained with TRE at Malvern until 1947 and then moved to RAE at Farnborough in the Guided Weapons Department. From 1954–7 he was based in Washington DC on the British Joint Services Mission. He then returned to RRE at Malvern as Senior Principal Scientific Officer, becoming Deputy Director in 1963. In 1971 he moved to the Admiralty Underwater Weapons Establishment at Portland as Director until his retirement in 1975.

Dr John M.M. Pinkerton, MA, Ph.D., D.Sc., C.Eng., FIEE (d. 1997)

'We were briefed by Watson-Watt
personally in his office in Whitehall.'

My journey to TRE started in July 1939 when I was beginning my third year reading for part II of the natural sciences tripos at Cambridge. It was usual for physics students to spend some weeks in Cambridge during the long vacation doing practical work because there were so many experiments to do which could not all be fitted in during the three academic terms.

A notice signed by Mr J.A. Ratcliffe appeared in the laboratory saying that there would be a short course later in the vacation to be sponsored by the Government and of special interest to radio enthusiasts. Anyone interested should speak to Mr Ratcliffe, which I did. He was somewhat mysterious saying I would have to be cleared by security. A week or two later he said I'd been cleared; later still I was told to join the course at a certain hotel in Folkestone.

There were other Cambridge people there including John Findlay. The upshot was that we spent about four or five weeks at the Dover CH radar station where, at 11 a.m. on Sunday 3 September we heard Mr Neville Chamberlain on the BBC declaring we were at war with Germany. We all assumed the first thing the Luftwaffe would do was to come over and take out all the radar stations. Dover seemed the most obvious one to start on being the nearest, but nothing of the kind happened (until the following year).

After four or five weeks in Dover we thought we knew all about CH radar practice. I wanted to join the research station, which we'd heard was at a remote place on the east coast. I was advised by the Cambridge University recruiting board to return as usual in October as I would be of more use to radar research if I had completed my degree. I was not called up but in June 1940 joined AMRE, which by then had moved to Swanage.

I was sent to a CH station near Scarborough to set up one of a number of posts to listen for German long-range VHF navigational beams. We were briefed by Watson-Watt personally in his office in Whitehall. Other listening posts were set up at Chain stations up and down the east coast. The German beams were used to locate and bomb British cities, including Coventry and Bristol. I later went on to establish a post at Dundee, where I got into trouble for disconnecting (for some reason I cannot now recall) the aerial system of a standby radar without getting the CO's approval. I must have taken Watson-Watt's instructions for the strictest security too literally: I made the cardinal error of not telling the CO what I was supposed to be doing on his station!

Back at Swanage I worked on aerial measurements, always out of doors and occasionally in a field where the local farmer's cows had a habit of scratching themselves on the dipoles which affected both the impedance and polar diagram.

I was sent to Dover during the Battle of Britain to install and set up a 50 cm aerial array on the back of the regular 1.5 m CHL array. The idea was to counter German jamming on 200 MHz. Unfortunately the additional dipoles added so much to the wind resistance that the whole thing blew down in a gale only a few days after it was set up and working. It had to be re-erected.

While I was at Dover, the town was regularly shelled from France and the radar stations on the cliff top were sometimes dive-bombed by Stukas. Most people took cover instantly in the station buildings, which were heavily sandbagged, but during one attack an RAF technician at the CHL site got so excited by what was happening that he stayed outside on the aerial platform giving a vivid running commentary, ignoring the Stukas and heavy AA fire all around him.

The main CH blocks were more substantial and were strengthened against bombs by two layers of concrete separated by six ft or more of shingle. One day a direct hit on the roof of the receiver block cracked both layers of concrete and the CO's office was filled to the ceiling with shingle. Luckily he was out at the time. The CH aerial feeders were constantly being cut which meant rephasing and recalibrating the system.

Another memory from Swanage days was examining the German 50 cm radar receiver brought back from the raid on Bruneval. This had nothing to do with my job but I found it a fascinating example of the thoroughness of German engineering. Special high-frequency valves of a totally unfamiliar type were used. The separate receiver stages were mounted in die-cast boxes with machined lids. Screws that had to be undone to gain access to what was inside the covers were ringed in red. On every component was an inspector's official stamp with the date. Most were in 1937, showing how far advanced they were in 50 cm radar technology before war began. The whole impression was that they had had, and had taken, all the time it needed to create a really thorough design.

I worked for Vivian Bowden (later Lord Bowden) on the airborne IFF interrogators code-named LUCERO, until he went to Washington to work on IFF Mark V. Working for him was a stimulating experience with never a dull moment.

I recall the South Wales trials of the IFF Mark III system. Bowden and Rennie Whitehead had been inspired to compute the possibility of 'interpooping' between IFF Mark III sets in concentrated groups, say of bomber aircraft.[1] They concluded on theoretical grounds that it could happen. If it did, of course genuine identification would be impaired. So the transmitters in IFF sets and the airborne interrogators were redesigned so as not to respond for about a millisecond after being triggered. I believe that the trials failed to prove that interpooping could occur since insufficient aircraft were involved. However, I spent three pleasant weeks on a Pembrokeshire farm near St Bride's Bay enjoying local bacon and eggs for breakfast every day. Rationing seemed to be unheard of out there.

The move to Malvern was precipitated by an early morning raid on Swanage by a couple of German planes. I was woken up by the sound of cannon fire seemingly right overhead, and ran downstairs much faster than usual to see the view of the bay completely obscured by smoke and dust. By then the raiders had gone, but not before dropping a few bombs and killing at least one member of TRE staff.

While at Swanage I ran a 1925 vintage car for a time – a Lancia Lambda bought from Nat Marshall who had paid 25s for it at a house auction he'd gone to intending to buy a piano. That went too high for him so he bid for the car instead, against the local scrap-metal dealer. The bidding advanced by only a shilling at a time. This exasperated the auctioneer who suggested advances of at least 5s, whereupon the dealer gave up, leaving Nat with a bargain. Sadly, on the journey to South Wales for the IFF trials, it ran its big

---

[1] Interpooping: in a close formation of aircraft, all carrying IFF, it was possible that the legitimate transmission from any one unit, in replying to an interrogating ground station, could appear as an interrogating pulse to other IFF sets in nearby aircraft. Although individual units were sweeping the IFF band and therefore unlikely at any instant to be on a common frequency, the closeness of the aircraft implied exceptionally strong pulses which might break through. The potential nightmare was a squadron of IFF-equipped bombers all triggering each other, spoiling their chances of identification and with their total radiation giving away their presence to the enemy.

ends. It struggled back to Swanage at 25 m.p.h with no oil pressure, but being hard up I had to sell it in Poole for scrap after all. It was an interesting car, being one of the first to have an independent front-wheel suspension of a unique design. It was great fun to drive. There were other notable cars at Swanage – an Alvis Speed 20 owned by Preist; a 3-litre Bentley owned by Doug Hogg and an enormous Lagonda owned by Sieger, which was reputed to do about 12 miles to the gallon.

In Malvern I lived in a Government hostel in School House 5. I was intrigued by Dr Uttley's H2S radar trainer. This consisted of a large shallow tank filled with water; at the bottom was a model of typical towns and the countryside to be overflown. A quartz crystal on a movable carriage emitted pulses of ultrasonic waves emulating the radar scanner, and received return echoes off these objects, which resembled those that would have been seen in actual flight.

This led me to consider, when I returned to Cambridge at the invitation of J.A. Ratcliffe, the use of ultrasonics for looking inside living creatures – an idea that has since taken off successfully. But in due course, ultrasonics got me into computers via J. Lyons at Cadby Hall.

After the war, Dr Pinkerton designed, for J. Lyons & Co., the first ever computer ('Leo') intended specifically for clerical work, and the later production versions, Marks II and III. He became Research Manager for English Electric Computers and later planned ICL's 2900 series. After retirement in 1984, he started a computer consultancy business.

Professor George E. Bacon, Sc.D. (Cantab), Ph.D.

'With the present-day long delays, poor deliveries,
terrible service and no sense of urgency, it seems
incredible what we managed to achieve in 1940'.

I joined TRE at Worth Matravers on Saturday 4 May 1940 aged twenty-two. I spent the first night, together with my colleague C.J. Banwell, at the Vicarage at Worth. Banwell was a New Zealander who had come to England the previous year to do radio research at Cambridge; while on his way by sea, war had been declared and the situation at Cambridge was rather different from what he had expected. Like most of the graduates at the Cavendish Laboratory, he was enlisted into RDF research and this is how I came to know him. I myself had graduated at Cambridge in June 1939. Many of us had been prepared for entering Air Ministry research a month or so earlier, and when war was declared I was in a train on my way to the Air Ministry Experimental Station (AMES) at Dover. I spent the next six months gaining experience on the Chain of 15 m radar stations on the south and east coasts.

After our first night at Worth I had to go to London to a meeting at the Air Ministry but Banwell explored the neighbourhood of Worth on his bike and found a home for us in Langton Matravers with Mrs Wingate, almost at the top of the hill opposite the Methodist Chapel. We had a sitting room to ourselves, complete with a piano, and were very comfortable and well fed, including our midday sandwiches; I have no recollection of any shortages as a result of rationing. My bedroom window looked up the valley to Corfe Castle; it was very pleasant and peaceful and I stayed there for the whole of the time that TRE was based at Worth.

My professional work at Worth was in ground radar – the location of aircraft from the ground – and I was particularly concerned with measuring their height which, in 1940, could not be done very accurately, especially when the detecting station was near to high ground. This meant that it was almost impossible to direct a fighter into a good position for attacking a night bomber. As the war proceeded, the accuracy of height-finding improved; eventually it became possible to position fighters close enough for them to use their own AI radar for the final attack.

In May 1940 we began the installation of our aerial system on a 240 ft wooden tower alongside Renscombe Farm. The system was called VEB (Vertically Elevated Beam) and was the radio equivalent of a vertically scanning searchlight, operating on a wavelength of 1.5 m. However, in order to increase its raid-handling capacity, it had to be a 'fan' beam, broad in the horizontal plane, rather than a 'pencil' beam. The basic idea was to produce a very narrow beam of radio energy by stacking horizontal dipole aerials one above the other on the tower. There were seventy-five of these, each separated by a vertical distance of 75 cm (half a wavelength) and extending up the centre of the tower from about 40 ft to 220 ft in height. Such an arrangement would produce a horizontal beam with a vertical width of about 1½ degrees, which could scan the sky like a searchlight. The vertical scanning was to be achieved by varying the frequency of the transmitter; optical theory shows that a frequency change of about 25 per cent is necessary in order to achieve the desired beam movement of 15 degrees. Although this was simple in principle, it posed immense technical difficulties in maintaining a constant load and a uniform distribution of power among the dipoles over such a wide range of frequency.[1]

This proposal was very soon abandoned in favour of a single-frequency system, which I suggested. The stack of dipoles was divided into a number of groups (seven or nine was suitable) which were linked to a phase-shifter, controlling the phase relationships of the radio waves transmitted by the individual groups. In turn, these phases determined the angle at which the groups of dipoles reinforced each other, so that by controlling the phases it was possible to change the angle of elevation of the beam. By suitable rotation of the arm of the phase-shifter, the beam scanned from, say, 0 to 15 degrees within a period of a few seconds. (The detail of the optical theory underlying my idea can be found in a paper published at the end of the war in the JIEE, vol. 93, 539–44, 1946.) At the present time, fifty years on, I have no recollection of actually testing the original frequency variation system before discarding it. However, we certainly pressed rapidly ahead with the new idea, which we were confident would be successful.

There was a good deal of outdoor work involved and, fortunately, the weather in May 1940 was very suitable for it. Indeed, early June was even better and, in spite of

---

[1] This system was ahead of its time: the enabling technology was not then available but after the war systems of this kind were more successful.

working seven days a week, there was always the possibility of sea bathing in the evening. Living at Langton Matravers I came to know the sea near Seacombe Cliff very well.

However, this idyllic situation was not to last. The evacuation from Dunkirk took place from 27 May to 4 June and France fell on 18 June. What had seemed to be only short-term plans for building our height-finding equipment had to be sacrificed to even more urgent needs, namely the provision of better basic radar cover around the coast in the face of expected invasion. This was needed particularly on the south coast, which now faced an enemy occupied coast stretching beyond Cherbourg. On 24 June I went to Beachy Head for three weeks. There was a curfew on the Parade at Eastbourne from 10 p.m. to 4 a.m. and men, women and children were filling sandbags with pebbles from the beach and placing them in the wheeled bathing machines that had been lined up as barricades across the ends of the streets which led to the sea front.

Provision of better radar cover for the likely invasion sites on the south coast was followed by the need to protect all ports. I visited a station in Lincolnshire which covered the Humber Estuary and another at Prestatyn which watched the approaches to Liverpool; yet a third in Scotland, a few miles from Wick, where a radar station had been erected to give better cover to the approaches to Scapa Flow. In each case my task was to see that the newly installed radar stations were operating satisfactorily and that the RAF personnel were well acquainted with the performance that could be expected from them.

On returning to Worth Matravers after a busy two months, I found the Battle of Britain had extended a good deal further westward. On 25 August I counted forty-two German aircraft passing over Worth in the afternoon; there were three alarms and the next day four more. A month later, 27 September, fifty-eight aircraft came over and we saw three shot down. After this, things quietened down and we were able to get on with our work more or less unhindered.

The installation and testing of our aerial system was largely complete. I remember flying a calibration balloon from St Alban's Head, carrying a small oscillator tuned to our exact frequency. Unfortunately a wind got up and the tethering rope broke: the balloon was last seen out at sea, heading towards Cherbourg. We sent a hurried message to our parent aerodrome at Warmwell asking for it to be shot down; we had no wish to make a gift of our frequency to the enemy. I have no recollection that we ever heard whether it was destroyed or not.

The installation work on the tower had proved enjoyable. It needed a certain head for heights, though what might be called the hazardous steeplejack work was done by the station's team of 'riggers' – five or six of whom had been on the job since before the war in the early days at Bawdsey. They were very experienced and capable.

Inevitably we on the scientific staff had to acquire a good many manual skills: having been used to soldering the connections on a simple electrical circuit in a laboratory, it was rather a change to try soldering heavy lead-sheathed cables and copper blocks in a howling gale 150 ft above the ground. Once we wrestled in a wind with a 4 ft square cover that had become detached from our phase-shifter box half way up the tower; we soon learned that double precautions were always necessary.

At the present day in face of long delays, poor deliveries, terrible service and no sense of urgency, it seems quite incredible what we managed to achieve in 1940. We used to say that no task or project could take more than six to eight weeks to complete. If some item did not exist it had to be made and the station's workshop was extremely versatile, knowing that anything they were asked for would be required within two to three days. Although we were nominally only making experimental sets, not operational prototypes or production runs – there was a limit to the specialised techniques, such as making castings, which could be achieved in a general workshop. I do remember putting out the manufacture and machining of about fifty brass castings to a foundry in Poole, for use in connecting large diameter cables. On receipt, the threads of some of these were decidedly tight and it is typical of our sense of urgency that we did not think of returning them to the manufacturers for further machining but set to work ourselves with a tin of metal polish and ran the threads in. (On our eventual move to Malvern we were able to call on all the 'back street' firms in Birmingham for almost any item we needed, ranging from a silver-plated waveguide from the jewellery quarter to a lorry mounted mobile radar set from a coach builder.)

There was scarcely any source of supply or recruitment for the combination of semi-scientific and semi-manual skills that were needed. By good fortune I had, for a long time, the help of Russell Aves, who had been a senior technician at the Cavendish Laboratory in Cambridge and had taught me glass-blowing and some workshop practice when I was an undergraduate. He was very able and willing to do almost anything – from, say, photography to welding – and at the same time was patient and encouraging as an instructor. He was also a very good 'acquirer' – a valuable skill in those days. One day he decided that we needed extra warm clothing for working up towers and managed to find a variety of garments, of which the prize item was the inside of a flying suit, nicknamed the teddy bear suit.

Our pattern of existence had now settled down to trying to get one rest day a week. For a while this was on the basis of a staggered day, so that in principle there were always six-sevenths of the staff working at Worth. By early 1941 the whole of the station had Saturday for its nominal rest day. For most of the year it was still possible to go to the Sunday evening service at Langton church with the aid of double summertime. However, because of the difficulties of providing blackout, the service was held in the afternoon in the darkest months. Starting in about May 1941 a special TRE service was held in Langton church – monthly I think – at the end of Friday afternoon. A similar practice was followed when we moved to Malvern, where we were able to hold the service in the college chapel.

My work proceeded well and the experimental height-finding aerial on the 240 ft tower did all that we had hoped. There was no shortage of test material: Worth was right on the main line for German bombers heading for the Midlands, and the diagram opposite is a copy of some of the early results recorded in our hut under the tower at Renscombe Farm. At that time these were the most accurate measurements of height of approaching bombers that had ever been made, and they could be made equally satisfactorily on any site, whether on hilly or level ground. Now, half a century later, they give a very positive picture of the layers of German aircraft, at about 15,000 ft up, which crossed the coast near us at that time.

As a result of these promising tests it was decided to produce a properly engineered set at an operational RAF station and this was erected on Boniface Down at Ventnor,

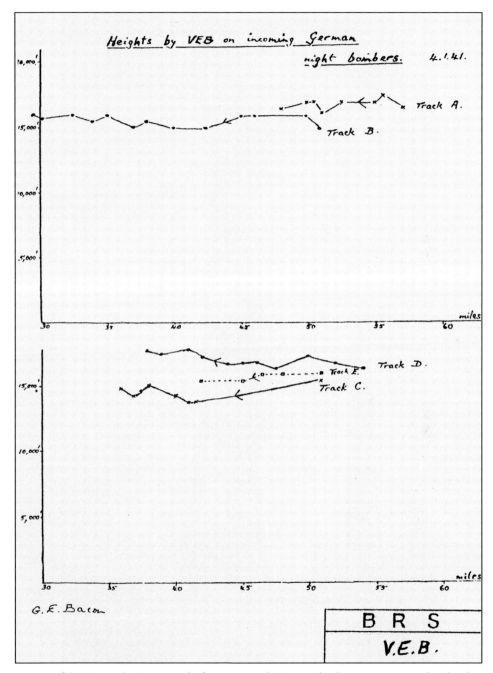

A copy of G.E. Bacon's 1941 record of experimental VEB results showing consistent height plots of approaching enemy aircraft at approximately 15,000 ft tracked from ranges of some 55 miles. Evidently Bawdsey (BRS) notepads were still in use.

Variable Elevation Beam aerials on a 240 ft wooden tower. The seven aerials were pivoted and ganged together mechanically, all being elevated by a common actuating cam, as seen in the picture opposite.

VEB actuating mechanism.

Isle of Wight. Accordingly, much of my time was spent in visits to London to the consulting engineers, Rendel, Palmer & Tritton, who were responsible for the mechanical design of the massive aerial system on the tower, to Westwoods who manufactured it on the Isle of Dogs in Millwall, and to Ventnor where it was erected at the end of 1941.

Later on a production contract was placed for seven other stations, to a simpler version of this design, but the contract was never completed. Like many other schemes in those days it was overtaken by something better, made possible by rapid technical progress. In this case the great advance was the development of powerful transmitters and sensitive receivers for the much shorter wavelength of 10 cm following the development of the magnetron.

Meanwhile at Worth we had set up another experimental Variable Elevation Beam system on a 120 ft tower. Having a smaller aerial system, it did not have such a long range of detection as the earlier proposals but it was vastly simpler mechanically, easy to erect, and it covered a wider range of angles of elevation. I was disappointed that this was not favoured for production, the actual choice being entirely determined by the greater range. However, my 120 ft model was not by any means wasted, being put into use at the GCI station at Appledore in Kent in 1942.

The advent of 10 cm equipment meant that a variable elevation beam system for height-finding could be made with an aerial fifteen times smaller than had been needed previously. If we gave it a height of 20 ft, it would be small enough to mount on a lorry and be mobile, yet be even more accurate than our original system. This was the task to which I moved in 1942. Initially this meant doing field tests on a 10 cm set at Sturminster Marshall where we had an outstation. This I did by commuting daily, by train and bicycle, from Langton and I continued to do this for some weeks after TRE had moved to Malvern College.

The 10 cm set at Sturminster had been developed by the British Thompson Houston Co. at Rugby for ack-ack gunlaying and consisted of twin paraboloid reflectors, about 6 ft in diameter and mounted side by side on a trailer. Both beams, for transmitting and reception, were pencil-like in shape, with an angular width of about 3 degrees. The receiver was equipped as a split-beam system in which the dipole successively occupied two slightly different positions, enabling an aircraft to be followed very accurately once it had been found. However, this was not adequate for our purposes where we needed to report rapidly and regularly on several aircraft at the same time. Nevertheless, it enabled us to get first-hand experience of operating 10 cm equipment for ground radar.

What we needed was a beam which, like our 1.5 m VEB array, was much wider in the horizontal plane than the vertical. A suitable aerial was a parabolic section measuring 20 ft vertically by 3 ft horizontally, a so-called 'cheese' aerial which could be fed by a horn system of waveguides. This gave a beam which was about 1 degree wide in the vertical plane and 7 degrees wide horizontally.

This aerial, mounted on an Austin chassis, formed the basis of the Type 13 heightfinder (seen at left). It oscillated continuously over a range of 15 degrees in elevation. The first three were completed in the spring of 1944 and served in Normandy soon after D-Day.

After the war, Professor Bacon was Deputy Chief Scientist at AERE Harwell. From 1963 he became Professor of Physics at Sheffield University and from 1968–71 was the Dean of the Faculty of Pure Science.

Bernard B. Kinsey, Ph.D., FRSC (d. 1995)

> *'On one occasion our plane was within seconds of being*
> *shot down by a Beaufighter on our tail, whose pilot must*
> *have wondered mightily about the dustbin carried beneath it.'*

My first contact with TRE was during that ominous summer of 1939. I had spent three years at the University of Liverpool, mostly working on the construction of a cyclotron. The machine was nearly complete and did not need much more effort in useful research to get it started. When instructions arrived to go to the RAF station near Dunkirk in Kent at the beginning of July, I was reluctant to go, but could hardly refuse; it was obvious what I had to do if war came. My old friend Vivian Bowden was in Liverpool at the time and received similar instructions. We went together to Canterbury and put up at the Falstaff Inn.

I shall not forget the amazement I felt when I first saw the radio direction-finding installation; its sophistication and the obvious efficiency of the uniformed RAF personnel who tended it. I had had no previous knowledge of the existence of the technology or of the purpose for which it was set up.

Our duty was to learn as much as possible about it and to think how it could be improved or altered to work more efficiently. We were sitting in the lounge of the Falstaff that fateful Sunday when Neville Chamberlain made his speech over the radio declaring war on Germany. Soon after, we heard the first air-raid sirens following a report, which was later proved to be false, of unidentified aircraft in the Thames Estuary. This apparently emanated from a CH station similar to that of Dunkirk, at Canewdon in Essex. After this there was no more thought of going back to Liverpool. My first job was to make a survey of the stations installed on the east coast starting at Canewdon and going north.

Coming new into this field, I was surprised at first at what must have been obvious, viz. that the power of the transmitted pulse at the aircraft must be proportional to the inverse square of the distance, and that of the echo at the receiver, therefore, as the inverse fourth power of the distance. Thus there existed a significant deterrent to increasing amplitudes (by transmitter power or by aerial gain) in order to increase the range at which an aircraft could be detected. All the more amazing, therefore, the achievement of a chain of defensive radar stations around the south and south-east of England attained apparently in complete secrecy.

The other factor affecting the range was the signal/noise ratio. The noise was derived mostly from the tuned receiving circuit, superimposed on a sizeable contribution from somewhere else. While I wondered about its origin, as I fiddled with the tuning controls, I was in no position to do anything about it. Years later, of course, it was the subject of very significant discoveries.[1]

The main difficulties with the chain of stations at this time was with maintenance. The transmission lines that passed the signals from the receiving aerials on the 200 ft wooden towers were hollow copper tubes into which was threaded a central conductor, prevented from touching the tubing by occasional insulators. Somehow rain water had a habit of getting into these tubes, causing a failure of reception or phase changes which nullified direction and height measurements. This happened often enough in that winter of 1939–40 to worry most of us. Very often the maintenance men on the station did not have the equipment necessary to dry out the lines, or they didn't have spares. After repairs had been made, the station had no means of calibrating its performance in

---

[1] At CH wavelengths much of the received noise came from extra-terrestrial sources. Investigations into it after the war formed the basis of radio astronomy.

measurement of height or direction. In due course I made a trip to the maintenance headquarters at Leighton Buzzard to find out the cause of these troubles.

As I studied the performance of these stations it seemed to me that while those on higher sites – the Northumberland hills or Yorkshire Wolds – had the advantage of longer range it was offset by potentially poorer height-finding accuracy in certain directions. It was worrying that gonio null readings for height measurements were less sharp than usual because of complex reflections from the rough and undulating terrain. No one at that time seemed to know how this affected the height measurements, if at all, or whether discrepancies in direction-finding occurred at the same azimuths. There was little or no time for a proper investigation of these effects for the stations had to be operational most of the time. Failure of the station was enhanced by the bad weather at the time.

1940

At Dundee I met the senior men in the electronics division who had been responsible for the remarkable electronics of the chain station receivers. These were Dippy, Jefferson and Fogg, and also the spiritual father of the whole scheme, 'Skip' Wilkins, a man who, it seemed to me, never received full credit after the war for what he had done.

I was soon put on another survey of the chain stations, to ensure their calibration, which was to be effected using a signal produced by a transmitter mounted on an autogyro. At that time the maintenance problems were still serious. The decision to calibrate the stations was presumably taken to ensure that they were in full working order should the war take a more dangerous turn. The azimuthal calibration presented few difficulties, even when the autogyro was made to hover over local objects such as churches whose position could be obtained directly from a map. The height calibration was made with the use of an extrapolation, which assumed that reflection from nearby terrain behaved similarly to that from the sea. I never had time or opportunity to look into the obvious difficulties presented by this assumption. What with weather restrictions, orders to the station from Fighter Command and similar requirements, it was difficult enough to snatch the time to make any calibration.[2]

The job I think was completed by May, when I reported to TRE, by then located at Swanage in Dorset. An extraordinary story from this time has come to light. Forty years on, Vivian Bowden sent me a typed admonitory notice, purporting to have come from a high officer at Fighter Command, in which were detailed complaints by the congregation of a village in Dorset whose church was used on a Sunday as a fixed point for the direction-finding calibration. Captain Brie, the pilot, had hovered over the church for sufficient time for the calibration to be made – unfortunately at a time when a service was being held.

From May 1940 onwards I spent most of the summer at Worth Matravers living, with Vivian, in a house on the road parallel with the sea front at Swanage. That summer

---

[2] The effect of ground reflections upon the bearing and height accuracies of CH stations was well appreciated and soon roving specialist calibration teams were set up. Aircraft – both autogyro and fixed-wing types – with radio communication links to the CH were used. The results of the calibration flights were programmed into the CH electrical calculators so that corrected plots were passed to Filter Rooms.

went all too quickly. We had hardly settled in there before Dunkirk occurred, followed rapidly by the fall of France.

Holt Smith became my division head. I myself had had some experience of radio frequency circuits but had had no experience of making impedance measurements. Bartlett, whom I got to know well that summer, had developed a well-deserved reputation by providing, in the nick of time, a reliable radio frequency communications system for the RAF, without which none of Fighter Command's resources would have been of much use in those critical months.

There were many discussions, as one might expect from an extended seminar in a beautiful place with perfect weather. Many of these were continued at the pub on the hill at the back of Worth Matravers. [The Square and Compass.] It was there that I met Don Preist and Betty Holding. In the hut that I occupied there were new colleagues: Hodges, Salmon, Meltzer (who introduced some of us to matrix algebra for the solution of electrical network problems). Later that summer I was transferred to a group studying air to sea radio direction-finding, working on a wavelength of a metre or two. This was a disappointing field. For some reason the box containing the electronics was mounted in the rear end of a bomber. My job was to get meaningful measurements of the range at which a ship (or better, a submarine) could be detected. I soon found, as doubtless others knew already, that the tuning of the receiver drifted with time and to put it right a member of the crew had to crawl through a long and very narrow space to get at the equipment. Naturally the crew – stiff and bored after hours futiley looking for submarines over the Atlantic, and with a device which was almost certainly out of tune – would be in no mood to perform this chore.

Soon my work changed to the supervision, installation and testing of a rotating 10 cm device, mounted in a Plexiglas [perspex] bucket, which could be lowered beneath the plane by a hydraulic motor. This took some weeks before it was ready for installation in a Blenheim. There followed some months of testing over the Atlantic and its approaches. It was a vast improvement on the metric RDF. On one occasion our plane was within seconds of being shot down by a Beaufighter on our tail, whose pilot must have wondered mightily about the dustbin carried beneath it.

From 1945–54 Dr Kinsey worked as research physicist in atomic energy in Canada. From 1955–8 he was Deputy Chief Scientific Officer at AERE Harwell, then in 1959 he moved to the University of Texas where he remained as Professor until 1975.

Dr W.H. Penley, CB, CBE, Ph.D., B.Eng., F.Eng., FIEE, FRAeS, FRSA

> *'With thick ice on the rungs it was really a foolhardy activity,*
> *but I don't think we thought of this at the time.'*

[In the following extracts from Dr W.H. Penley's autobiography and lecture notes we read how from the very start he was involved in CHL (Chain Home, Lowflying). Sited as high as possible – often on hills, cliff tops, specially designed wooden towers, or on the platforms of existing CH towers – CHL became a major link in the UK early warning chain, but much effort and ingenuity was needed before this could be achieved. The concept of CHL represented an advance from CH but several techniques remained still to be mastered, e.g. the use of a common aerial for transmitting and receiving, and the PPI display. The solutions to these problems for CHL, as well as the development of a new rapid height-finding system, led directly to the 1.5 m radars for GCI (Types 7, 8, 15).]

When I was nearing the end of my Ph.D. work at Liverpool, Eric Seward, whose research I was continuing and from whom I had taken over the equipment, visited the labs. He said he was having a grand time but couldn't tell me what he was doing as it was very secret. Wouldn't I be wanting a job very soon? They were looking for recruits where he was working and he said I was just the kind of person they wanted. Why didn't I apply for a job with them?

He had application forms sent to me, to be returned before 23 June that year – 1939. I sent them in to 'The Superintendent, Bawdsey Research Station, Bawdsey Manor, Woodbridge, Suffolk' . . . and waited!

[In the event he did not have to wait unduly long while completing his Ph.D. thesis. An interview was arranged at the Air Ministry in London in August; he took the Ph.D. viva in January 1940 and entered his Civil Service post at the beginning of February, by which time BRS had moved to Dundee.]

I presented myself at the reception room at the Teachers' Training College, Park Place, Dundee at 10 a.m. on Thursday 8 February, and so commenced my career in the Civil Service as a Junior Scientific Officer.

After signing the usual papers, Official Secrets Act etc., I was taken to the library to read the RDF 'bible'. This typewritten folder gave the reader the outline of the sequence of events which had led to the development of RDF. There was reference to the choice of frequencies to seek the maximum reflected signal from aircraft targets, and the development of the CH stations which formed a protective chain in the most vulnerable parts of the east and south coasts, and which were still being manufactured and installed. I think I was given the rest of the day and the next day to read and ask questions about RDF.

As I had been working on high-power oscillators, I was taken to a lecture room where work was being done on transmitters. This team was being run by Jim Phillips, who had come from GEC, and seemed to be understudied by Don Preist. I was intrigued to see work being done to make major reductions in the size of transmitters by using micro-pup valves and smaller tuned circuits and components.

I was taken to join a team which was being set up to put a CHL aerial system on the 200 ft platform of one of the 360 ft steel CH transmitter towers at Douglas Wood, near Dundee. As a transmitter 'expert' (T-man), I was to deal particularly with the transmission side, which was to involve getting the transmitter power up the tower to an aerial mounted under its 200-ft platform. The idea was for the receiver aerial to be mounted above the platform, and if the simple tests with fixed aerials were successful, the concept for operational use was for them to be mounted on some kind of turning gear operating through the platform and turning them together.

I think most of the major bits of equipment we needed had already been requisitioned and we were warned that in such bitterly cold weather we would need to wear long johns and balaclava helmets as well as several thicknesses of pullovers and wind-proof overcoats. How right this was! We found a hut which was to take the CHL transmitter erected under the middle of the tower we were to use, with another hut as a lab and receiver room.

The first time we climbed the tower was quite an ordeal. We went up to see what it would be like on the 200 ft platform. Each ladder stage was 50 ft. With thick ice on the rungs it was really a foolhardy activity, but I don't think we thought of this at the time; just held on as best we could and struggled up in the time-honoured way of moving only one limb at a time. When we got used to it, we could make the climb in five minutes and reckoned that this was equivalent to about one-quarter horsepower as we always had things to carry up with us.

The platforms had protective rails round them but as those in front of the receiving aerial would interfere with reception of radar echoes, they had to be removed. This would clearly be another hazard so we decided always to tie ourselves to strong ropes attached to the platform when working in exposed positions. To get heavy aerials and other equipment up the tower, a winch system was fitted up. The steel cable drum with winding handles was on the ground and a pulley was fitted in a suitable position on the platform. I think the team of 'riggers' fitted this and took up the aerial sections for us to erect and connect up and also fitted the aerial array under the platform. However, we had to do the electrical connections and matching etc. John Duckworth did a lot of this, a hair-raising task, clambering down below the platform with questionable safety ropes tied to him! However, we got the Tx and Rx aerials set up facing out to sea and then had to connect them up.

As the 'T-man' I was horrified at the length of the feeders from the Tx hut to the aerial, particularly when I found that the standard transmission line was '200 lb copper wire' [a pair of solid bare conductors of about ¼ in diameter] with perspex spacers at about 3 in intervals with the wire crimped to hold them in place. I was told that this line was very troublesome in wet weather even on short runs. I therefore decided to use a strained line with the wires under high tension, and a minimum of spacers. Initially the wires went straight to beehive insulators on the roof of the Tx hut, which had to take the strain. But we began to learn about ¼ wave stubs and the mysteries of matching lines and aerials; so we soon used shorted ¼ wave sections to take the strain. Sometimes the wind hum was very loud but the system seemed promising.

A standard CHL transmitter was now installed in the hut. I had very little information on it, but sorted out its operation as best I could with verbal help from Jim Phillips and others in the Transmitter Group. The two aircooled bright emitter tungsten filament type VT58 valves were set up in a self-oscillating circuit with silver-plated copper tube lines shorted at approximately ¼ and ¾ wavelength positions. The ¾ wavelength line tuned the anodes and was arranged in an arc of a circle with the shorting bar adjustable from outside the enclosed box to provide some tuning. The transmitter pulse started from random noise, built up to maximum output within about a micro-second and then tailed off in about five microseconds due to the buildup of a high negative voltage on the valve grids. This gradually reduced via a grid leak resistor and the process repeated. This was called 'squegging' and the grid leak was adjusted to give about 1,000 pulses per second – the pulse repetition rate.

[Dr Penley goes on to describe further technical activities in setting up the CHL. A test flight Anson aircraft was provided from RAF Leuchars but, with a radar detection range of only 30 miles, improvement was essential and the hard work continued. Of life at Dundee Dr Penley makes the following comments.]

While at the Training College in Dundee it was the practice to congregate for coffee in the library and there we got to know more about the other activities going on. In particular we got a better feel for the basic principles involved in this new art and science and found that great interest was shown by everyone in what was being done. There was no hesitation in putting forward ideas or criticism, or helping where necessary. There was a great team spirit and this was to continue throughout the war. We heard something about work on height-finding being done by Ken Budden at Arbroath, testing the vertical polar diagram achieved by 200 MHz aerials at various heights above the sea to see if height-finding could be done on 200 MHz as it was at CH frequencies. This work confirmed theoretical predictions made by the mathematicians on the variation of signal with angle of elevation at this frequency, and laid the foundation for the subsequent development of height-finding for 200 MHz GCI.

Towards the end of April we were told that we were to move to a place called Worth Matravers in Dorset early in May and that we were to pack up all our equipment which was to be taken there within a few days.

[NOTE: some lines about lines. The problem confronting Dr Penley and his colleagues – the linking of the CHL transmitter at ground level to the aerial at 200 ft – was far more complex than the connection of an ordinary cable for a normal electrical appliance running from the electricity supply mains. The high radio-frequency alternating currents at 200 MHz, which formed the output of the transmitter, would do their best to radiate from any conductor; they would also tend to cause power loss, by heating, in insulating materials. A means of minimising the loss *en route* and thereby getting the maximum power up to the aerial was to use a pair of air-spaced parallel conductors in the form of a 'transmission line'. Using the fewest insulating spacers, the wires were placed as close as possible to minimise radiation but just far enough apart to prevent flash-over.

Such a line, consisting of a pair of wires at a constant spacing, assumes a natural preference for the amount of current it will take in proportion to the applied voltage: this is known as its 'characteristic impedance'. It is rated in ohms and depends upon the spacing and thickness of the wires. The full power of the transmitter is only transferred to the aerial when the resistive load (in ohms) of the latter appears equal to the characteristic impedance of the line: in other words the line must be 'matched'. If a detector is run along a matched line it will indicate a constant reading of alternating voltage from end to end and the line is then shown to be carrying 'travelling waves'. A varying reading indicates the presence – in some degree – of 'standing waves' when a mismatch is indicated and less power is transferred.

The scientists and engineers had to maintain the characteristic impedance by ensuring constant clearance of the conductors; they had also to arrange the correct electrical match at the end of the line. They would assess their success by checking for minimum standing waves. But standing waves can have their value too: by introducing specific lengths of deliberately unmatched line – with their ends even short-circuited or open-circuited – it is possible to achieve matching at the junctions and intersections of complex transmission line layouts. It is also possible to provide mechanically strong low-loss all-metallic 'insulators'. While the theory of transmission lines is fascinating and offers great scope for ingenuity in design, it is better enjoyed in the comfort of a laboratory rather than up an open steel tower in mid-winter in wartime. A difficult job was done under the most appalling conditions.

As an alternative to air-spaced parallel conductors a line may take a co-axial form. One conductor of circular cross-section then runs through the centre of an outer cylindrical conductor from which it is insulated, various means being used to achieve constant spacing and so maintain the impedance of the line throughout its length. The screening effect of the outer conductor is useful in avoiding radiation from the line, especially desirable in very high frequency (short wavelength) applications. However, at the extremely short wavelengths encountered in centimetric radars it is more efficient to transfer power by the radiation of radio waves constrained within hollow metal tubes – usually of rectangular cross-section – known as waveguides. Although their mode of operation differs from conventional transmission lines, waveguides also exhibit a form of characteristic impedance and, like lines, need to be correctly matched if standing waves are to be avoided and maximum power transferred.]

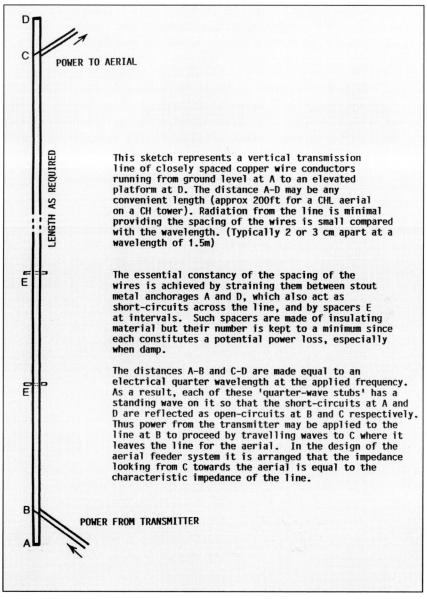

A matched radio-frequency transmission line.

TRE Moves to Worth Matravers

We travelled down to Swanage on 8 May 1940. Buses had been arranged to take us to the establishment site, which was being set up in open farmland outside the village of Worth Matravers. On arriving we found what seemed like chaos. One large field – about 20 acres – was to be the home of the establishment and many huts of various shapes and sizes were under construction, some with blast walls supporting earth ramparts for protection against air attack. A 240 ft wooden CH tower was being erected for research use on this site. In an adjoining compound there were two 240 ft towers linked to transmitter, receiver and operations rooms and near the south fence a CHL station with two 20 ft platforms supporting transmitter and receiver aerials was being set up. This we were told was 'A' site and was an RAF operational station. Our main establishment was on 'B' site and Renscombe Farm was between them. The farmer had agreed to provide milk and would make tea and possibly sell some food from a little hut between the sites. To the north of the establishment site, a 360 ft steel tower was under construction and huts were being built to house the CH transmitters for the RAF operational station in due course. This was 'E' site.

Duckworth and I were to work in Hut No. 50 in the far south-east corner of the main compound. This involved getting as much as we could of the furniture and equipment and tools we needed. The good relationship we had built up with the stores

Aerial view of the layout in the early days of TRE at Worth Matravers.

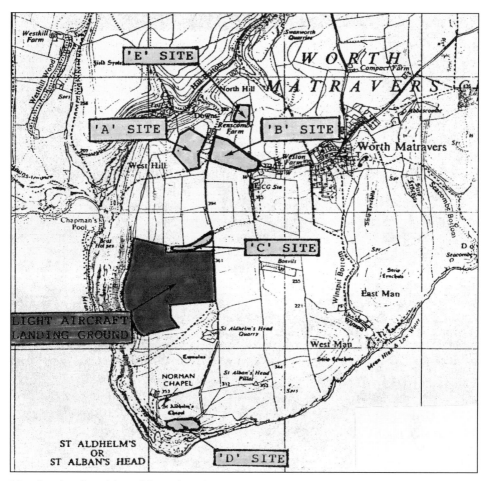

Map showing disposition of the various sites.

and workshop people at Dundee helped considerably, and we even got coal for the crude stove, to provide rudimentary heating.

Our first main task was to improve the performance of the 200 MHz CHL equipments which were then being installed round the south and east coasts to increase the ability to detect low-flying aircraft. We learned that CHL had been evolved very quickly from the 200 MHz Coastal Defence (CD) equipment being developed by the Army radar team which had moved from Bawdsey to Christchurch. In addition to detecting intruding ships and boats, it was required to provide the most accurate information possible on their positions for our coastal defence guns.

An experimental station was to be set up at St Alban's Head near the coastguard station. This was 'D' site. The aerials there would be nearly 300 ft above the sea, on a true cliff site from which the radiation patterns obtained in the vertical plane should be fully formed by the combination of direct signals with those reflected from the surface of the sea. In sharp contrast it was expected that the station erected on 'A' site about a mile and a half from the sea would have its radiation patterns determined by reflections from the ground within a half-mile radius. This was pretty level and about 30 ft below the centre line of the aerial.

It was quickly apparent that the inland CHL was little better than the CH for early warning of low-flying aircraft and that high aerials were essential for CHL equipments. It was therefore decided to install an operational CHL station for the RAF on the cliff site. Our operational research group had been using the inland CHL to develop more accurate methods of directing aircraft. One project they put a lot of effort into was the task of dispensing the Long Aerial Mines in the path of incoming raids. Professor Lindemann was very keen on this concept in which it was visualised that if an aircraft flew into a long length of steel wire trailing below a small parachute, the drag of the parachute would pull the wire up across the wing and bring an explosive charge fitted to the wire into contact with it. This 'LAM' concept, whether dispensed from aircraft or by rockets, did not give satisfactory results.

The other main project was to find a way of using the high accuracy which it should be possible to obtain from a CHL-type beam station to direct a fighter to the best position from which to engage an incoming bomber. Many schemes were tried using the split-beam plotting techniques with various mechanical navigation computing instruments – certainly doing better than could be achieved with the main CH station.

I set out with Taylor and Duckworth on midsummer day 24 June in a staff car to take each of us to one of the recently installed CHL stations so that we could help set them up to give the best performance. We made our way eastwards – I was to get to Truleigh Hill which was said to be near Shoreham.

The station was not working very well and we changed over to a Yagi 'T' aerial but this, if anything, made matters worse and we thought the differing heights of the aerials and the lobe pattern produced as a result of the sloping ground configuration might be a cause. We therefore decided to try feeding the transmitter to one bay and use three bays for the receiver aerial to preserve a split beam operation for direction-finding. This we did and much better detection ranges were obtained. I think this configuration was left as the operational setup for a time, and we journeyed on to Beachy Head at Eastbourne, arriving there on 6 July. Though the installation was on the landward side of the coastal road, the position probably allowed it to operate as a true cliff site, at longer ranges, and the performance was good.

[Radar transmitters, necessarily producing very high power pulses, do not make ideal bedfellows with radar receivers having extreme sensitivity. If both are connected directly to the same aerial, the receiver cannot operate correctly: at best it will be overdriven and made insensitive, or at worst – and more likely – permanently damaged. Accordingly, the T and R aerials of early CHLs were built on separate manually rotated mounts; and as each was directional, both had always to point at the same target.

Dr Penley and his companions, visiting several CHLs, found that under operational conditions this essential alignment was not being maintained sufficiently well and was therefore a cause of poor performance. Each CHL aerial had several stacks of dipoles: a series of experiments was made in which different combinations of dipoles on a single mount were used for transmitting and receiving. While the transmitting and receiving aerials were then theoretically less efficient than before (since each used less elements) they did at least all point in the same direction at all times and overall station performance actually improved. After leaving Beachy Head the team extended their CHL investigations to stations on the south coast, the Bristol Channel and South Wales.

Eventually, as will be seen, a 'common T–R' system was developed whereby a complete single aerial could be switched from transmitter to receiver at the pulse repetition rate: the full performance of the aerial was then realised both when transmitting and receiving.]

In August 1940, after we had returned from our trip to the CHLs, we heard that special mobile equipment for Ground Controlled Interception (GCI) suitable for inland use was to be made. This was to be based on the Worth trials and what had been achieved at Foreness and take into account a suggestion that using low aerials in a saucer-shaped site with higher ground about half a mile away might reduce the level of ground returns which degraded overland tracking from standard CHL stations. It had been decided to use CHL aerials mounted on cabins designed by the Army team for their gun-laying sets. The two aerials still had to be swung to and fro and kept in step, but a PPI would be fitted as well as a standard 'A' scope.

Work started and the first equipment was installed at Durrington, near the Poling CH station, on 18 October, but the urgency was such that the RAF had decided that six more were needed before Christmas, and work on these had been put in hand before any testing had been carried out.

Duckworth and I found that the plotting rate was too slow for accurate control and that height information from the CH at Poling was ineffective. There were also gaps in cover – targets being lost at critical times. Nevertheless, it provided better control than the Chain. Gradual improvements were made, step by step, by changes to the equipment. The receiver aerial was divided into upper and lower sections at about 7.5 ft and 12.5 ft and the 'split' switch used to switch between them so that the different vertical polar diagrams could be used for elevation determination. The transmitter aerial was sectioned in the same way and arrangements made to feed these sections either in phase or in antiphase to alter the vertical pattern. These two changes effectively overcame the serious gaps in cover and enabled some rudimentary height-finding to be achieved; but plotting rate and height accuracy were still inadequate.

Teething Troubles

Meanwhile at Worth we were struggling to overcome the many shortcomings of the CHL technology. In addition to our experimental setup on the 'cliff' site, the operational CHL station had now been erected there and the original CHL on 'A' Site was now being used intensively by Larnder and his Operational Research team to study the problems involved in the interception of single aircraft using information extracted from the radar on the positions of target and fighter and trying out all kinds of ways to get the fighter into the best position for a successful attack on the 'bandit'. This had now taken precedence over the Long Aerial Mine work.

The standard way of extracting and plotting the positions of the two aircraft (enemy bomber and attacking fighter) on to a map table separately and then determining relative motion had its drawbacks and many ways of trying to use the received signals to give relative position and movement directly were dreamed up and tried. (Burning the midnight oil: Harry Poole, E.J. Smith and Ian Cole.) Differential 'split' systems and many mechanical navigational instruments were devised to aid in determining the directional instructions to be relayed to the fighter which had to be guided to a position about two miles behind the 'bandit' and pointing towards it so that his AI radar could detect it and provide the information necessary to achieve an effective tail-chase operation.

The limitations in accuracy and poor performance resulting from having to swing the receiver aerial to and fro and hoping that the transmitter would follow, together with the inaccuracies of the plotting methods and the lack of good height information, were very daunting, even when an early experimental PPI was introduced. Overland operation was greatly hampered too by intense ground returns. It was expected that with the success achieved against daylight raids in the Battle of Britain, there would be a rapid increase in night attacks by single aircraft or small groups. This intensified the pressure on us to overcome all these limitations as quickly as possible.

A third CHL gantry fitted with turntable and aerial had been installed on 'A' site to the west of the initial operational CHL. This was made available for testing any improvements we could make with the hope that it might be used to feed signals to the experimental GCI operations room being used by Larnder's team.

Dr C.H. Westcott – a very able research scientist – was asked to take charge of our ground radar activities at Worth. Several very important technical developments were based on ideas first put forward by him. However, he was not very well attuned to the hurly-burly of applications work and equipment development; and so the management of the team was given to me with Westcott as scientific advisor.

The Common Aerial

We undertook many tasks to improve the performance of the 200 MHz equipments. One of the most important was to find a way of using the same aerial for transmission and reception. The very high pulse output powers of the transmitters (up to 150 kW) had to be prevented from wrecking the receivers and many ideas were tried. I decided to try mechanical switching and with Fishenden got a switch designed and operating. The rapidity of switching required made this very unpromising and we could not overcome the intense sparking which occurred.

The use of spark gaps which would flash over during the transmission pulse was tried. By the use of suitable stubs, these could provide a near short circuit on the feeder to the receiver when flashing – with very little waste of T-power – and when not flashing would allow a clear path for the received signal and also isolate the transmitter so that it would not waste received power, provided the remaining ionisation in the spark gap could be cleared quickly enough. Many designs of gap were tried and the most successful were tungsten wires sealed in glass tubes with a mixture of gases selected for the best overall performance. Complete experimental rigs were set up on the third gantry and the performance was compared with the two-aerial station. Signals reflected from aircraft and the ground were studied, both with and without a 'split' arrangement.

The results were very encouraging and were supported by measurements made with our crude test gear. This system was developed by Banwell and Lees and by the end of 1940 had been shown by them to be by far the best and most practical solution. The principle was adopted thereafter, for all future high power 'common aerial working' equipments.

To make effective use of the Radial Time Base or Plan Position Indicator (PPI) continuous rotation of the 'common T and R' aerial was essential and with the large and very heavy transmitters so far developed, this required a means of passing transmitter power and received signals through rotating connections of some kind from the rotating aerial to stationary transmitting and receiving equipment.

An arrangement of two single-turn loops to form an HF transformer – one fixed and the other rotating with the aerial – was devised at RAE and tried. It gave large variations of coupling and impedance when rotating but was clearly much more serviceable than any arrangement with rubbing contacts. Fishenden tried out various arrangements and improved the design. A rotating receiver link to operate at the intermediate frequency was then produced too and was adopted for Service use.

During this period Dr Lewis was taking a very keen interest in ground radar activities, and came forward with many ideas and proposals. One operational problem on CHL stations was to distinguish quickly between signals from aircraft and those from ships. He suggested that the Döppler principle might be used to help in this task and called me to his office in Durnford to ask whether a small oscillator placed in the transmitter compartment could survive and at the same time feed out enough signal at the transmitter frequency to provide a reference signal on the A scope of the receiver. If so, he predicted that a beating signal would result which should show a slow beat for ships and a much quicker beat for approaching aircraft.

Fishenden and I made up an oscillator and fitted it to the experimental set on the cliff site. After a little adjustment the results were exactly as Dr Lewis had predicted. I judge that this was the start of all the very extensive work subsequently done on 'coherent' radar,[1] and was certainly a crucial simple experiment.

Dr Penley's distinguished postwar career included eight years as Head of the Guided Weapons Department at RRE Malvern, then as Director of RRE itself before becoming Director-General of Electronics R. & D. at the Ministry of Aviation. From 1964–7 he was Deputy Controller of Electronics there, then Director of the Royal Armament R. & D. Establishment. He was Chief Scientist (Army) from 1970–5 and following other senior appointments he became Professional Head of the Civil Service Science Group. From 1982–5 he was Engineering Director of Marconi's Underwater Systems.

---

[1] A radar echo is a short burst of radio waves whose precise frequency depends upon any relative movement between the radar and the reflecting target. When the range is constant the transmitted and returning frequencies are identical – if reducing, frequency is very slightly higher and vice versa (Döppler effect). To assess the instantaneous velocity of a target – or to check its nature by detecting any movements of its parts – this very small frequency change may be detected if it can be compared, at the time of the echo's return, with a replica of the previously transmitted pulse.

To permit this, a low power 'coherent oscillator' may be locked to the transmitter pulse and allowed to run throughout the following reception period. This is the basis of many subsequent clutter-cancellation techniques. The work described above is believed to be the first occasion on which the theory was tried out.

Kenneth ('Hoppy') Hopkinson, B.Eng.

*'Next day was Monday and the washing had been put in to soak
and Hitler or no Hitler we were not leaving our clothes!'*

That first summer in Swanage, 1940, was quite delightful. The resort had a lot of spare accommodation and I soon had my family with me enjoying the beach and the sea before the defensive screen was put up across the bay.

We took over several schools – Langton, Durnford etc. – before we finally settled down at RAF Worth Matravers. Lasting memories are of mud and bikes and rather expensive bus fares (Western National had a monopoly, or am I being unkind?). Bicycles were a favourite means of travel between the main site and the CHL station on the cliff edge some mile or so away. I'd trundle mine up the hill from Swanage in the fresh morning air and coast down at night. One night the searchlights got too close to an enemy plane and the response was the 'rat-tat-tat' of machine-gun fire with tracer coming my way. Why I took to the hedge bottom I will never know; looking for the bike in the dark was no fun.

At some stage it became the law that we should work on Sundays so that top brass, ministers etc. could come to be suitably impressed with our work and go back to London refreshed in mind and spirit. These 'Sunday Soviets' became quite a feature. Sometimes we were given pep talks which were no doubt intended to inspire us to even greater efforts.

One Sunday there was an invasion scare and I told the family that we had to pack a small bag and be ready to leave at a moment's notice during the night. I was told in no uncertain terms that we could not possibly leave because tomorrow was Monday – washing day – and the clothes had been put in to soak already, and Hitler or no Hitler, we were not leaving our clothes. In the end, it was a false alarm anyway.

The CHL equipment was adapted to become GCI (Ground Controlled Interception). Someone – I think it was a New Zealander, Banwell – had developed a TR switching system using ¼ wavelength stubs and spark gaps to suppress the transmitter pulse to a level which the receiver could withstand and to allow a single aerial system to be used for both transmitting and receiving. In turn this allowed the aerial to be rotated continuously for all-round looking, which was essential for inland GCI stations. Someone had the idea of a CRT display with a trace which started at the centre of the screen instead of at the side, and could be rotated in phase with the aerial. Signals could be arranged to increase the brilliance of the trace and the CRT given an afterglow screen so that aircraft echoes could be seen and identified after the trace and aerial had passed.

When not actually at work I found that I wasn't the only member of the CHL/GCI team who was interested in music. One could go into the lab and hum the first phrase of, say, Bach's E minor Violin Concerto and somebody would finish it, and somebody else start the next. Swanage did not enjoy good reception of the BBC and as I seemed to be the only member with a home and a gramophone, friends and colleagues would come round to listen to some of our collection of 78s and bring some of their own. I don't know where all the coffee, milk and biscuits came from, but it was very pleasant and years afterwards the start of Beethoven's 4th Symphony on the radio would always trigger the comment 'Fishenden', in memory of his invariable habit of conducting it.

Ground-controlled Interception

One of the GCI sites was at Sopley, a few miles north of Christchurch, and the first attempt to install a suitable display was not at all successful. The display used deflection coils which could be rotated round the neck of the CRT in synchronisation with the rotation of the aerial. The deflection coil turning mechanism was driven through gearing by a Selsyn motor coupled to a driver Selsyn mounted through the same-ratio gearing on the aerial. The circuitry for the deflection coils seemed to be highly complicated and very difficult to adjust and control.

The time-bases on the existing CHL displays used saw-tooth voltage waveforms and it had been necessary to generate the high voltage waveform using a push-pull pair of triode valves. What was now required was a saw-tooth current waveform but as the deflecting coils possessed both inductance and resistance, it required only simple maths to suggest that they should be fed with a composite waveform: a square wave to produce a linear saw-tooth deflection through the inductance and a saw-tooth waveform to compensate for the resistive element. It seemed obvious to connect the coils into the cathode circuit of the output valve and to drive the grid beyond cut-off by means of a suitably large negative-going square wave so that the trace would start in the middle of the screen. The circuitry turned out to be delightfully simple and easy to adjust to give a very linear CRT trace once the optimum deflector coil had been produced. I think that it took longer for permission to be given to raid the Sopley gear than it did to construct it.

Close-up of the mechanism for rotating the deflecting coils around the neck of the first magnetically deflected PPI tube.

Alec Tutchings
who contributed to
the development of
GCI displays and
devised the method
of assessing heights.

Eventually Alec Tutchings and I arrived on site at Sopley. Alec was fairly well known there, having helped survey the site in the first place and perhaps helped with its installation. We had planned the equipment changeover fairly thoroughly by the change of complete units but the sight of us degutting the original equipment was too much for the station staff and they all departed for Bournemouth.

Two or three nights later, Sopley claimed its first 'kill' and someone cut a notch on a broom handle in the lab and over the next weeks we kept score, cricket fashion. When the Sopley equipment was replaced some time later, the old equipment was driven away with forty-eight swastikas painted on one of the panels for all to see. The furore that we had caused by the 'unauthorised' changeover was quite something – we would hardly have been surprised if we'd been committed to the Tower. However, all the other stations were converted. We converted all the other display units in the lab with a gang of Canadian RAF erks and an RAF lad who was promoted to officer rank.

The Ground Controllers soon came up with a problem. They could direct the night fighter behind the unsuspecting raider and if they were somewhere near the same height, 'Cat's-Eyes-Cunningham' and his fellow pilots could see the exhausts of the enemy and usually add one more to the score, otherwise the operation would be likely to fail. Rapid assessment of the raiders and the intercepted heights was essential.

After a visit to one of the sites, Alec came back suitably chastened but with a bright idea. He dropped some cards one after another on my desk. Each card had two vertical lines of varying height spaced about an eighth of an inch apart.

'Guess the ratio in heights of the two lines.'
'1:2, 3:4, 5:4, 2:1'

He sketched the vertical radiation diagrams of two similar aerials at different heights from the ground and suggested that we could split the GCI aerials so that they had different vertical radiation patterns and that we could shift slightly the horizontal time-base at the same time. The operator could then judge the ratio of the two signals for each aircraft and control the fighter up or down until the two ratios were the same. It worked beautifully. There was a lot of research into better and better long-afterglow CRTs and a fairly constant traffic between the GEC research labs at Wembley and Swanage.

In keeping with the idea of the 'Sunday Soviets', our friends from the GEC research labs at Wembley usually arrived on Thursday evening or Friday morning and returned home some time during the weekend. I remember one occasion when a whole party of us assembled in one of the bedrooms at the Grosvenor Hotel to listen to ITMA[1] on the

---

[1] ITMA – 'It's That Man Again'. This was a nationally popular BBC wartime radio programme featuring comedian Tommy Handley.

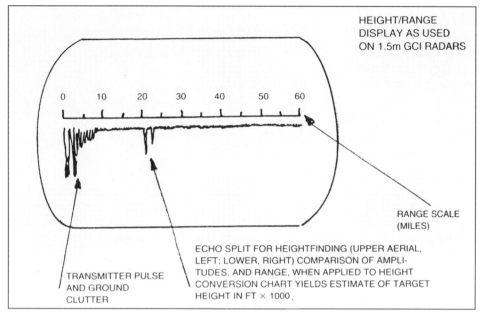

HEIGHT/RANGE
DISPLAY AS USED
ON 1.5m GCI RADARS

0   10   20   30   40   50   60

RANGE SCALE
(MILES)

ECHO SPLIT FOR HEIGHTFINDING (UPPER AERIAL,
LEFT; LOWER, RIGHT) COMPARISON OF AMPLI-
TUDES, AND RANGE, WHEN APPLIED TO HEIGHT
CONVERSION CHART YIELDS ESTIMATE OF TARGET
HEIGHT IN FT × 1000 .

TRANSMITTER PULSE
AND GROUND
CLUTTER

The height/range display as used on 1.5 m GCI radars.

radio. I think we had a couple of foreigners with us; they thought we were bonkers but they cheered up during the subsequent dinner dance. Those Friday-night dinner dances were quite a feature and we usually walked home along the Prom warmed up by a cup of tasty hot soup handed out as we left the hotel.

Messrs Sharpe and Jesty from GEC became very good friends and Jesty was overjoyed when we took him up to the churchyard at Worth Matravers where he found a tombstone to one of his ancestors, probably his grandfather. The tombstone was inscribed with the information that the said grandfather had been the first doctor successfully to use vaccination, with his wife as the patient.

There were several attempts to produce large-screen PPIs using projection tubes. There were very many problems and I don't think we ever got anywhere near solving them. The dark-trace tube or Skiatron showed some promise and seemed to meet the Navy's requirements. We were invited to fit one in the control room of HMS *Ark Royal* when she was in dry dock in the Liverpool area. The PPI trace was projected on to the underneath of a glass screen which was about 1 m square mounted horizontally so that identifying counters could be moved to indicate friend or foe. It seemed to work OK but we never heard whether it had been successful or not. Naval tradition required us to wear hats and to raise them to the officer on duty when we stepped aboard. I duly raised my hat but forgot to lift my feet high enough on the gang plank, so I arrived more or less horizontal when piped aboard and hit the Duty Officer amidships.

Birth of Oboe

One day we were asked to provide an audible guidance system to help pilots to fly along a given track. Sharpe made up an oscillator circuit which would feed short pulses of sound into the left side of a telephone headset and long pulses into the right ear. 'Dits' and 'Dahs' as it were. In the middle there was a constant note. We took the unit up to RAF Boscombe Down and guided a pilot in a Link trainer. The crab[2] moved quite nicely along a railway line and a road and made quite accurate turnings. The wing commander chap from HQ was most impressed. 'What does that noise sound like?'

'An Oboe, Sir.'

[Little could the last speaker in that narrative have realised how prophetic his answer was to be: the most sophisticated and precise of all the radio aids to bombing employed in the war developed at TRE, Oboe, guided the pilot by just such an aural signal.]

After the war, Kenneth Hopkinson was invited to form an electronic valve group for RRE. He became the British delegate to IEC and NATO technical committees for the specification of valves and semi-conductors.

Margaret Waters

> *'Are there still orchids at the side of the*
> *road leading to Studland Golf Course?'*

Swanage was a rather busy place when we were there in the first half of the war – full of troops as well as the staff of TRE. The cinema at the top of Station Road was the main attraction: always full, changing programmes twice a week. Occasionally we would go to Bournemouth and I remember once, when we'd been there to see Charlie Chaplin in *The Great Dictator*, having to wait for over two hours on the blacked-out station for a train back to Swanage. There had been an air raid further up the line; the train had been halted and the firebox damped down so that enemy aircraft could not see it.

A canteen was set up for the forces in one of the cafés in Swanage and a number of TRE wives formed a rota and undertook to run the kitchen on Sundays, which was a working day for the establishment. I recall one occasion when the Grenadier Guards were moving out and the Suffolks taking over, but there was an overlap. For a long time after that I couldn't face beans on toast!

Southampton began to be heavily bombed so the children were brought to Swanage for safety. The local people willingly took them into their homes to care for them and as they had few clothes, sewing parties were organised where dresses were cut down to fit the girls, and husbands' trousers for the boys. Some of the children, due to the harsh conditions they had faced in air-raid shelters, were suffering from scabies and impetigo, so a sick bay was set up near Burlington Road until the sufferers were fit again.

---

[2] 'Crab' – automatic writing device.

At first we were not allowed on the beach, which had been covered with scaffolding in case the Germans tried to land there. So, with petrol still available in small amounts, we would go over to Arne for our swim, much to the delight of the pilot of a small seaplane who used to practise his 'circuits and bumps' as close as he could to frighten us. Later, when the fear of invasion had lessened, those who lived within 10 miles of Swanage were allowed on the beach by showing their identity cards.

Because of double summertime, it was not dark until about 11 p.m., so after dinner we would go over to Corfe to try to catch trout. I think we were poaching but there was no bailiff and our catch was greatly welcomed by our landlady.

I remember one strange time when suddenly all the shops were full of lemons! We hadn't seen lemons for over a year and even in peacetime the shops would never have bought so many. Everyone was buying them and sending them off to their families in boxes or anything they could find. My theory is that they were meant for Swansea, not Swanage. (If only we had had more sugar!).

I have fond memories of Swanage and not least of the kindnesses shown to us by the local families and landladies. Are there still orchids at the side of the road leading to Studland Golf Course? And in the fields past the lighthouse? Adders in Godlingston? And do woodpeckers still make their holes in Rempston?

R.L. (Les) Elliott

> *'We found ourselves much in demand to give demonstrations*
> *to visiting VIPs, especially on Sundays.'*

I arrived at Swanage in May 1940 having moved down from Dundee as a member of AMRE Group I, and for two years shared office and laboratory space in Building 52 at Worth. This was a large purpose-built U-shaped building – one wing being laboratory space for automatic equipment and the other laid out as a Sector/Group type operations room, complete with a large round plotting table and a dais for controllers.

The responsibilities of Group I started at the Cathode Ray Tube and covered the transmission and use of the radar information so obtained. During my two years at Worth, I was involved, with Group I, in four equipments using automatic telephone apparatus.

First of the four was the electrical Calculator, Type Q, known as the 'fruit machine', which was designed by G.A. Roberts at Bawdsey and developed by Siemens Brothers and the GPO Engineer-in-Chief's Circuit Laboratory. By the end of 1940 the calc had been installed in the MkII receiver buildings of the east coast CH stations and replaced the optical converter which other CH stations such as Worth itself continued to use to convert a range and bearing to a grid reference.

Our first task was to arrange the installation of a complete CH receiver and Calculator in Building 52, where it was used for demonstrations and by Alan Bruce for testing the prototype Message Recorder Equipment. As a result, we found ourselves much in demand to give demonstrations to visiting VIPs, especially on Sundays.

During the period July to November 1940 I was attached to RAF 60 Group, together with D.A. Weir and A.E. Bennett also of Group I, to tour the east coast CH

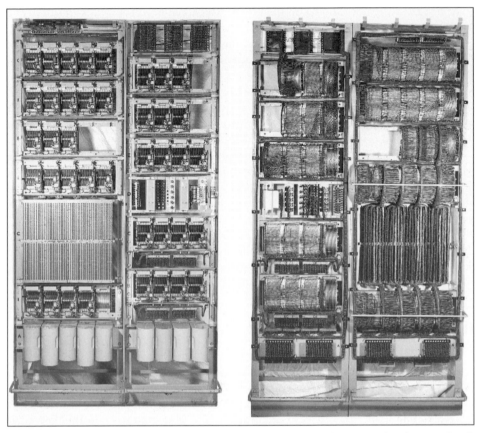

Electrical calculator Type Q (front on left) used on CH, familiarly known as the 'fruit machine'.
Right, rear view of the calculator.

stations, transposing the DF and height calibration information into wiring schedules,
ready for application to the calculators.

The second of my four jobs was working on a CH Interception Desk which was then
installed in the receiver room at Pevensey CH station in December 1940. The idea was
that information taken direct from the Calculator together with radio facilities would
allow a controller to direct a fighter to an incoming raid. This project was overtaken by
the opening of GCI stations, which allowed much more convenient and accurate
control of intercepting aircraft.

Next, I designed and built a prototype Height Signalling Equipment for MkII GCI
stations, which could accept the measured heights of a fighter aircraft and of a selected
target as keyed in by the radar height operator, and automatically calculate the difference
in height. This information was then displayed to the Interception Controller in a
control room overlooking the main plotting table in the operations room. The

prototype equipment was assembled at Worth and the first installation was at Durrington MkII GCI station in 1942.

My fourth project was the responsibility of Don A. Weir, who with ST&C[1] designed a system for calculating the bomb release point for Pathfinder aircraft under the control of Cat and Mouse Oboe stations.

After the war Mr Elliott worked at UKAEA, AERE Harwell on the design and development of automatic data-processing and control systems for atomic energy experiments.

Richard H.G. Martin

> *'If you stayed off work due to illness, you were not paid.'*

Dundee

I had just completed my second year of an electrical engineering course at Imperial College London. The previous summer (1938) I had taken a vacation job on a Bibby liner doing the return trip Liverpool–Cochin–London. We were approaching Marseilles on the way home at the time of the Munich crisis and there was talk of having the deck strengthened to take a gun. There was a feeling of inevitable war.

I returned to college in October and the talk was about volunteering early in order to get quicker promotion – probably good advice. The summer vacation arrived and I thought of my options: engineering in the RN seemed an obvious choice based on my vacation experience. However, there had been rumours of the Air Ministry looking for electrical engineers, so I made some enquiries, sent in an application and had an interview on 1 September 1939. After war was declared I heard nothing for a while, so volunteered for the Navy, but the Air Ministry asked me to report to their Research Station at Dundee, where I headed on 27 October as a Scientific Assistant III on £120 per annum.

I duly signed a number of forms, including the Official Secrets Act, and found myself digs some 2 miles from the Research Establishment – a room, breakfast and evening meal for 37s 6d per week. The tram to work cost 2d; half a pint of beer could be had for 3d, and entry to the local dance hall on a Saturday evening was 1s.

Everybody was very busy at AMRE and it was difficult to get a thorough briefing. I learned from my first boss, Dr Denis Taylor, and from various papers I'd been given to read, that the subject was RDF (Radio Direction Finding). A limited number of RDF stations (CH) were fully operational between Southampton and the Tees; these had been erected as a matter of great urgency, primarily for the defence of London.

One of my first jobs, as a member of a team under Denis Taylor, was erecting the transmitter array at Douglas Wood CH station on the Sidlaw Hills just to the north of

---

[1] Standard Telephones & Cables.

Dundee. The winter of 1939–40 was extremely cold with ice on the Thames and around the coast; not surprisingly it became bitterly cold working on the platforms of the 360 ft high transmitter towers. Somehow, Denis managed to keep himself busy in the little hut where tea and cocoa were brewed, but then, he was the boss! Perhaps he wondered sometimes why we descended so often to ask for some extra 'explanation' or maybe he knew we came to thaw out and get a warm drink.

When that job was complete I worked with Dr Wynne Williams on the development of the CH calculator – basically an electro-mechanical computer with a wired-in programme.

About this time I developed a dose of influenza. If you stayed off work due to illness, you were not paid. So most of us could not afford to stay at home in bed, even for a day. My friends came to the rescue: when I arrived in the morning they put me under the bench in the laboratory and wrapped me in their coats, bringing me a sandwich or something if I wanted it at lunchtime. Soon the worst was over and in a day or two I was up and about again.

My last move in Dundee was to the display section, where I was joined by Jimmy Stewart who had recently arrived after graduating at Newcastle. We were now working under Freddy Lutkin who had joined Bawdsey from the National Physical Laboratory at Teddington. In the spring of 1940 Jimmy and I were sent to one of the first CHLs at Walton-on-the-Naze. Minelaying aircraft had been taking a toll of shipping in the Thames Estuary, laying mines mostly at night in order to avoid being seen. We were equipped with a Baird photographic recorder specially modified for the purpose. A film recorded the linear trace of the CHL display together with an azimuth dial driven in synchronism with the receiver aerial.

Apart from filming the range and bearing of each signal, the film was processed by the recorder itself. We fed the recorder with film and chemicals and each morning had a processed film ready to be sent to the Admiralty for analysis where the tracks of minelaying aircraft could be deduced and the mines swept during the following day.

Walton-on-the-Naze was a pleasant contrast to Dundee, not the least attraction being the subsistence allowance which improved our financial situation. Eventually this work was taken over by the RAF and we returned to Dundee where we heard we were to move to Worth Matravers near Swanage at the end of April 1940.

Stewart and I were back in the display team and were joined by Joe Sieger, who had arrived from Scophony Television. I left Dundee at the end of the last week in April which gave me the opportunity of a weekend in London on the way. Sieger gave me a lift from there in his Lagonda car on the Monday and what a wonderful sight as we entered Swanage on a glorious, sunny May day with the brilliant white cliffs of Ballard Down contrasting with the deep blue of the sea. On arrival, I found myself billeted in Avenue House in Victoria Avenue, together with Jimmy Stewart, George Jeckell, Maurice Jones and Ian McLusky.

Swanage

It was almost as though our move to Swanage was a signal for the end of the 'phoney' war – the time of preparations by both sides during the previous nine months for the battles to come. On 10 May 1940 Hitler invaded France and the Low Countries. The lightning speed of the German advance was both surprising and alarming. On the evening of 25 May I was, with others, in the office of A.P. Rowe, which was in one of the temporary wooden buildings at Worth. It was dark, for I remember that a hurricane lamp on his desk was the only form of lighting, possibly because the windows had not been fitted with suitable blackouts. Rowe gravely informed us that Boulogne had fallen to the Germans and so they were now at the Channel coast. He emphasised the probability of heavy air and perhaps seaborne attacks, and therefore the extreme urgency of providing the RAF with the various developments in hand. Certainly nobody doubted that as soon as Hitler had beaten France he would immediately launch an attack upon Britain.

The miraculous evacuation of British and French forces from Dunkirk was completed by 4 June and Winston Churchill spoke in the House. His speech was broadcast in the evening and relayed to everyone in the Ship pub in Swanage and I was there to hear him say, 'We shall go on to the end. We shall fight in France; we shall fight on the seas and oceans, we shall fight with growing confidence and growing strength in the air. We shall fight on the beaches, we shall fight on the landing-grounds, we shall fight in the fields and in the streets, we shall fight in the hills. We shall never surrender.' It was truly inspiring to all who heard that great man.

In the early weeks of the Battle of Britain, which started in July 1940, the CH stations at Dunkirk (near Canterbury), Dover, Rye, Pevensey, Poling and Ventnor were all hit, together with the airfields of Tangmere, Biggin Hill, Manston, Hornchurch and others. Tactical control of our fighter aircraft was undertaken from the Sector Operations Rooms under the broad direction of Group Headquarters and Fighter Command Headquarters at Stanmore, where Air Marshal Sir Hugh Dowding exercised strategic control.

Fortunately, the Battle of Britain was almost exclusively fought in daylight; this meant that Sector Controllers could vector an entire squadron to intercept the enemy raiders as reported by the CH stations. So once the enemy had been sighted by our fighters they could attack from the most advantageous position. Such 'loose' control would have been impossible at night. As the fortunes of the Battle of Britain flowed in our favour, it was evident that eventually the enemy would turn to night raiding as a means of reducing their losses. Efforts were then directed by the establishment to providing the means of 'close' controlling our night fighters from the rapidly deployed GCI stations and to the development of radar to be fitted in the night fighters.

Early in September I was installing some experimental equipment in the CH operations building at Worth Matravers, which was staffed by RAF and WAAF personnel. I couldn't help noticing one particular WAAF who, apart from being most attractive, seemed to be bubbling with life and a centre of attention. One thing I noted particularly was her ability to throw the RAF sergeant's wellington boots up into the rafters of the hut! I met this WAAF again a couple of months later at one of the Saturday night dances at the Grand Hotel in Swanage. We married eighteen months later, in May 1942. In spite of working long hours, there was plenty of entertainment at Swanage such as dancing, and also a good cinema and plenty of pubs.

Germany never gained command of the skies and accordingly Hitler's invasion plans were withdrawn in mid-September 1940. I was in Slough on the evening of 7 September and remember the enormous red glow to the east as the London Docks came under heavy attack. Throughout the following months, as soon as darkness fell, the air-raid sirens would sound and Londoners flocked to the underground stations for the night. One night in October I was in London with Jimmy Stewart, staying at the Regent Palace Hotel just off Piccadilly Circus. We had just started dinner when the sirens sounded and the first bombs began to fall. We decided we'd be happier outside, so we walked out into the cool evening air and looked up at the waving searchlight beams, accompanied by the crump of bombs and the burst of anti-aircraft shells. We were on the lower side of the Circus when there was an almighty crump which shook the ground beneath us. This was the bomb which scored a direct hit on the Café de Paris in Coventry Street. It passed straight through the building, exploding in the middle of the basement dance floor. Casualties were appalling and included the singer 'Snakehips' Johnson.

In the autumn of 1940 the night raids were becoming intense on London and other cities. On the evening of 14 November 1940 I had been working late and was walking back to Swanage under a full moon. Above me was the roar of enemy bombers heading north: nobody who lived through the raids will ever forget the beat of the bomber engines – the deep throb and the 'wow-wow'. I learned next day that these were the bombers heading for Coventry and the virtual destruction of that city.

GCI

Three of the earliest GCI stations were at Durrington near Worthing, Sopley near Christchurch and Sturminster Marshall near Blandford. At first these were put together as quickly as possible, being continually modified and updated. By Christmas 1940, six mobile GCIs were on their operational sites to be followed shortly by six more.

At the beginning of 1941 I began to spend more time at the GCI stations, trying to learn something of the developing art of close-controlled interception at night, and to assist in any technical developments which might improve the effectiveness of the controllers' task. As civilians, we were able to discuss problems with any Service rank. It transpired after the war that in Germany things were very different, resulting in barriers between the armed forces, scientists and industry, which slowed technical development and application.

The Type 7 GCI stations at Durrington and Sopley were two of the first to be equipped with additional 10 cm radars – the new Type 13 height-finder and Type 14 surveillance radars – and were regularly visited. These stations were also among the first to be housed in permanent buildings known as 'Happidromes'. This name originated with the form of the building, in the centre of which was the large operations table overlooked by the Chief Controller and other operational staff, giving an impression of a theatre, with stage and circle.

On 7 December 1941 the Japanese attack on Pearl Harbor brought America into the war. We had fought the Germans alone for eighteen months, between June 1940 and December 1941, and for all the might of the German war machine we had survived. There were now great hopes that, with the Germans having difficulties on their Eastern front, the combined strength of ourselves and the United States could finally put an end to the war.

Reporting Room of final GCI station, AMES Type 7, generally known as the 'Happidrome'.

V1s and V2s

When we began to hear that the Germans had a secret weapon we had hoped the war would be over before they had a chance to use it. But I remember driving across Beachy Head one day when a 'Doodlebug', popping along like some toy, passed little more than 100 ft above me. At meetings in London, talk used to falter momentarily as the popping stopped and the explosion followed a second or two later. The V2, first used in September 1944, was a much more sinister weapon, travelling so fast that it was not possible to hear its approach before the explosion of its warhead. It seemed there was no defence against such a weapon but the Big Ben radar project helped Bomber Command to eliminate the launching sites.

'Dinner Wagon'

In August 1944 a Requirement was raised by HQ Allied Air Forces for AMES Type 65, code-named 'Dinner Wagon'. The requirement called for a Horsa glider fitted

Horsa glider equipped with 'Dinner Wagon' radar installation (AMES Type 65).

with radar and communication facilities sufficient to allow the glider, on landing, to operate as:

— an Early Warning Station,
— a Night Interception Station, or
— a Fighter Direction Station.

I was given overall responsibility by TRE for the installation work. Two radars, the AMES Type 6 MkIII (1.5 m 'Light Warning') and the American AN/TPS3 (50 cm, RAF's Type 63) were to be installed in the Horsa together with equipment and facilities for VHF/HF communications, IFF, radar displays, telephone links and power generation. (It might report in to a mobile control and reporting station such as AMES Type 70.)

The installation was undertaken at RAF Defford, the aircraft facility of TRE Malvern. RAF crews, consisting of two aircrew together with some ten radar mechanics, were attached to Defford to assist and familiarise themselves with the installation. The project was awarded the highest priority, given direct and immediate access to RAF Maintenance Units for all equipment and spares and priority in the workshops at Defford.

By 11 November 1944 the 'Dinner Wagon' installation and testing was complete and, with the aid of a Stirling bomber as tug aircraft, was flown to RAF Wethersfield near Braintree. The Stirling had a single crew member – a very young but efficient pilot – and he had been accompanied to Defford by an equally young member of the Glider Pilot Regiment. My confidence was about to be tested as I stood on the flight deck of the Stirling and the engines revved for take-off. I couldn't see what was happening behind but felt the snatch as the glider was pulled forward and relief when the pilot reported that take-off had been successful. The pilot did his own navigation by heading due east until he crossed the east coast, then on to the reciprocal to pick up a railway line, which he followed in a southerly direction until he picked up his final bearings in the Colchester area. Simple, but effective when flying at a few hundred feet below cloud.

We arrived at Wethersfield during the afternoon and made the installation operational within an hour. That evening the installation and its operational capabilities were inspected by, and demonstrated to, Lt Gen Browning, Deputy Commander of the Allied Airborne Army. Following this, the glider was flown to the Airborne Air Forces airfield at Tarrant Rushton in Dorset for further deployment trials.

'Dinner Wagon' was being installed at the time of the ill-fated airborne landings at Arnhem in September 1944. These showed the vulnerability of gliders in a troop dropping zone where close-range enemy fire could be expected, and the risk of damage on landing. It was recognised that such equipment would be most useful if deployed on a captured airfield behind the front line in order to direct fighter aircraft or provide guidance and control for supply aircraft. Nevertheless, the Allied Expeditionary Air Forces still felt that rapid deployment of some form of radar defence and control in the dropping zone was required.

As a result, AEAF suggested that a plan position radar equipment, together with HF and VHF communication facilities, should be mounted in one or two vehicles so that they could be transported by glider and then rapidly deployed away from the immediate landing site. The use of armoured vehicles was not considered essential since speed and manoeuvrability were equally as important as armour. But a four-wheel drive was essential. A requirement was issued in December 1944 for a second Horsa ('Dinner Wagon') installation, but this was cancelled before work started.

Victory in Europe was finally declared on 8 May 1945 after nearly six years of war. Efforts at TRE were then directed towards the war in the Far East and I was given the task of developing a man-transportable radar for use by troops in the jungle. Before the work was complete the atom bombs were dropped, followed immediately by Japan's unconditional surrender on 14 August.

[NOTE: while glider-transported ground radars came late in the war and appear not to have been used greatly in operations at the time, the concept – like ACI (see Hodges, p. 168) – heralded future military thinking. After the war a growing demand for air-transportable ground-based radar systems was met by the progressive development of new radars and large transport aircraft.]

Richard Martin continued to work at Malvern for RRE after the war until 1964 when he became head of the Technical Division E1 Eurocontrol Agency, Brussels. He was Chairman of the Technical Concept Group for the Maastricht Upper Area Control Centre.

R.M. Fishenden, MA (Cantab)

> *'In the severe gale the aerial was blown down. This did*
> *the structure no good at all but the event was greeted with*
> *shrieks of merriment by those lucky enough to see it.'*

Looking back on my days at TRE, one of the things that stands out is the number of my colleagues who subsequently reached distinguished positions in the world of science.

My first group leader was J.A. Ratcliffe who had taught me at the Cavendish Laboratory, Cambridge and who after the war became Director of the Radio Research Laboratory. He was followed by W.H. Penley who was later to be the first engineer to be head of the Scientific Civil Service. Among my immediate colleagues were Roland Lees who became director of the Royal Radar Establishment (successor to TRE) after the war; George Bacon who was appointed to a Chair at Sheffield University; and for a time, Martin Ryle, later Professor Sir Martin Ryle, the distinguished radio-astronomer and Astronomer Royal, who shared our hut. He could be short tempered and was known to throw things when his experiments were not going well. These names are taken from quite a small group and they illustrate the intellectual power that was concentrated upon TRE's work.

Much of my time at Worth was devoted to work on aerials for the CHL stations, working on a wavelength of 1.5 m. An important part of this work was measuring polar diagrams, for which the setup was crude but effective. It was based on a circle, perhaps 100 yds in diameter, on the flattest available piece of field, with stone markers round the circumference at 5 degree intervals. It was known as 'Stonehenge' or the 'Druids' Circle'.

The aerial under test was placed at the centre of the circle and connected to a small 1.5 m transmitter. A receiver consisting of a single dipole and reflector, mounted on a wooden stand about 2 m high, was connected to a thermocouple, and the voltage measured on a sensitive meter. The receiver was carried round the circle by hand from one 5 degree marker to the next. As the voltage from the thermocouple took about a minute to reach a steady state, taking the seventy-two readings required for a complete polar diagram was a slow and tedious business.

The Yagi aerial now used for most television receivers was then a new invention, and seemed to offer a relatively light and simple alternative to the large and cumbersome arrays of about sixteen dipoles in front of a wire mesh reflector – then in use at CHL stations. So a lot of measurements were made on Yagis to determine, for example, the effect of changes in director length, number of directors and the diameter of a metal tube on which the directors were mounted. This work was written up in one of the IEE articles published when details of radar were declassified at the end of the war. (Proc. IEE, Vol. 96, Pt III, No. 39, January 1949.) All the measurements on which this article was based were made on the Druids' Circle.

Some of the experiments carried out were at a remarkable level of sophistication. For example, it was important to discover whether the performance of stations would be affected when the aerials were soaked by heavy rain. A test aerial was therefore set up at the centre of the 'Druids' Circle'; the receiver placed in the maximum of the beam; and the received signal measured. Several buckets of water were then thrown over the test aerial and the reduction in received signal observed. I believe the effect was remarkably small except for Yagis mounted on wooden frames and these were soon abandoned in favour of those mounted on metal tubes.

An important improvement achieved at Worth Matravers – I think mainly by George Bacon – was to use the same aerial for transmitting and receiving. It was known as the 'common T & R' system. The lines from the transmitter and the receiver were joined inside the operating hut. Half a wavelength along the receiving line from the junction a spark gap was placed across the line. When the outgoing pulse was delivered, the spark gap fired; this protected the receiver, and the transmitter 'saw' nothing but a short-circuited ¼ wave stub, which has no effect. When the reflected pulse was received, the spark gap was out, and it was arranged that the line to the transmitter appeared as an open circuit. Development of spark gaps with an adequate life took some time, but once this was achieved the system worked well. Apart from the economy in staff and equipment, performance was improved because there was no longer any misalignment of the transmitting and receiving aerials.

However, the transmit/receive system was still connected to the aerial by means of a transmission line of limited flexibility. This had two disadvantages: first, the aerial had to be swept backwards and forwards, so adding to the complication of the mechanical system. And when plan position indicators (PPIs) replaced the linear timebase display, there was a gap in the coverage. Second, as the transmission line was rotated, the distance between the pair of wires changed slightly between spacers, so affecting the characteristic impedance of the line. This was sufficient to make a measureable difference in the received signal and when Ground Control Interception (GCI) stations were introduced, on which the height of aircraft was measured by comparing the signal from two aerials at different heights, significant inaccuracies were introduced.

These problems were solved by a device that I designed which permitted continuous rotation of the aerial. Rubbing contacts are no good for kilowatts of RF power, and the only practicable solution seemed to be an inductive link. After some crude calculations, assisted by the TRE maths group, I came up with a device consisting of two flat rings of about 8 in in diameter and 1 in wide, separated by about ½ in. The device had a very low impedance, so it had to be connected to the standard 350 ohm transmission line by a low impedance transformer, consisting of two 1 in wide strips of brass at about ⅛ inch separation, which could conveniently be brazed on to each ring. A simple mechanical arrangement allowed one ring to rotate relative to the other. It worked quite efficiently, apart from a small disturbance when the stubs on the two rings were opposite one another [later cured by a Faraday screen].

Towards the end of our time at Worth Matravers, work began on CHL stations operating on a wavelength of 50 cm. To get the maximum advantage out of the shorter wavelength in terms of a narrower beam, and hence greater angular accuracy (and also higher aerial gain), a large experimental array was constructed, the same size as the standard 1.5 m aerials, and using the same pattern of dipoles, but of course with many more elements. This was mounted on a standard short tower and turntable on the main site at Worth. Unfortunately this coincided with a severe gale and the aerial was blown down. It did the structure no good at all, but the event was greeted with shrieks of merriment by those lucky enough to see it. It was a feature of those times that disaster was greeted with laughter, but also with a renewed determination to get on with the job. Before any 50 cm stations became operational, the CHL type aerial was replaced by a large circular dish. [Forerunner of AMES Type 16.]

During the summer months at Worth we often took our picnic lunches down to the cliff site at St Alban's Head, a delightful spot with the sea several hundred feet below. A particular delight was to tip boulders over the edge of the cliff and watch them

A rotating joint for coupling transmitter power to a rotating aerial array on 1.5 m radars including CHL and GCI. The slotted disc in the centre is the Faraday screen to ensure reasonably constant coupling, irrespective of angle of rotation.

thunder down to the sea. We spent much effort and ingenuity getting the biggest possible boulders dispatched in this way.

In summer 1940 there was a series of air raids on south coastal radar stations. The day following the raid on the Isle of Wight – Ventnor, the nearest station to Worth – we saw on the radar screens connected to our experimental CHL set a German bomber force apparently heading straight for us and in considerable strength. Those not directly engaged thought it prudent to push off to an air-raid shelter midway between the main site and the cliffs. (There always seemed to be bicycles available for moves of this kind.) The shelter was no more than a large slit-trench in the chalk, approached by a steep chalk slope. Shortly after my arrival a voice was heard enquiring from above, 'How do you get down?' 'Slide down on your arse!', I shouted back, then saw with some embarrassment that the new arrival was our Chief Superintendent, A.P. Rowe. The raiders passed overhead to targets elsewhere.

In fact I don't think the site ever suffered a German bombing attack. It was once shot up by a German fighter, but I was away that day, perhaps fortunately – a bullet hit the back of an empty chair – the one in which I normally sat.

After the war Martin Fishenden worked at AERE Harwell in scientific administration and was Division Head and member of the Management Committee.

Harry Bisby, B.Sc.

> *'I packed my worldly goods into a rucksack and*
> *mounted the only transport I had – a bicycle – and rode*
> *the 85 miles from Bristol to Swanage in one day.'*

It was in July 1940 that I joined AMRE, Worth Matravers, from King's College, London University (at that time evacuated to Bristol). I was in my second year of postgraduate research, using microwave radiation to investigate the dielectric characteristics of polymers. The radiation wavelength was 5 cm, generated by one of the very scarce split-anode magnetrons, designed and made by Dr J.J. Hull of the Royal College of Science.

I was familiar, therefore, with short-wave radiation and its properties and, on the outbreak of war, our work was soon redirected to the design of a short-wave aerial for fitting in the nose of an aircraft. The project, which was under the direction of Professor C.D. Ellis, was visited at Bristol in February 1940 by Dr Watson-Watt. This encounter resulted in my being requested to spend the Easter vacation of 1940 on a 'defence project' at Bawdsey.

However, by the time the Easter vacation arrived, the defence project had moved from Bawdsey to Dundee, so I went there to spend a few days seeing J.A. Ratcliffe and visiting an outstation near Edinburgh. From there I was sent to the CHL station at Flamborough Head, where C.L. Smith was the 'scientific observer'. During the ten days of that vacation I learned the basics of RDF. Returning to Bristol, I awaited the decision of a Joint Recruitment Board held by Brundrett at the Admiralty in June. The result came soon and I was detailed to join AMRE at Worth Matravers as a Junior Scientific Officer on an annual salary of £240.

The location of AMRE was given to me in a letter marked 'Secret' and I was to report to J.A. Ratcliffe on arrival. I was almost penniless at the time since my research grant only allowed me £50 per annum to live on in Bristol. So I packed my worldly goods into a rucksack and mounted the only transport I happened to have – a bicycle – and rode the 85 miles from Bristol to Swanage in one day. That night I found accommodation in a small family hotel.

The next day I cycled to Worth Matravers and reported as instructed, but Ratcliffe must have been absent and no one anticipated my arrival. I was shown into an empty office and given the RDF 'bible' to read. The same happened the following day, at the end of which I was given a rail ticket to Shoreham and told to report to the AMES at Truleigh Hill (a CHL) as a Scientific Observer. I was to check the performance, since the CO had reported that they weren't getting any echoes at all. It appeared that after two days of reading the 'Bible' I was supposed to be an expert. I did discover that, compared with the RAF personnel who were operating at Truleigh, I was indeed an expert!

On arrival at Shoreham – again with my possessions in a rucksack and wearing a pair of old corduroys and a deerstalker hat – I called at the post office for directions to Truleigh Hill. The locals obviously knew that it was a hush-hush place and the clerk kept me waiting, saying he would have to ask someone. After a few minutes, a burly policeman arrived and asked me to 'step along with him to the station'. There I had to prove who I was and why I wanted to know the location of Truleigh Hill. Worth Matravers was contacted on the telephone for verification, and only then was I taken up to the AMES by police car.

I could get no accommodation that night in Shoreham, since Worth had failed to inform the CO of my visit. I went back to the police station but they could only suggest that I made use of an old car out on the sand dunes. The sergeant kindly shared his sandwiches with me and I made my way out to the dunes and spent a most uncomfortable, sleepless, cold night. Early next morning, I found a snack bar for breakfast then walked – unwashed and unshaven – the 2 miles back up the hill to the radar station. There I set about finding out why they were getting no echoes.

On those early CHL sets, the transmitter aerial had to follow the receiver aerial as the latter was scanned round through about +/− 135 degrees of south. This was achieved using a potentiometer on each connected in a bridge network, so that if the aerials were pointing in the same direction, a centre-zero meter in the transmitter room indicated zero. Both aerials were rotated separately by manpower. It so happened that the padding resistors used in the bridge circuit had been incorrectly wired up (values interchanged)

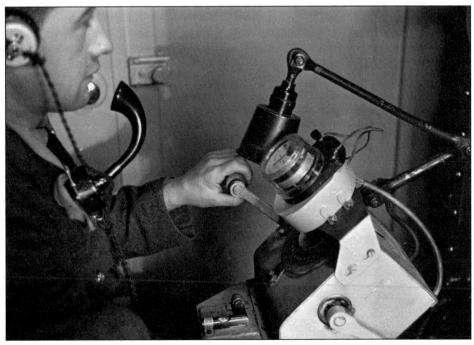

'Binder' at work in a rotating aerial cabin. By watching the centre-zero meter he tried – by turning the hand cranks – to keep his transmitting aerial aligned with the rotating receiver aerial. This was tough work in windy weather!

so that when the meter was reading zero, the transmitter aerial was about 35 degrees out of line with the receiver aerial.

No one had noticed this amazing situation. When it was corrected and the CO instructed in the mysteries of 'polar diagrams' (both vertical and horizontal) for the aerials, the station had echoes, although these fluctuated markedly due to the height of the station above sea level (500 ft I think).

My bed and breakfast at the Ship Inn at Shoreham cost me 6s 6d per day. After fourteen days I was asked to go and check the station performance at Beachy Head and this I did, finding a marvellous billet in a private house in Eastbourne at 3s per day. I spent most of August and September at Beachy Head during the Battle of Britain and I remember the glorious hot weather and sunny blue skies streaked with vapour trails.

The performance at Beachy Head had to be kept on top line since Pevensey and other CH stations were badly damaged by air raids. Most nights I spent with the RAF crew repairing, testing and checking performance ready for the next day. On one such night we observed the first E-Boat battle in the Channel off Beachy Head. Our aerials were so high above sea level that we could get echoes back from even quite small boats passing by. As far as I know, mine was the first reported sighting of shipping.

GCI

In late September I returned to Worth Matravers and worked with the design teams of mobile GCI (Ground Controlled Interception). This work culminated in the commissioning of the first GCI at Durrington near Worthing. Alec Tutchings, Peter Hall and 'Doc' Franklin were also there and we had terrible problems sorting out all the design and production errors – nothing worked at first. I recall one day when it absolutely poured with rain and the spark-gaps and feeder lines on the transmitter aerial simply wouldn't work. Tutchings and I got thoroughly soaked working on the aerials, so much so that when we finally got them going we took off our trousers and were checking the performance in our underpants. (This was before the WAAFs arrived to manage the operating!). Suddenly a fleet of staff cars arrived and who should walk into the operations wagon but ACM 'Stuffy' Dowding, together with more brass than we had ever seen before. We hurriedly wrapped our coats around our legs and sat down hastily at the PPI and demonstrated the operation of the sets as if nothing was amiss. They all departed quite impressed but somewhat bemused by the dress style of the 'boffins'.

In December the WAAFs arrived to take over the operations at Durrington, so the TRE team, with the addition of George K. Budden, transferred its attention to Sopley GCI station. It became operational by the end of 1940, manned by WAAFs, so there were great celebrations at the Woolpack Inn during Christmas of that year.

On New Year's Day, in terrible icy weather, I set off with a brand new GCI for Avebury in Wiltshire, staying at the Red Lion village pub in which I and a retired church missionary were the only residents. I have never been so cold – the ground was hard frozen and out on the open Wiltshire downs the wind cut through any clothing like a knife.

There was no sign of RAF personnel so I abandoned the convoy on site and returned to pick up another GCI convoy and take it to a site at Wherwell near RAF Middle Wallop. There was about 2 ft of snow at Wherwell; the rigours of trying to get the installation working in the middle of a field in deep snow were unbelievable. A couple of RAF sergeants turned up after a week to assist Ray Turner (of TRE) and me with the work and long before we got it operational, a whole lot of WAAFs arrived. They were quickly dispatched to the warmth and comfort of RAF Middle Wallop with strict orders not to show up until we said so. One day, an RAF person showed up in a staff car and when challenged turned out to be AVM Joubert, wanting to be shown round.

By the beginning of February the Wherwell and Avebury sets were all on top line, so I was sent to Martlesham Heath to help Alec Tutchings and George Budden try out the new technique of height-finding, using a 'split' aerial. This was done by comparison of the relative amplitudes of the two signals received on the top and lower halves of the receiver aerial. By reference to a chart of ratios and range of signal, the height of the detected aircraft could be found. The ratios were expressed in tenths, i.e $\frac{5}{10}$ if one signal was half the amplitude of the other. It was quite surprisingly successful.

Harry Bisby with a mobile GCI in France soon after D–Day. (PPI left, height-range display right). As one of the civilian TRE scientific staff who provided practical technical support to RAF ground radar crews, he travelled extensively on the continent during the invasion campaign, often under harsh and dangerous conditions. Such authoritative on–the–job backing from design staff enhanced the effectiveness of the mobile GCI stations and contributed significantly to victory.

In March 1941 I was back with the design team at TRE Swanage and designed the original rotating, capacitative feeder linkage. This allowed the aerials to rotate continuously in one direction so that now they could be motor-driven in angular synchronism using the Selsyn[1] system. At last, the days of man-powered aerials were gone for ever. The coupling was housed in a square section box on the top of the aerials where the feeder connected to the aerial and after a proving model was tested and found satisfactory, it was soon fitted to all the GCIs.

By April I was back at Martlesham Heath to train a clutch of newly recruited WAAFs on the height-finding technique. Later on that month I was sent to the GCI at Orby on the Lincolnshire coastal plain. I was flown from Martlesham in a small Cessna or equivalent at a height of about 300 ft the whole way. My first flight – I thought it was marvellous – and I did all the navigating using a road map!

Harry Bisby rejoined TRE at Malvern in May 1945 and in 1946 he joined the Electronics Division of UKAEA at Malvern. He moved to AERE Harwell in 1949 to work on the betaspectrometer. In June 1950 he joined the Weapons Research Project at Fort Halstead, then on to Montebello Island, Australia in 1952 for the first British atomic bomb testing. Then he moved to South Africa to work on developing an analyser for uranium mining. In 1960 he returned to Harwell AERE, working for the 2000 series instrumentation group. He then went to Belgium where he joined ESONE Commission at GEEL. He retired from AERE in November 1975, after being elected founder Chairman of the European CAMAC Association.

Olga Ward, Widow of Arnold Ward

> '*There were air-raid warnings and many nights spent under a strong dining-room table, but at least we were together as the German planes roared overhead on their way to Poole and Southampton.*'

As for many young scientists, Arnold's directive to Swanage was a very hurried affair. Given two days' leave to be married in July 1940 (initially arranged for September), we were able to borrow a caravan and car from my father-in-law and journeyed to Swanage after our 9 a.m. wedding breakfast, spending the night in Ringwood *en route*.

We found farmland accommodation for the caravan near the coast in Swanage and settled down to our new life; but not for long: an order from the powers that be said that if we were to stay in our caravan the wheels must be removed. (To this day I never understood why.) We applied for a ration of petrol to take the caravan back from whence it came and then looked for a flat or house, which had to be furnished, since we possessed nothing. Luck was with us and we found a summer home for a reasonable rent in Bonfields Avenue, Swanage. There were air-raid warnings and many nights spent under a strong dining-room table with pillows and blankets, but at least we were

---

[1] Trade name for the self-synchronising system developed by BTH (British Thomson Houston Co. Ltd, Rugby).

together while the enemy planes roared overhead on their way to Poole and Southampton. We stayed in that house for two years.

One evening we were invited to dinner at St Nicholas Court in Worth Matravers where our friends Henry and Adelaide Booker lived. There was an air-raid warning and they both departed to their shelter built in the basement, while Arnold and I spent yet another night under a table! We heard a tremendous swish and thought 'this is it!' but the bomb landed in a field just above us, for which we were deeply thankful.

Another event I remember was a violent storm with a fierce east wind which washed sea and shingle into the High Street. 'It's an ill wind that blows no good' though, because Tatchells the drapers had a super storm-damage sale and I was able to purchase some single sheets for 6s a pair.

Our days at Swanage were very happy in spite of the war – we were able to swim and fish and we made many friends there. We fished out at Dancing Ledge and Arnold caught a memorable bass there one day. Then there was Dr Penley's choir which was a great joy, meeting weekly for rehearsals, and we were quite proud of our rendering of 'Torrents in Summer'.

Ellis Wiblin, MA (dec.)

'Our team had but one official bike, so you must picture Holmes, me and
the future Astronomer Royal (Martin Ryle) riding it – one on the bar
doing nothing, one on the saddle steering and one on the carrier pedalling.'

The declaration of war came while I was on the beach at Ilfracombe. I rushed back at once to the Cavendish Laboratory at Cambridge to start work for the Air Ministry.

Under Jack Ratcliffe's leadership, I and K.G. Budden, M. Ryle and R. Aves were directed to conduct research and development on directional aerials at a wavelength of 50 cm. As the needs of AMRE became clearer, various members dispersed and the team eventually comprised Ryle, me and a young assistant, Holmes, who had been at Bawdsey. We three stayed at Cambridge until 17 May 1940 when we were sent to Swanage just in time to coincide with Dunkirk and the arrival of the German presence across the water.

Our first task was to find digs and all three of us joined a gang already installed at Blechynden in Station Road. My chief memories of this period are of the Battle of Britain and the great Churchill speeches. And also of Tommy Handley and friends – 'ITMA' played no small part in maintaining national morale at that time.

May found us setting up our model aerial work on C-Site at Worth Matravers. Others too were assembling and as an example, which was to have enormous implications later on, our hut on C-Site was shared – until we were thrown out of it! – by a team including Oliphant, Lovell and Atkinson, as well as a big, strange chunk of hardware – a cm wave klystron. Continuously evacuated, it did not look at all like what it was to become – an ancestor of airborne radar – but I well remember one of the team holding a sheet of tin down the field and producing some echoes.

Our first attempt at 50 cm working was undertaken by Budden. It was to make an oscillator to a pattern given in an American article, using a Western Electric Doorknob valve which needed a lot of HT supply. With the recipe given, we could not get anything below 60 cm (our measurements were always by lecher wire). We therefore tried many other ideas and got furthest with Barkhausen-Kurz oscillators: the only snag was that the old R valves lasted only for about five minutes.[1]

Soon after this Ryle and I were on our own and we acquired some miniature triodes (Acorn type) so we made up oscillators to feed model aerial arrays. The problem then was stray radiation from the twin wire feeders and other bits of the rig. So we made up some good concentric feeders and junctions, and behold – polar diagrams became the right shape, at the right wavelength and we could concentrate on the arrays.

The first problem put to us was that of back-to-front ratio of CH transmitter aerials. A number of arrays were tried, mostly in an attempt to get high front-to-back signal ratio and to get narrow main beams free of side lobes. One of the promising types (in general – not for CH) was the Yagi, following the initial recipe of H. Yagi of Tokyo, as a single array or in combinations. We worked up to one with forty-two directors which showed great promise of a 'pure' beam and was later tried on the early 'Radio Lighthouse' at Worth.

Fortunately we quickly learned that it was no good mounting such a parasitic array on wood which could get wet. The first model concentrated its polar diagram mostly backwards. Fishenden and I made a number of later multiple arrays, including the so-called GRB, and these showed up the fundamental fault of long parasitic arrays: the bad current distribution meant a low overall gain.[2] Henceforth we concentrated on multiple arrays with not more than four directors and a reflector each. Some of these were very successful, including the 4 x 4 used for the mobile sets (e.g. LW – Light Warning). Arrays of this type (four element) were used for 1.5 m ASV on Wellington, Whitley and Liberator aircraft and on Sunderland flying boats, until centimetre gear came into use.

Yagi arrays of this simple form and their much more sophisticated later derivatives are now of course, and have been for many years, the mainstay of domestic TV installations. The all-metal type now used exclusively and which we developed to eliminate 'wet wood trouble' were inspired, as was so often the case, by an almost chance remark by Ratcliffe.

Two developments of prime importance during the Swanage era were those of common aerial working and of the Plan Position Indicator. The first of these gave the obvious advantage of real co-ordination of T and R aerials in a rotating beam setup as well as the equally real relief to the tribe of RAF 'binders' who had manually to rotate the cabins. Having achieved proper T and R alignment, the use of a PPI was possible and the elegant versions, such as the small 12 in magnetic tube one, in which 'Hoppy' and Tutchings played a big part, were of vital importance to many applications.

On the lighter side, I can recall how in those early days we, as good civil servants, needed tea and this came via a hut near one of the other sites. Our team had but one

---

[1] R valves were simple early triodes made in great quantities during the First World War. Not noted for long life anyway, they would have suffered much in B-K circuits, which unkindly imposed high positive grid bias and negative anode voltage, the converse of normal operating conditions.
[2] GRB: Ground Rotating Beam, an early term for the project that led to GCI radars.

A typical Yagi aerial array attached to the underside of an aircraft wing.

official bike so you must picture Holmes, me and the future Astronomer Royal (Martin Ryle) riding it – one on the bar doing nothing, one on the saddle steering and one on the carrier pedalling.

One day we all had our first close-up view of a shot-down German aircraft – an ME109. We all scrambled up a 120 ft tower to watch it land nearby and then on our bikes to find it, still hot on the ground. The pilot, a chunky major, came to his arrest back at the site in charge of Flt Lt Len Pittendrigh, who was the Technical Officer of the radar station. Another early recollection is of a talk given by Bainbridge-Bell on his return from a visit he made to the scuttled *Graf Spee* to have a good snoop at its radar. To make this easier he is believed to have bought the hulk.[3]

Visitors to Worth during that period included the King's brother, the Duke of Kent (later killed in an air crash); Professor Lindemann with his bag of vegetarian sandwiches; AM Sholto Douglas and Lord Brabazon. At the time I was engaged in getting a miniature radar set going in a converted Lloyd infantry carrier and it was my pleasure to shove each of the latter large gentlemen through the very small entrance.

There were so many episodes – humorous, serious and thrilling – over this time and it was satisfying to know that we were making a valuable contribution to the war effort.

___

[3] Curiously, Bainbridge-Bell's formal report seems to have been shelved and ignored in Whitehall, although it had shown conclusively that Germany had radar in service in 1939.

A highlight for me was a visit one night to a new mobile GCI. The Controller was trying to find 'customers' for the Beaufighter pilot and this demonstrated the value of the various 'bits' – from aerials to PPI – born at TRE. The realisation of that project, together with the whole centimetre development, must surely have been among the peak achievements of TRE at Swanage.

When Ellis Wiblin left TRE he worked at AERE Harwell on linear accelerators and later he and his team did original work on heart pacemakers. He was a Principal Scientific Officer and continued at Harwell throughout his working life.

Professor Sir Martin Ryle, FRS (d. 1984)

'There was a loud bang and I felt the blast of the
bullet going by on the right side of my face.'

[From a paper by the late Sir Martin Ryle transcribed from handwritten text received from Lady Rowena Ryle.]

Early on in the Battle of Britain it was realised very clearly that if that battle were won, the Luftwaffe would turn to night bombing; the development of a radar-equipped night fighter and the necessary accurate ground radar to control it near enough to the bomber was therefore urgent. Earlier work had shown that a separate radar operator in the aircraft was necessary and tests were made using a light bomber – the Blenheim.

Apart from the future problems of the correct distribution of responsibility between pilot and observer, the aerial system (which provided four 'beam' positions, the relative responses of which allowed the direction of the bomber to be established) was not satisfactory. So a small group, E.R. Wiblin, myself and a good technician, Holmes, set about the design of an improved aerial system. This involved preliminary work at our small lab at the Worth Matravers radar site.

Because of the need to avoid reflections from buildings, fences etc. when measuring the reception patterns of aerials, our lab was at C-site on St Alban's Head south of the main station enclosure.

Having designed 'mock-up' aerial systems, transmitter, azimuth (port and starboard) and elevation (up and down), these were taken to RAF Christchurch and tested again on the actual aircraft to determine the effect of engines etc. on the performance. If necessary, modifications were made and then a proper version was built and installed for flight trials.

This early long-wave (1.5 m) night fighter radar (AI MkIV) meant that each type of aircraft had to be considered anew. At the time of Dunkirk a number of French Air Force pilots flew out some Bostons – an American light bomber. These were slightly faster than the Blenheim, which did not have the margin of speed needed to intercept some of the Luftwaffe bombers. As there were enough Bostons to form a couple of squadrons, it was decided to equip them with AI MkIV and to fit them with machine-guns in the bottom of the bomb-bay. The modified aircraft was known as the Havoc.

One was delivered to Christchurch, and I was looking at the best place to site the azimuth aerials (either side of the rather long nose). There was an armourer fiddling about with the port machine-gun. I'd been looking at the port side of the nose, but to check that the arrangement of Perspex was symmetrical, had just moved straight in front of the nose in order to see both sides at once. There was a loud bang and I felt the blast of the bullet going by on the right side of my face. 'What the hell do you think you're doing?'

'Sorry, Sir, didn't know there was one up the spout!'

'Well, bloody well look next time!'

So we fitted aerials for the Havoc too. The test flying (during the Battle of Britain) was complicated. We were not supposed to fly during alerts (we had a scarcity value!) and as there were often six in a day there tended to be a mad dash to get airborne as soon as the 'All Clear' went (the communications system was totally inadequate to recall us).

But the Blenheim and the Havoc were not the answer – they were too slow – and what was to become the night Blitz relied on a new aircraft developed by the Bristol Aeroplane Co. – the Beaufighter. As well as greatly improved performance, it was fitted with 20 mm cannon. It also took a more serious view of the problem of baling out, by the provision of excellent pilot and observer escape hatches. The first production Beaufighters were due in the latter half of September 1940, and we were expecting one for aerial design, which because of its short nose would have to be something new.

In about mid-September 1940 I took my lunch sandwiches to the Square and Compass in Worth Matravers for some cider and company. On my way back to C-Site I called in the operations room of the CH radar to see what was going on. One WAAF was urgently passing plots to Fighter Control, the other beckoned me over to the other display, where there was the largest formation of aircraft I had ever seen. 'How many?'

'100 plus.'

'Where are they heading?'

'Here!'

Now that was interesting; a few weeks earlier the bombing of fighter stations having proved ineffective, the Luftwaffe turned its attention to the radar chain. Starting with Teutonic thoroughness at the bottom right-hand corner of Britain, they had worked their way along the south coast and Ventnor, the next station to Worth Matravers, had been bombed a few days earlier. In fact, the radar stations were usually back on the air, maybe with reduced power or without height-finding, within a couple of days and the programme was ineffective. But for the sake of completeness, the latest station in the CH chain was a likely target. They were still twenty minutes flying time away, so after exchanging mutual wishes of good luck I returned to C-Site. We were in any case supposed to be in our own air-raid shelters, although the C-Site one was so far only an excavated ditch.

Soon the bombers were within earshot and then visible – a compact formation heading straight for us. But they flew on, except for one which was caught by a few Hurricanes nibbling at a corner of the formation. He was straight overhead and came down with his engines flat out – a sound which once heard can never be forgotten. There was no chance of anyone baling out and the aircraft hit the sea just off the cliff; the earthquake through the rock reached our ditch before the sound. About an hour and a half later the main formation returned, straight over us again, in the meantime having bombed Bristol and severely damaged the Bristol Aeroplane Co.

A Beaufighter equipped with 1.5 m AI radar.

In order to speed things up we were sent a Beaufighter's starboard wing. By mounting it on trestles we could measure the reception pattern of the azimuth aerials, and by standing it vertically (with strong ropes against the south-westerly gales) we could measure the patterns of the elevation aerials. But besides establishing the appropriate positions of the aerials, we could see exactly where they had to be to miss wing ribs, rivet lines etc. In this way the drawing office were able to make detailed drawings of mounting brackets, cable runs etc., before the first production aircraft emerged.

Nos 1 and 2 were kept at Bristol for further tests, flying and installation work; No. 3 crashed; No. 4 was for pilot training and we had No. 5. But there was very little test flying needed and it soon joined No. 4 for operational trials. It was to be the Beaufighter fitted with AI MkIV that won the night Battle of Britain in the period early 1941 to the end of 1942.

At about this time Skinner, Dee, Lovell, Burcham, Atkinson and Ward moved into our hut, with laboratory glassware, vacuum pumps etc. for developing centimetre wavelength equipment. Soon the Randall and Boot development of the magnetron at Birmingham, which increased the 100 W or so available from the klystron to 5, then 50, then 200 kW! – and the discovery of how to make, repeatedly, crystal rectifiers, and of course the TR cell and Sutton tube local oscillators which were also vital – revolutionised the possibilities of successful centimetre wave radar. Before long we had witnessed the first cm target: an assistant, Reg Batt despatched on a bicycle down the track to the coastguard station, holding (with difficulty) a sheet of aluminium.

But our hut was now altogether too crowded and a new one was built for us nearer the cliffs at the west of St Alban's Head. Here we developed the long-range homing aerial system for the ASV MkII of Coastal Command, installed in Wellingtons, Sunderlands and Catalinas.

By the end of 1942, a new aircraft, known only as B1/40, was nearing production; its performance was considerably better than the Beaufighter and we were again given the job of designing the aerials. But this meant something totally new: the aircraft was made of wood, and so the reflecting properties of the skin could not be used for forming the desired reception patterns. In addition, the increased speed meant that as much as possible of the aerial system should be inside the wing. De Havillands sent a section of wing and also a large sheet of skin plywood and dope, to measure the absorption which would be produced by internal mounting (which was in fact negligible despite the shiny appearance of the aluminium undercoat). Again the complete aerial system was designed and incorporated during the construction of the wing. The B1/40 became the Mosquito.

But the days of 2.5 m radar for night fighting and Coastal Command were numbered. The success in developing transmitters and receivers for 9 cm wavelength had led to an ingenious spirally scanning dish, invented by Alan Hodgkin and engineered by Nash and Thompson. The first was installed in the nose of one of the Christchurch Blenheims. The test flights were immediately encouraging, but occasionally responses were observed which showed no physical reality – you just flew through them. They were not flocks of migrating birds; they occurred under a wide range of weather conditions, including completely clean air. A camera gun repeatedly showed nothing as the target was approached. Could there be some great fallacy in cm wave radar? Was there some non-obvious atmospheric effect that would render the large effort made in its development useless?

The pulse recurrence frequency was 3,000 per second. This meant that an aircraft at, say, 5 km, could be simulated by one at 55 km or 105 km – if the echoing area were sufficiently large – one at 55 km would have to be more than 15,000 times larger. This seemed totally impossible.[1] But when the position of the aircraft as it 'intercepted' one of these ghosts was checked, it seemed that the answer was found – the city of Portsmouth! But how could compact bits of Portsmouth (for the ghosts often showed small components) give such a huge echo? The answer turned out to be in the fact that man-made buildings tend to be vertical, with right-angled corners, so that the effect can be the same as in a 'cat's-eye' road reflector: the energy is reflected back in the direction from which it has come and not scattered over the sky. This conclusion was soon confirmed, and because of its suddenly perceived importance, was awarded overriding secrecy. For here was something that could show up man-made structures in the landscape: it could be used to navigate beyond the horizon of other radar navigational systems, and it could be used to bomb cities.

And so, in parallel with the first operational cm radar – AI MkVII, installed in Beaufighters and then Mosquitos – was developed the H$_2$S navigational system under the direction of Bernard Lovell.

At about this time a new airfield at Hurn, just north of Bournemouth, was completed. With its concrete runway it allowed the faster and larger aircraft now becoming relevant to TRE to operate safely. But our occupancy was short: the danger of invasion was very real and the Isle of Purbeck has, besides the ferry across Poole Harbour, only one road passing through a steep valley at Corfe (hence the castle). It had been decided that in the event of invasion TRE would run away: those with cars were to pick up others and get out (if German paratroops were not already holding Corfe).

Sir Martin Ryle was elected Fellow of the Royal Society in 1952 and in 1974 was joint Nobel Prizewinner for Physics. He achieved distinction in the field of radio astronomy, becoming professor in that subject at Cambridge, Director of the Mullard Radio Astronomy Observatory and Astronomer Royal from 1972–82. He died in 1984 aged sixty-six.

Douglas Wootton, B.Sc., DIC, FIEE, C.Eng., (d. 1994)

*'The head of our Group was delighted to demonstrate to
visitors the power that was then obtainable at this frequency
by lighting his cigarette from the output probe.'*

I graduated at Imperial College London in 1939, but continued with a postgraduate course in the autumn while offering my services at the outbreak of war. It wasn't until February 1940 that I was summoned to appear before a joint recruiting board composed of representatives of the Army, Navy, Air Force and Government research

---

[1] With a repetition rate of 3,000 pulses per second echoes could be displayed up to a range of 30 miles on the cathode ray tube trace that immediately followed the transmitter pulse. If echoes were received from (very large) targets at much longer ranges they would also appear on the display, but several traces later. The observer had no obvious means of telling whether echoes were within the 30 miles or at much longer ranges.

establishments. As a result, I was directed to join the Air Ministry Research Establishment in Dundee. They were getting ready to move, though, so it wasn't until 7 May 1940 that I finally joined them on their arrival at Worth Matravers.

Every new recruit was given three days in which to digest the contents of the 'bible' on radio direction-finding techniques, after which he was allocated to a specific area. I was fortunate enough to be put in a department working on a new form of radar for use against the night fighter or bomber [AI]. This required the use of very high radio frequencies of centimetric wavelengths, so that the signal could be directed in a beam from an aerial small enough to be used in an aircraft. Everything had to be developed from scratch; it was certainly a great privilege for a young man to be a member, albeit very junior, of such a team largely recruited from established members of academe.

Worth Matravers was a very small village, so most members of the establishment lived in Swanage; arrangements were made to provide a private bus service operating on a fixed schedule. Some of the senior men had cars, but for us juniors wishing to work later than the buses ran, it meant cycling up to Worth Matravers – a hard slog in the morning, but a joy in the evenings of double summertime to sit on the bike and coast most of the way down to Swanage, admiring the lovely views on all sides.

Swanage itself was a pleasant place to live with some excellent landladies. In the early summer of 1940, sailing was still allowed in the waters around the coast and the view from the town across to the Isle of Wight made a pretty picture with sails lit by the evening sun. Later, as France fell, sailing ceased and the pier was chopped in two in order to make a sea-borne invasion more difficult.

For outdoor recreation we had the picturesque country lanes and coastal paths on which to walk or cycle. I remember in particular the splendid display put on by the glow-worms as dusk fell on the cliff path near Ballard Point. For the more energetic there was badminton and tennis, while indoor activities included concerts organised by musical groups who pooled their limited supply of gramophone records. Some of the friendships formed during those activities have continued to this day.

As the size of the team working on centimetric activities grew, we withdrew from the building on the main site to a Nissen type hut at C-Site near the cliff above Chapmans Pool. This hut was inadequately heated by a stove which we managed to get red hot during the particularly cold weather in the winter months of 1940–1.

A group at Birmingham University had been working on the generation of microwave power, and provided us with a two-cavity klystron giving a continuous wave output power of 300 W at a frequency of 3 gigahertz. The head of our group was delighted to demonstrate to visitors the power that was then obtainable at this frequency by lighting his cigarette from the output probe.

Among the more amusing incidents that occurred at this time was a visit by ACM Dowding, then Chief of Fighter Command, who was not so much interested in our work as in reprimanding us for the delay in progress of installation of aerials on an aircraft. He had us lined up in military fashion for his lecture. Fortunately for us, the work turned out not to be our responsibility.

After the fall of France the Germans turned their attention to softening up Britain prior to their planned invasion. Indeed, there was on one day a yellow alert and we stood by ready to smash up the equipment that had been built. The first targets for the massed raids by German aircraft were near to the south coast, and due to the cloud-free skies of the summer of 1940, we had a grandstand view of the dogfights with their vapour trails, the sun glinting on the aircrafts' wings making them look like fish swimming in the sky. Fortunately the bombers were flying at about 15,000 ft, a height which enabled early detection by the existing CH radars and allowed sufficient time to scramble Hurricanes and Spitfires and get them into the best position from which to attack the enemy.

The Group was obtaining some success and it was felt that microwave techniques had been developed sufficiently to warrant building an experimental radar. There was a need to find suitable targets on which experience could be gained and improvements found for the ground-based radar before installing it in an aircraft. Some aircraft and ships were made available as targets, but they were in short supply in those days, so I was unwise enough to suggest that a substitute target might well be made from suitably reflecting objects suspended beneath a balloon. I was taken aback when I was given the job of organising it.

When all the necessary equipment had been prepared, the launch day arrived and the local police and the Air Ministry informed. We filled the balloon with hydrogen in a field, but it turned out to be larger than anticipated and became somewhat difficult to control as it swirled around in a gusty wind. As it rose high in the air, we were embarrassed by the arrival of some local inhabitants, who of course wanted to know what was going on. We couldn't tell them of course, so on being pressed, said we were taking fresh air samples. To cap it all, a police constable approached and said that a man in the crowd was suspected of being a spy. I wondered whether he was pulling my leg, but in wartime it was difficult always to get at the truth. In the event we just carried on. I suppose those targets were the forerunners of the corner reflectors now to be seen on the masthead of most seagoing yachts, which enable them to be visible on the radar screens of larger vessels.

Whitsun 1942 saw the establishment departing for Malvern, where it occupied the college for the duration of the war, eventually moving to a former naval training establishment called HMS *Duke*, where it has remained ever since.

Douglas Wootton joined EMI's research labs at Hayes in 1947 and remained with them until 1985. He then was employed at, and later headed, Microwave Solid State Section. He worked on Cymbeline and Searchwater military radars. In 1975 he took over responsibility for the newly formed Medical Ultrasonics Section. He later contributed to the 'Mainsborne Programme' – trials of this involved electricity, gas and water authorities taking meter readings and transmitting them via telephone cables to a centralised computer.

Sir Bernard Lovell, OBE, FRS

[In *Echoes of War* (IOP Publishing, 1991), Sir Bernard Lovell describes the then novel introduction of microwaves to three applications of airborne radar: air interception of night intruders (AI); location of enemy shipping including submarines (ASV) and blind bombing over Germany beyond the ranges of UK ground-based navigational aids (H_2S).

During the development of these radars, continual modifications and improvements led to many additional subtitles and type numbers. The various resulting Marks are described in detail as are the opposing viewpoints of different high officials on the perceived priorities for Service use. These disputes sometimes resulted in equipment originally conceived for one application being diverted to another, as in the case of the modification of H_2S for ASV against submarines, a contentious decision which nevertheless hastened the end of the Battle of the Atlantic and thereby foiled Germany's attempts to block the vital marine supply lines to island Britain. The comprehensive treatment of complex matters, interspersed with extracts from official minutes and statements made during the fluid war situation, tend to limit the extent to which mere extracts are appropriate. Nevertheless, we are grateful to Sir Bernard and to IOP Publishing Ltd for permission to quote the following abridged passages from his book.]

1. The First Centimetric Radars

As soon as the sealed-off cavity magnetron arrived on 19 July [Worth Matravers, 1940], plans were made to wire it into a crude pulsed system as quickly as possible. Atkinson and Burcham had been working on the pulsing of the klystron and now had the job of making the modulator to pulse the magnetron. Skinner collaborated with A.G. Ward in making a receiver using a crystal mixer and on 8 and 9 August, with the equipment connected to fixed paraboloids, echoes were obtained from the coastguard houses [on the cliffs at St Aldhelm's (or Alban's) Head].

In the absence of any common transmit-receive device I asked the workshops to make a swivel on which to mount the two 3-foot paraboloids. By this time Rowe had placed Dee in overall charge of us and with only one piece of equipment a good deal of confusion reigned. However, on 12 August, the day I got the double paraboloid swivel from the workshop, Dee, Skinner and Atkinson were away and the site was unusually quiet. Burcham made cables to carry the magnetron power to one paraboloid and the receiver to the other. At 6 p.m. we were ready. By chance an aeroplane was flying along the coast a few miles away and from that unidentified aeroplane we received the first 10 cm echoes using the cavity magnetron.

The next day (13 August) there were more echoes from aircraft. Dee had returned and brought down Watson-Watt and Rowe to see these historic echoes. In the afternoon we sent one of our junior assistants, Reg Batt, with a tin sheet and told him to cycle along the cliff in front of us. The ground rose slightly to the face of the cliff and where that young man cycled the ground was behind the tin sheet as viewed from our paraboloids. As we swivelled the paraboloids to follow Batt and the tin sheet, a strong echo appeared on the cathode-ray tube. I merely noted that it was 'amazing considering it should be right in the ground returns'. None of us had any inkling on that afternoon of the immense significance of that somewhat casual experiment.

[The fact that the echo from the tin sheet was so strong as to be clearly visible despite a background of returns from the cliffs was significant in that it augured well for the success of microwaves for two possibilities: terrain mapping by detecting reflections from objects such as buildings against a background of general ground clutter, as was soon to be realised with H_2S; and for the detection of small targets such as submarine periscopes amidst sea clutter with new centimetric versions of ASV radar.]

2. The 'Sunday Soviet' of 26 October 1941

Few 'Soviets' could have had the significance of this one. Although the whole of my work for the remainder of the war was to be determined by that meeting I was not a participant. In fact it was customary for Rowe to summon only the senior scientists who had interests related to the subject under discussion. In any event the most significant

TRE person present on that day was Dee whose diary entry reads only: 'Big VCCE meeting/Soviet at TRE on how to locate targets'.

This meeting was, perhaps, the most significant outcome of Churchill's 3 September minute to the Chief of Air Staff [on the inability of Bomber Command to locate targets accurately]. No minutes of the 'Sunday Soviets' were kept but it seems probable that it was stimulated by Sir Robert Renwick whom Cherwell had recently arranged to be responsible in the Ministry of Aircraft Production for the coordination of all research, development and production of radar and radio aids in aircraft. Rowe's reference to the meeting states that: 'Late in October 1941 I held a "Sunday Soviet" on how to help Bomber Command to bomb unseen targets'.

Although both Gee and Oboe were to prove of great importance to Bomber Command operations, they were ruled out of discussion at the meeting because Cherwell insisted that great ranges of operation were needed to enable Bomber Command to penetrate deep into German territory.

At the meeting, Cherwell insisted also that Bomber Command must have a radar bombing aid self-contained in the aircraft. Although on that afternoon, as Rowe recalled, the meeting ended 'without an idea', the discussion had stimulated Dee to reflect on the possibilities inherent in the centimetre system. Those in the field at Leeson House clearly revealed the radar reflections from the small town of Swanage a few miles distant down the hill. The strong echo from the tin sheet standing out against the ground scatter, observed in the first ground tests of the centimetre system at Worth in August 1941, seemed significant. Also several of the centimetre AI systems were now airborne on which coastlines were well defined. Early in the tests of the spiral scanning AIS system, submarines had been detected with only the conning tower exposed.

These features led Dee, a day or so after Rowe's meeting, to organise a specific test to discover whether a centimetre radar flying several thousand feet above the ground could distinguish the echoes from a town among the echoes scattered from the ground.

[Sir Bernard goes on to describe in some detail how an AI scanner (common T & R aerial reflector) was modified for a fixed angle of depression and flown in a Blenheim aircraft, with Dr B.J. O'Kane (GEC) and G.S. Hensby (TRE), on 1 November. They photographed the radar display and obtained such convincing results that H_2S was born.]

3. Responsibility for H_2S

On 29 December 1941 Rowe had summoned me to his office and told me I was to cease working on the lock-follow AI and take charge of the development of a new device, then known as BN (blind navigation) to help Bomber Command. I responded that I did not want to do this because I was anxious to get the AIF system into a Beaufighter. Dee was absent but when he returned on 31 December he said I had to do this and insisted on driving me to the new aerodrome at Hurn, hoping thereby to lessen my resistance. Early the next morning I was again taken to Rowe's office whose patience was rapidly evaporating as he abruptly terminated my further objections by the terse statement that 'there was no alternative'. In that manner I was ordered rather than 'given charge of' a task that I did not want to do and knew little about.

I was soon to be made aware of the circumstances which were as follows. After the evacuation of the BEF from France there was little scope for offensive action against the enemy apart from bombing. Indeed on 15 January 1941 the Air Staff issued a directive to the C-in-C Bomber Command that the 'sole primary aim of your bomber offensive should be the destruction of Germany's synthetic oil plants . . .'. However, the U-boat menace to essential shipping was so serious that in March 1941 Churchill issued a directive giving absolute priority to the Battle of the Atlantic, and on 9 March the C-in-C Bomber Command received another directive from the Vice Chief of Air Staff: 'I am directed to inform you that the Prime Minister has ruled that for the next four months we should devote our energies to defeating the attempt of the enemy to strangle our food supplies and our connection with the United States . . .'. A considerable proportion of the available Bomber Command effort then became involved in mine-laying and in the bombing of the German battleships in dock or under construction. Although a number of German ports suffered some damage there was little effect on industrial and other targets inland.

4. The U-Boat Attacks in the North Atlantic

When the move to Worth Matravers had occurred early in May 1940 I became immersed in the development of centimetre radar and it seemed most unlikely that I should have any further connection with ASV systems. However, this was not the case and I must now describe the circumstances that led to the involvement of a substantial part of my group with Coastal Command, coincident with the first operational use of H$_2$S over enemy territory.

During 1942 the shipping losses from U-boat attacks in the North Atlantic reached 600,000 tons per month. Churchill and the Cabinet were extremely concerned, and in his account of those years Churchill states that his great fear was that Hitler would decide to stake all on the U-boat campaign. By midsummer the War Cabinet considered that the losses to the Atlantic merchant fleet 'constituted a terrible event in a very bad time' and that the U-boat attacks were then our worst evil. Every history of that period reveals the critical nature of these U-boat attacks on the ships bringing oil and essential supplies to Britain.

[Sir Bernard then describes how Coastal Command Wellington aircraft fitted with 1.5 m ASV and aided by the Leigh Light accounted successfully for U-boats in the Bay of Biscay – their transit area from French ports to the Atlantic – until the enemy fitted them with Metox receivers, giving enough early warning of approaching aircraft for the submarine to dive to safety. To re-establish the Wellington's success a centimetric ASV development was started within TRE but for various reasons a decision was soon taken (at first causing disruption of staff within TRE, upsetting Bomber Command and failing to satisfy Coastal Command) to abandon it in favour of a crash plan to modify H$_2$S radars for ASV.]

The uneasy relations between Coastal and Bomber Commands were greatly exacerbated by the decision to use the H$_2$S equipment for ASV. The crash programme to produce a few Mark I H$_2$S systems by the end of 1942 was merely beginning at the time of this decision and Bomber Command fought bitterly to prevent this diversion of the scarce equipment they needed.

Furthermore, Harris and his senior staff argued that far more damage would be inflicted on the U-boats by bombing the U-boat pens in the French west coast ports than by attempting to sink them at sea.

For their part the senior officers of Coastal Command were very greatly annoyed by the decision to cancel the development of the system being undertaken specifically for their use.

The Coastal Command hierarchy would not face the reality that they *could* have the H$_2$S/ASV system almost immediately whereas they had no hope of getting their own ASVS system for many months. Further, the logical (to us) procedure of fitting a few extra four-engined bombers to be used by Coastal was violently opposed by both Coastal and Bomber Commands for different reasons.

It would have been logical to fit the scanners in the underbelly position of the Wellingtons as we had done for the four-engined bombers but that position was occupied by the retractable Leigh Light and the only feasible alternative was to use the nose position. However, this meant removing the forward guns, and since the Leigh Light had already replaced the under-turret guns there was quite naturally further argument and dispute. Eventually a Perspex 'chin' was fitted under the nose of Wellingtons, but the scanner had to be redesigned to an aperture of 28 in instead of 36 in. The chin position prevented complete all-round-looking and caused a blackout in a 40 degree sector directly behind the aircraft.

By December 1942 we had fitted two Wellington VIIIs (LB129 and LB135) with the modified H$_2$S equipment and with the scanner in the nose position. There seemed to be endless teething troubles and the lack of enthusiasm and general antagonism of Coastal Command increased our difficulties. They demanded that we should include various beacon facilities and this caused delays and was of insignificant value compared with the major issues at stake. Many of the modifications were carried out on the top floor of the Malvern College Preston Laboratory by a few members of my group and, by the end of January 1943, we had sent two Wellington XII aircraft fitted with the H$_2$S/ASV and one of our prototypes to the Coastal Command Squadron based at Chivenor in North Devon. By mid-February we had sent seven Wellingtons to Chivenor and there were a dozen there by the end of the month.

Whereas the Bomber Command aircraft were operating at 20,000 ft the normal Bay patrols of Coastal Command were at 2,000 ft. The Wellingtons arrived at Chivenor with the normal dipole feed used in the H$_2$S scanners. In order to improve the coverage and give better performance when flying at the 2,000 ft level we decided to replace the dipole by a waveguide feed.

The Coastal Command officers exhibited negligible interest and with O'Kane and seven members of my group at Chivenor maintaining and giving instructions in the use of the equipment, one of my senior staff, Richard Fortescue, most generously offered to don RAF uniform and fly over the Bay as operator of the ASV.

March–April 1943

Although the aerodrome at Chivenor was in the midst of the attractive region of North Devon and close to popular peacetime seaside resorts, my memory of the March days of 1943 are not pleasant ones. On the night of 1 March two of our 10 cm ASV-equipped

Wellingtons took off from Chivenor for their first Bay patrol. Fervently believing that major issues were involved, we had connived with the diversion of H_2S units from Bomber Command to their great annoyance and in the face of opposition we had staked nearly half of our group and much of our reputation to get these two aircraft operating over the Bay.

I have no record of the name of the Station Commander at that time but he had absorbed the antagonism of his superiors and vented a good measure of it on me as we waited for the return of the patrol. His faith in our equipment was entirely lacking. For him it was another nuisance. 'What good do you think that gadget of yours is going to do out there? You ought to fly out and look for yourself at that great featureless expanse, then you would realise that your rotating thing would never stand a chance of catching a sub.'

I would gladly have flown out and looked for myself but it had been nearly impossible to arrange for Fortescue to go and if I had been there my eyes would have been glued to the cathode ray tube – as Fortescue's were. It was as well that he was looking at the tube. At last he returned. No, there had been no submarines but they had been attacked by a German fighter and he had been able to give the pilot instructions for evasive action. The crew of that Wellington spread the news and the tensions of our presence on the aerodrome began to ease.

For two weeks the patrols continued without incident. With seven specialists from my group looking after the equipment, the serviceability was good and then, during the night of 17 March, the equipment in Wellington H538 saw an echo from a U-boat at a range of 9 miles. The attack on the U-boat was foiled by the jamming of the Leigh Light. The next night H538 obtained another contact at a range of 7 miles and this time the U-boat was attacked with six depth charges. The pilot's log read: 'Both times the submarine was fully surfaced and under way, showing no signs of suspecting attack.' . . . 'March 27th. Chivenor had a good haul in the Bay this week – four good attacks!'

The centimetre ASV – now coded as ASV MkIII in this 172 Squadron based at Chivenor, made thirteen sightings before the end of March and another 24 in April. The U-boat crews did not relish these night attacks and Doenitz ordered his crews to stay on the surface and fight it out with the aircraft, not only on the Bay transit routes but around our convoys. Now, long-range aircraft operating from both sides of the Atlantic closed the mid-Atlantic gap, and a grim slaughter of the U-boats ensued. During the decisive months of April and May 1943, fifty-six U-boats were destroyed and at the end of May the Naval Staff 'noted with a relief that can still be felt today the sudden cessation of U-boat activity which occurred on or about the 23rd of May'.

The few 10 cm ASV-equipped Wellingtons in 172 Squadron had, within a few weeks, transformed the strategic situation to such an extent that in May 1943 every U-boat crossing the Bay, on average, suffered one attack. The shipping losses in the North Atlantic had reached 400,000 tons in March but, instead of rising to the unprecedented levels feared by the War Cabinet they then fell abruptly and by August were less than 100,000 tons per month. In a radio broadcast Hitler complained that 'the temporary setback to our U-boat campaign is due to one single technical invention of our enemies'.

[After some delay the Germans fitted submarines with Naxos, a 10 cm successor to their 1.5 m Metox warning receiver.]

. . . the delay in their understanding that the Coastal Command ASV was now radiating on a shorter wavelength illustrates the lack of close liaison between the scientists and the operational staffs. It is inconceivable that such a delay could have occurred with the Allies where the scientific/operational liaison was so close. The consequence of this delay was that by the autumn of 1943 when evidence arose that the Germans were now listening to the 10 cm ASV transmission we had completed our development of ASV Marks VI and VII.

[These equipments marked another step forward in microwave technology by working not at the 9–10 cm wavelength of the first centimetric airborne radars but at 3 cm which, once again, evaded the U-boat listening device. The 3 cm H_2S equipment was also introduced to the Pathfinder Group of Bomber Command late in 1943 with consequent improvement in target discrimination. Subsequent chapters of *Echoes of War* cover the successful use of H_2S in the role for which it was first conceived – as a blind-bombing aid against targets in Germany (but not without some controversy), for minelaying and in applications with the Army.]

On returning to academic life after the war, Sir Bernard soon became involved in research into radio astronomy at the University of Manchester, at first adapting surplus ex-wartime radar gear before embarking on the giant Jodrell Bank Radio Telescope project with which his name has become inseparably connected. His professorship of Radio Astronomy and numerous academic honours at home and abroad, together with a wide range of publications, has established his reputation internationally as a pioneer and leader in the science of radio astronomy.

Reg Batt

> *'It was sheer magic! The transmitter problem had been*
> *solved – the age of the magnetron had arrived!'*

I arrived on the scene early in May 1940 at the time when the new, purpose-built site at Worth Matravers had been opened up. I came from the Post Office Engineering Department in London. Significantly I was at that time the most junior member of the group but the only one with formal radio engineering qualifications. I was soon to learn that the less one knew about radio the better one could assimilate these new and strange concepts. The time it took for electrons to travel between valve electrodes had become important (goodness!); the shortest piece of connecting wire was no longer just a piece of connecting wire but in itself a tuned circuit and one of embarrassing proportions. What kind of madhouse had I volunteered to enter?

I was put to work assisting a well-built Canadian by the name of A.G. Ward who had been given the job of concocting a 10 cm receiver more or less from a standing start. Close on my heels on 15 May came P.I. Dee and W.E. Burcham from the Cavendish Laboratory at Cambridge University where before the war they had been involved with what is nowadays referred to as high-energy physics.

Dee was tall, slim, impatiently active and businesslike. He was to be a joint group leader with Dr Skinner who, with tousled hair and crumpled suit, appeared like

Professor W.E.
Burcham.

Professor P.I. Dee.

Dr H.W.B. Skinner.
(Photograph by
courtesy of his
daughter, Mrs Elaine
Wheatley.)

everyone's idea of a mad scientist. Such an impression gained credence when early on in our relationship I heard him talk about using crystal detectors – complete with catswhisker as in my father's 1924 wireless set! Then, when I heard him say that he considered the target for the establishment was not just 10 cm but 1 cm, I thought he really must be mad. But in the weeks, months and years that I was to work under him, I was to learn what a remarkable prescience this man possessed – in little more than two years the group would be down to 1.25 cm (K band). Dee and Skinner – such a diverse pair of characters – were nevertheless remarkably complementary in their function as joint group leaders. Though their methods of working were so different, they were in close agreement as to the course of the work.

Yet another great character was to arrive as a senior member of the group – Dr (now Sir Bernard) Lovell, to join the select band who were 'always furiously engaged in argument, breaking fresh ground in centimetres', to quote none other than Sir John Cockcroft who had been largely instrumental in recruiting many of the university scientists into radar in the summer of 1939. From Manchester University Lovell had, in those first nine months of the war, been working with Bowen on the 1.5 m AI at Perth and latterly St Athan airfield. He therefore came to the new group with knowledge and experience in AI systems and in the problems of fitting equipment into the confined spaces of aircraft. He was a tireless and enthusiastic worker, and sharply critical of any shortcomings on the part of ministries, management, storekeepers, industry or anything else that threatened to obstruct the progress of a project. In this respect he was at one with Dee.

It seemed that those in the upper echelons of the establishment had little faith, time, or patience for such a way-out undertaking as centimetres, less still for a dissident bunch of academics none of whom had professional experience of radio. It was as well therefore that the group's number included Jimmy Atkinson. His experience in Bawdsey days had given him an unrivalled knowledge of the RAF stores system. This, together with his innate charm, enabled him to acquire the most scarce of wartime commodities from would-be unco-operative storekeepers and administrators.

The Klystron

The group had been allocated a hut on C site, which was a whole field removed from the main area encompassing A and B sites. It was as if centimetres was a contagious disease which must be kept at a respectable distance from legitimate radio men. One look inside this hut would have confirmed a sceptics' worst suspicions: it certainly took me aback when I first saw it. In the corner nearest the door was a most extraordinary array of apparatus – its central item a large and strange transmitting valve, made more of copper and brass than glass. This was a klystron, a new type of microwave valve invented by the Varian brothers in the USA. Based on their original design, it had been developed by the team at Birmingham University led by Professor (later Sir Mark) Oliphant.

High-frequency power was produced within a coupled pair of resonant cavities referred to by the Americans as 'rhumbatrons', which were energised by a beam of electrons produced in a like manner to that within a TV picture tube. To get work started without delay, Dee had had this one made at the Mond Laboratory at Cambridge to Oliphant's design. To bring it to life was a network of umbilical cords feeding it not only with electrical power but with cooling water pumped from a cistern which stood outside the window. Yet more rubber tubing connected it with a vacuum pumping system complete with its motor-driven backing pump which clack-clacked away noisily day by day.

Alongside the bench supporting the klystron and its pumping equipment was a lethal-looking assembly of oil-filled transformers the size of a packing case, and high voltage capacitors as large as a small suitcase, and all bearing menacing-looking porcelain insulators which in themselves were warning enough of the 10,000 to 20,000 volts the setup could produce at a not insignificant current. I surveyed this scene with incredulity, remarking to Ward that I thought we were supposed to be working on something to go into an aeroplane! He just smiled gently – Ward always smiled gently – and in his slow Canadian drawl made some reassuring remark which nevertheless failed to convince me.

The klystron – a device of brilliant scientific conception – was a temperamental animal. Everything had to be just right for it to perform. Day after day Skinner, Dee, Burcham and Atkinson worked away tirelessly with small reward. While Skinner pressed on doggedly, Dee impatiently complained of the capricious device which 'can only be persuaded to oscillate for a mere ten minutes once a fortnight'. There was some substance to Dee's complaint, for in my first three weeks of working in the hut, I only witnessed two occasions when the klystron could be persuaded to oscillate and produce power. But when it did, its performance was spectacular. We watched as Skinner drew off an arc from the output stub with a screwdriver. The resulting ionisation of the surrounding air produced a continuous blue glow as if it were a spirit flame. If you held your hand nearby you could feel heat being radiated.

Waveguides

The question had been raised as to how this power could be fed to an aerial since coaxial cable was relatively new and at microwave frequencies hopelessly lossy. It was decided to experiment with the entirely new concept of waveguides. A waveguide was a metal tube which at 10 cm would be of the order of 2 in in diameter; launched into the tube the radiation would pass along its length as a wavefront with, hopefully, little loss. Accordingly, about a 12 ft length of metal tubing was set up along the bench supported by retort stands with the output stub of the klystron 'looking' into one end.

At the time we had the impression that the piping had been bought from a local ironmonger, but later we learned from Atkinson that it was vent piping from Elsan chemical toilets which were used on site, Worth being without main drainage. He had persuaded a disbelieving storekeeper to supply him with two, which although providing us with tubing of the required diameter, left him with a bizarre disposal problem because the storekeeper could issue only complete sets. Notwithstanding the dubious source of our waveguide, it can be reported that the experiment was an undoubted success. Once the klystron had been prodded into oscillation the results were amazing: a neon lamp held at the far end of the tube glowed brightly indicating the radio frequency power issuing from it and the heat could be felt as if from a blast of hot air rather than high-frequency radiation.

Spectacular as these occasional bursts of klystron activity were, it was far from providing a solution to the problem of producing a 10 cm transmitter which could be made to fly. Neither were the receiver experiments that Ward, myself and another colleague, Wootton, had been conducting any more rewarding. The main problem was to produce a local oscillator from a selection of thermionic valves which were never designed to operate at 1 m let alone 10 cm. The apparent answer was to operate them in what was termed the Barkhausen-Kurz mode in which the circuit conditions were set to match the rate of electron flow between the valve electrodes (i.e. the transit time). We never achieved a wavelength shorter than 80 cm by this method and with the valves available. So we fell back on a more conventional transmission line oscillator on 20 cm (at which frequency we could use the second harmonic). For this we used a Western Electric Samuel Tube commonly called a 'double-doorknob' since its glass-sealed connections came out each side of a doughnut-shaped glass envelope. It was designed to operate down to about 1 m, hence at five times that frequency it ran excessively hot. In consequence it would run merrily for about half an hour before suddenly stopping due to the connections becoming oxidised – potentially embarrassing when giving demonstrations to VIPs.

The Aerials

Least problematical was the work on centimetre aerials, which progressed steadily in the hands of Bernard Lovell. The consistently fine summer of 1940 was ideal for aerial experiments, most of which needed to be done in the field. To assist was the able Chapman, a laboratory technician whom Lovell had 'borrowed' from Manchester University for the duration, along with a useful selection of lab equipment (which would be returned with interest in the form of some surplus radar equipment when the war ended). Chapman was a calm, conscientious and unflappable worker – a perfect complement to Lovell's hyperactive zeal.

To produce a narrow beam at centimetre wavelengths one could use a horn or a parabolic reflector (also referred to as a 'mirror' or a 'dish'). The main problem was not the design of the aerial element itself but the means of connecting it to transmitter or receiver. Not until ICI's new wonder material polythene became generally available was a satisfactory coaxial cable found for this application. Nevertheless, Lovell and Chapman made good progress accompanied by generous helpings of self-criticism and congratulation in equal measure from the loquacious Dr Lovell.

Whoever among Dee, Skinner or Lovell could sing the best chorus of complaint against adversity or the administration was immaterial to the rest of us in the group, for the interplay of these remarkable personalities was a constant source of entertainment. Never was there a dull moment. At the height of the Battle of Britain, while dogfights were raging above us, one could hear Dee complaining to Skinner about some ministerial cockup as they sat under a hedge (which was where we were advised to go before air-raid shelters had been built).

The Magnetron

The tide of events began to turn on 19 July 1940 – the day Jimmy Atkinson arrived back from GEC with one of the first production samples of a device which was to revolutionise radar and to keep Britain ahead of not only the enemy but of her great ally the United States. It was the cavity magnetron, which just five months previously had been invented by two of Professor Oliphant's Birmingham team – John Randall and Harry Boot.

Aware of the problems of the klystron, Randall – like the well-ordered scientist that he was – went back to basics. To 1887 to be precise, to the work of Heinrich Hertz. Hertz laid the foundations of electromagnetic theory. His experiments involved resonant loops. Here then was the key to the Randall and Boot concept. They applied the principle to an already known microwave valve known as the 'split anode magnetron'. In its original form it was of limited power, somewhat unstable and required an external tuned circuit for it to function as an oscillator, which precluded its use for wavelengths much below 50 cm.

From the principle of the magnetron (which as the name implied operated within a magnetic field causing the electrons emitted from the cathode to take an orbital path on their journey towards the anode) they had the idea of using a resonant cavity as their tuned circuit, following Hertzian principles: furthermore not just one cavity but a series of them together forming the anode, thereby avoiding the need for external connections. Hence the unique form, made largely from a solid block of copper, whose interior with its six cavities appeared remarkably like the chambers inside the barrel of a revolver. (In fact in the early stages of development this was what was used as an accurate drilling jig, since the bore of a Colt revolver's chambers was just about the right size.)

With the help of their laboratory technician and with what material and equipment was available or could be scrounged, Randall and Boot constructed their first cavity magnetron (now in the Science Museum) which exceeded their expectations. The output power was so great that until they were able to measure the wavelength it was thought that it could not be as short as 10 cm. In fact it was (thanks to Mr Colt) 9.8 cm, and the date of its first memorable test was 21 February 1940.

Little time was lost in its subsequent development, which was placed in the hands of GEC, one of whose senior engineers was E.C.S. Megaw who was recognised for his own work before the war on the split anode magnetron. A design suitable for quantity manufacture was soon evolved and it was the second of the pre-production batch of magnetrons designated E1189 which arrived in our hut that sunny morning of 19 July.

The klystron was quickly moved to one side; the magnetron – supported between the poles of its accompanying permanent magnet – was set up on the bench with an air blower for cooling; the supplies connected, and with a deft adjustment of the high voltage supply, it promptly burst into oscillation (indicated by the bright glow of the ubiquitous neon lamp held near to the output stub.) Jimmy Atkinson promptly lit his pipe from the powerful arc it produced. It was sheer magic! The transmitter problem had been solved – the age of the magnetron had arrived.

Nearly sixty years on, the magnetron, substantially as Randall and Boot had originally conceived it, is still with us and in daily use the world over. It is serving us all, whether in travel by air or sea in navigation systems or in our kitchens generating the heat in a microwave oven.

The cavity magnetron was undoubtedly one of the significant inventions of the war. When in the autumn of 1940 the Tizard Commission went to America to initiate a war-winning partnership by disclosing our radar and other technical secrets (at the time covertly since the USA was a neutral country) they took one of the first pre-production magnetrons to demonstrate. It made a deep impression, such that an official American report described it as 'the most valuable cargo ever brought to our shores'. By the end of the war a total of a quarter of a million magnetrons had been manufactured in Britain, the USA and Canada.

The Receiver

Now, with a dependable 10 cm transmitter and Lovell's aerial systems in good shape, what about the receiver? We had a local oscillator (albeit not as reliable as we'd have wished) and an intermediate frequency amplifier which was a unit originally designed by Pye Radio as a pre-war TV receiver, operating at a frequency of 45 MHz and first used for airborne radar by Bowen for his 1.5 m systems. This left us with the problem of finding some form of detector for the signal mixer. Nothing better came to light than the seemingly wacky idea of a crystal detector.

The development and indeed the initial manufacture was assumed by Skinner personally. Basically it was no different from the 1920s '2LO' crystal and catswhisker arrangement, except that it had to be as small as possible and immune from vibration (in an aeroplane there could be no fiddling with the catswhisker like grandad trying to pick up the BBC.). Skinner created a sound design shown in the sketch, in which the small chipping of silicon crystal and the tungsten catswhisker were sealed into a piece of glass tubing. He then checked its performance using an Avometer (which he jealously guarded for his sole use in testing his crystals) at the same time tapping the tube, hopefully to improve the performance (though sometimes ruining a good one.) but essentially to check its stability. When finally satisfied, he would fill the tube with molten wax through the pinch hole, to protect the setting against vibration.

For days on end Skinner would sit at a bench sealing the crystal assemblies into small lengths of glass tube with the aid of a glassblower's burner. Since there was no gas supply to the hut, the burner ran on a mixture of Calor gas and oxygen from a cylinder. At the end of a session the bench would be liberally strewn with spent matches – as many from constantly relighting his pipe as from relighting the burner, which frequently blew out with a loud bang when he turned on too much oxygen.

Once the best form of manufacture had been established, Skinner personally became a one-man crystal-making factory to supply crystals for the group's work, since no one else could

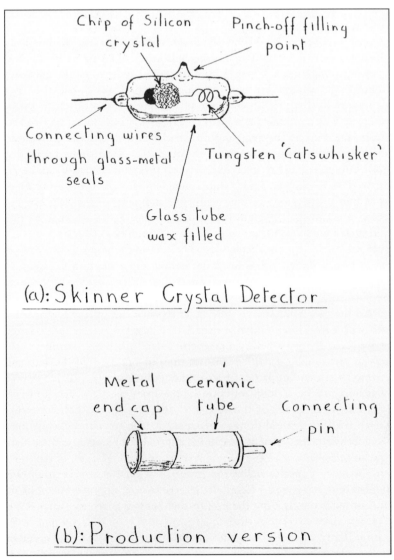

Chip of Silicon
crystal

Pinch-off filling
point

Connecting wires
through glass-metal
seals

Tungsten 'Catswhisker'

Glass tube
wax filled

(a): Skinner Crystal Detector

Metal
end cap

Ceramic
tube

Connecting
pin

(b): Production version

Silicon crystal diodes as microwave mixers. (a) Skinner's experimental model; (b) BTH's production version.

match his glass-blowing skill. He became the sole source of this vital component until the BTH Company took on the job and developed a version suitable for quantity production. Here a ceramic tube with metal end caps replaced the glass tube with wire ends, but the basic internal arrangement of crystal and catswhisker was the same. After the war, when Schockley and his associates at Bell Labs in the States set out to discover and explain exactly how the humble crystal detector actually worked, their findings led them to invent the transistor.

Setbacks

We now had all the essential ingredients of a simple radar system and the time had come to put it to the test. Jimmy Atkinson with his infallible knack of laying his hands on whatever material or facilities were needed, waved his magic wand and two empty gunlaying trailers appeared outside the group's hut one morning. Into one was installed the magnetron transmitter rig and into its neighbour went all the bits and pieces which made up our receiver complete with a cathode ray tube to display what echoes might be received.

Aerials were lined up on the ancient Norman chapel and its accompanying terrace of eighteenth-century coastguard cottages on St Alban's headland about a mile distant; the receiver was deftly tuned and to everyone's elation up came echoes. Centimetre echoes! We had arrived! A.P. Rowe, TRE's Superintendent, noted in his book *One Story of Radar* that to him this was one of the memorable moments of the war. For Rowe this was his 'Road to Damascus', for until centimetres were shown to work he had shown little faith in such a wild project, much to Dee's and Skinner's chagrin.

There was, of course, the inevitable snag. The transmitter and receiver each had their own aerial dishes (a shared aerial for transmission and reception – essential for the airborne application – would come much later). Lovell had arranged for a pukka twin mirror assembly complete with 'gunsight' to be made in TRE workshops, but until it was completed the two aerial dishes were quite separate, set up outside their respective trailers, each with a man to aim them at the selected target.

Now it was one thing to get echoes – good strong echoes – from sizeable static objects such as our buildings, with plenty of time to optimise all the settings. But to track a moving target, and in particular an aircraft (which is what the job was all about) proved in practice to be an impossibility. In the brief moment that a target aircraft swooped in across our piece of the sky, we soon discovered that the two separate operators each with their aerial dishes were quite unable to follow the swiftly moving object in synchronism. In short, it was quite impossible to obtain and to demonstrate echoes from an aeroplane.

We were all very conscious that the group was on borrowed time. Without a convincing demonstration with a target aircraft, continued support – financial and moral – would not be forthcoming from the powers that be. It was yet another setback for the frustrated Dee to chafe over.

In the hope that continued practice on the part of the two independent aerial operators would bring success, further tests with an aircraft (usually an Anson) from the Telecommunications Flying Unit at Christchurch airfield were carried out. During this period there came a day when Dee, Skinner, Atkinson and Ward were due to attend a progress meeting at GEC Wembley.

GEC was to co-operate with TRE in the development of the 10 cm system. Unfortunately as far as Dee and Skinner were concerned, the firm was already involved with a 25 cm version launched by Bowen the previous year, and they were distinctly reluctant to scrap what they had achieved in favour of some hairbrained scheme of a bunch of academics. It was therefore very galling for the TRE party to be taken up to a hut on the roof of the GEC laboratories and given an impressive demonstration of GEC's 25 cm pet, while Dee and his group had little of real substance to report.

While this was taking place, Lovell and Burcham with some assistance were having yet another attempt at tracking an aircraft with the usual frustrating result. Aware that we had been seeing echoes from vehicles as they drove back and forth along the track to the headland, I suggested that I might fix a sheet of tinplate to my bicycle and cycle round the headland to provide a moving target. The idea met with a rather cool reception on the part of Lovell and Burcham but I persisted.

With the tin sheet in position, I rode off in the direction of the headland and reaching the area beyond St Alban's quarry, which in those days was all scrubland, I cycled back and forth across the rough ground where I presented a broadside target. I even dismounted and lifted the bike shoulder high to increase the chance of being 'seen' by the beam.

I'd been away half an hour or so and it was late in the afternoon. When I got back to the hut I was surprised to find the sets switched off and the two trailers shut. Lovell was standing outside the hut nearby looking out into space. 'Weren't you watching me?' I enquired, somewhat hurt.

'Oh yes – marvellous. Echoes up to saturation,' he replied. Saturation meant that the received signal had been at maximum strength, which seemed to me very unlikely; I felt I was being patronised.

The next morning when Dee, Skinner, Atkinson and Ward arrived back from their soul-destroying meeting, they were telling us all the sorry story when Lovell interrupted them saying, 'You should have had GEC down *here* yesterday,' and proceeded to describe my performance on the bike and its results. So he hadn't been kidding me after all! I promptly had to fix the sheet of metal to the bike again and do a repeat performance for the benefit of the four incredulous scientists who found that the sun still shone.

All Systems Go

Very soon I found myself performing in what seemed like the 'greatest show on earth', for as soon as word reached the upper echelons of power, the world seemed to beat a path to our door. Demonstration followed demonstration and until Lovell's twin aerial assembly (shown in the foreground of the sketch) arrived from workshops, and aircraft could be tracked successfully, I had to perform my circus act each time. First came Watson-Watt with a whole bevy of service chiefs giving it the air of a royal visit. Then came Professor Lindemann (later Lord Cherwell), who in the hot summer sun appeared incongruously dressed as a city banker complete with bowler hat. His sole concession to the heat of the day was to tip his bowler to the back of his head, which matched perfectly the music-hall atmosphere of these occasions.

Yet another notable visitor was Professor Oliphant from Birmingham. During all these demonstrations, Ward and I had been at the edge of a volcano lest our temperamental oscillator should pack up at a crucial moment. On one occasion it did so just as the VIP motorcade arrived in the customary cloud of dust. 'Heck!' cried Ward, 'what do we do now?' At that moment providence obliged and the air-raid siren sounded. But even the possibility of a raid wasn't going to let us off the hook. The VIPs, having made the long, tiring journey, weren't going to let Hitler deny them the demonstration, so, after a hasty conference, we were told to carry on. During this brief

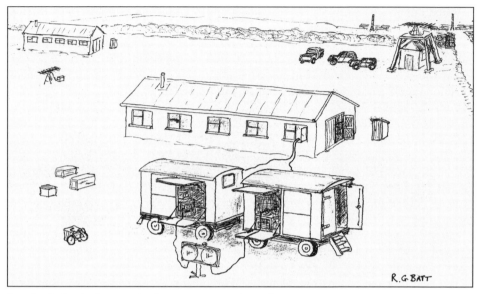

Reg Batt's sketch showing the first centimetre radar trials.

period the set had been switched off. Ward held his breath, switched it on and to his relief it burst into oscillation and kept going for the duration of the demonstration.

Help was at hand in the form of two gentlemen from the Admiralty Research Laboratory at Bristol. They were Sutton and Thompson, who had devised the perfect solution – the reflecting klystron – known as the Sutton tube. Like the magnetron transmitter, it was amazingly simple in operation. One had only to set the correct voltages and behold – it would oscillate at a wavelength determined by the single ring-doughnut shaped resonator. It had none of the complexities of the original Varian klystron which had a pair of interconnected resonators. With Sutton's magic tube (see opposite) we were home and dry. From thenceforth the reflecting klystron was to become the standard centimetre local oscillator.

Before an airborne system could become a practical possibility, means would have to be found to combine transmitter and receiver feeds to a single scanning aerial – but this would come within a year – otherwise all the pieces had come together. Now we had the basic ingredients, the time had come to evolve working systems – first and foremost being AI. Among many new faces then joining the group was Dr (later Sir Alan) Hodgkin, who devised a unique spiral aerial scanner and display for what would become AI Mark VII and later Mark VIII. It was a most remarkable piece of work on the part of a man who far from being a radio man was not even a physicist. He was a Cambridge biologist who after the war became a joint Nobel prizewinner for medicine.

Many other applications for centimetre radar were to follow before the war ended, not only airborne but marine and land-based as well. The most outstanding in terms of its contribution to final victory was H$_2$S which gave RAF bombers a map presentation

Production version of reflex klystron used as local oscillator in centimetric radars. Also known as the 'Sutton tube'.

of the terrain below; enabling them to locate targets accurately at any range, the most important being Berlin. It was Bernard Lovell who, from the end of 1941, was to direct H_2S development. Very soon the technology had been extended down to 3 cm, which for a given size of aerial assembly offered increased resolution; to be followed in due course by 1.25 cm. Skinner's way-out conjecture had become reality.

After the war Reg Batt continued working in radar development at Bush Radio Ltd, before joining UKAEA Harwell. He later moved to Dorset when the Atomic Energy Establishment at Winfrith was set up. He was concerned with reactor instrumentation development and provided reactor control instruments for almost all the authority's reactors including Calder Hall and Windscale.

Dr W.D. Allen, B.Sc., D.Phil. (Oxon), Hon. D.Sc., FIEE

One Saturday I was digging in my garden near Swanage when a chap came up and said, 'Can you tell me the name of the person living in this house?'

'Dr Allen,' I replied.

'Oh,' he said, 'is your father in?'

Well, I'd just received my D.Phil., so I raised myself up to my full D.Phil. height and said solemnly: '*I* am Dr Allen.'

'Oh,' said the chap, eyebrows highly uplifted. He turned out to be a Jehovah's Witness and, becoming pally, he said: 'Have you built up a good practice?'

'Well,' I said, 'as a matter of fact, I'm not a medico, I'm a scientist.'

'Oh, you're not a doctor of medicine, you're a doctor of science?'

'Well,' said I, 'they don't call it a doctor of science, they call it a doctor of philosophy.'

By this time he was convinced he was talking to a lunatic, or charlatan, or both. 'I must be getting along,' he said, and departed.

It was a golden summer in 1940 and some of us would sit on Ballard Down and watch a fleet of German bombers drone overhead, or a squadron of our fighters circling around awaiting their arrival. One had the feeling of witnessing a gladiatorial conflict; murder was the name of the game. I never actually saw a dogfight, although once I heard one taking place above a thick layer of low cloud which ended with a tiny figure dangling from a parachute and coming down in the sea about a mile out. Apart from that I myself saw few signs of war at Swanage, though two or three times there were oil-burning exercises in Poole Harbour which were a reminder of the possibilities.

I am glad to have lived through those crucial months of war in England in 1940: the Churchill speeches at 9 p.m. on Sundays; sometimes J.B. Priestley; the steady intensification of the fighter war; the reminders that all the time Hitler's invasion fleet was filling every available waterway opposite Britain; the BBC's nightly playing of all the national anthems of the Allies.

Later on, in March 1943, half a million tons of Allied shipping were lost; in May a fifth of a million tons – at a cost to the Germans of forty-one U-boats. At the Führer's Naval Conference of 31 May 1943, Doenitz said: 'Our most urgent need is for a radar interception set. We do not have such a set. We do not even know on what wavelength the enemy locates us.'

This simply meant that the Germans paid the price for treating us with contempt. To begin with, with S-band sets beaming from Leeson (TRE Swanage) towards Cherbourg, weather conditions of temperature inversion were not uncommon so that Cherbourg turned up on the screen.[1] Therefore, at Cherbourg itself, the signal must have been high; and simply a 1920-style crystal detector, in the focus of a parabolic mirror and feeding a reasonably wide band amplifier, would have been sufficient to give an indication from which everything else would follow.

In 1943 I was working on aerials, and an assistant set up a mirror with a waveguide feed working on X band [wavelength about 3 cm]. This was in the Malvern school playing fields beyond the railway line. I don't remember whether they were within the fence but 45 acres was quite a large area. But even if there was a wire, all that was expected of an enemy agent was that, with binoculars, he should observe and report the mirror and the approximate dimensions of the pipe leading to the centre of the mirror.

---

[1] Temperature Inversion is a weather condition in which the upper atmosphere is warmer than that below. It is one cause of anomalous propagation ('anaprop') whereby radio waves follow the curvature of the earth (or sea) and radar ranges are extended greatly. It may be common or rare, according to climate. It is also known as ducting, superrefraction and trapping.

That would have been enough to identify the X-band story. So if I, with my very limited observation, had seen such things that a German agent could have spotted, the total available to agents must have been enormous. It is astonishing that there should have been so few agents and that they should have been so ineffectual.

Incidentally in May 1942, when the trailers were departing from Leeson House (for Malvern), someone happened to notice a magnetron embedded in the mud: if left it would have been an interesting archeological exhibit for someone to find!

I have one special memory of my time at Swanage. Double summertime was in operation so sunrise was not 3.45 GMT but 5.45 a.m. We rose at 4.30 a.m., climbed Ballard Down and paused to empty our Thermoses and take in the view. It was a perfect morning (fairly nippy of course), with the sea like glass surrounding us in an arc of some 200 degrees. Poole Harbour, Swanage Bay, and the Isle of Wight opposite looking as if you could throw a stone over to it. Far to the east, in the orange light preceding the rising of the sun, there was a swarm of little black specks which appeared stationary but – because of the distance – must have been high up. It was the balloon barrage above Southampton, 30 miles to the east. As the light intensified the specks vanished.

We wandered down to the Old Harry Rocks, past hedges full of honeysuckle, then made our way slowly back to Studland, to early service in the Saxon church; then home to breakfast. An unforgettable morning.

Dr Allen has had a distinguished postwar career, first as a Government scientist for the Ministry of Supply, then in nuclear physics with UKAEA. He has also pursued academic activities at the universities of Reading and Southampton.

Sir Alan Hodgkin, OM, KBE, FRS (d. 1998)

[We are grateful to Sir Alan Hodgkin and the Cambridge University Press for permission to reproduce the following extracts from his book *Chance and Design*, Cambridge University Press, 1992.]

At the end of June I found that Hut 40, where I occupied part of a bench, had filled up with interesting people. As well as Ryle, Wiblin and Lovell we were joined by the distinguished physicist Philip Dee and his younger colleague William Burcham. Dee had got a klystron made at Cambridge to Mark Oliphant's design and he and Herbert Skinner were trying to extract as much power from it as possible. We had several visits from Oliphant and he told us about the work at Birmingham. In particular he talked about Randall and Boot's cavity magnetron, of which we received an engineered version from GEC on 18 August [*sic*]. Atkinson and Burcham got this going in a few weeks while Skinner, Ward and others designed a 10 cm receiver with a crystal as detector and a reflection klystron as local oscillator. The klystron was known to us as a Sutton tube after its inventor Dr R.W. Sutton.

It now seems extraordinary that all this high-powered work went on in a small isolated hut, reached only by a muddy track, with no gas, and only makeshift water and electricity supplies. Nevertheless a great deal of work got done and an echo from a Battle aeroplane was recorded at a range of 2 miles, before the end of August, using a cavity magnetron.

From Left to Right: 'Taffy' Bowen, Hanbury Brown and Alan Hodgkin enjoying lunch outside the Square and Compass pub.

Someone, probably Dee, had suggested that I get a prototype scanner going, first on the ground and then in an air-to-air test by Christmas. This was a tall order, as we had no way of transmitting and receiving on the same aerial. Nor did we know how to make a satisfactory rotating joint in a concentric cable or waveguide at centimetric wavelengths.

With some difficulty I persuaded the workshops to build a crude scanner in which the dipole emitting or receiving was vibrated vertically about five times per second through the focus, while the whole paraboloid was oscillated over 120 degrees in the horizontal plane within a period of two seconds or so. The aerial was vibrated by a powerful high-speed windscreen wiper I had obtained from Farnborough.

The problem of transmitting and receiving on the same aerial at centimetre wavelengths was not solved satisfactorily until May 1941 when Ward, Skinner and Starr produced an elegant switching device with a klystron-type resonator filled with gas at a low pressure that flashed over when the radar pulse was transmitted but not when it was received.

Towards the end of September 1940, all the centimetre work and much of the rest of TRE were moved from Worth Matravers to an empty girls' school, Leeson House, in the village of Langton Matravers, about half way between Swanage and Worth. The centimetre group was housed partly in a classroom and partly in stables. On finding that

Boffins working on 10 cm AI scanner in nose of Beaufighter. This work was led by Alan Hodgkin.

the electricity supply was completely inadequate we installed heavier fuses until the walls became dangerously hot. This was appreciated by the mice which multiplied to a vast population and caused havoc by eating any notebooks left lying around.

One very distinct advantage of the new site was that it looked down across the town of Swanage to the sea and in the distance to the Isle of Wight. This area, sometimes called centimetre alley, provided an excellent place for testing 9 cm or 3 cm radar on aeroplanes or ships. After our experience in the bitter cold of the previous winter, Lovell was rightly determined to be able to measure polar diagrams in reasonable comfort. He achieved this by ordering enough perspex to build a large greenhouse-like structure. By then we had mastered the business of filling in Air Ministry forms in pentuplicate and Lovell, who knew that it was as easy to order several thousand square feet of perspex as a smaller quantity, built himself a fine Crystal Palace.

During the late autumn of 1940 we had three trailers fitted with 10 cm radar. In the middle trailer, run mainly by Burcham and Atkinson with help from Lovell, every effort had been made to maximise the range on aeroplanes or marine targets, the cliffs of the Isle of Wight at a distance of 40 miles providing an excellent standard signal. It was from this trailer that 9 cm radar was 'sold' to the Navy.

After the move to Leeson House the centimetre group expanded rapidly with people of the quality of S.C. Curran, A.D. Starr and G. Hensby joining us during the autumn and winter. The establishment was beginning to recruit some first-class people at a more junior level. A curious feature of the build-up was that Dee's team was largely composed of physicists and we had hardly any mechanical or electrical engineers. However, we could always obtain help from people like R.C. Williams and Hanbury Brown and the imbalance was partly rectified by a close collaboration with GEC.

Gradually some sort of administrative structure emerged. People naturally specialised in different subjects; for instance Burcham was the expert on the magnetron and transmission in general, Curran looked after the development of the high power modulators. Skinner, Ward and Starr worked on the crystal receiver and helped to solve the all-important problem of transmitting and receiving on one aerial. Bernard Lovell was initially in charge of work on aerials and paraboloids but did a great deal to promote the use of centimetric radar for ship detection and later for detecting cities (H_2S). He was also involved in the design of a lock-follow scheme which later became AI Mark IX. I was supposed to look after scanning and display systems for AI and for the initial air trials, a job which we could not possibly have carried out without much help from the research laboratories of GEC.

Some other important activities at TRE were navigation by means of Gee and Oboe (R.J. Dippy, A.H. Reeves, F.E. Jones); Countermeasures (R. Cockburn and M. Ryle); GCI (W.B. Lewis, D. Taylor, F.C. Williams); trainers (G.W. Dummer, R.A. Smith, J.W.S. Pringle). In addition there was a large section devoted to techniques, including a

Swanage Bay viewed from Leeson House.

mathematics pool where H. Booker, M.V. Wilks and G. McFarlane did high-powered work on anomalous propagation but were always prepared to help with *ad hoc* problems as they arose.

Much centimetre radar was pushed into service long before it would have satisfied any peacetime criterion of reliability. This was only possible because J.A. Ratcliffe, who controlled about one-third of TRE's personnel, had built up an excellent post-development service, whose job it was to 'wet-nurse' equipment during its early career, and often for long periods thereafter.

Although we naturally grumbled a good deal, I now consider the administrative structure of TRE to have been flexible and imaginative, particularly in the way that it allowed young scientists and engineers to take responsibility for major ventures. In 1940 when I was still a junior scientific officer earning £300 per annum I was encouraged to write and sign letters to firms on technical matters, and Dee's authority was required only if some point of major policy were involved. In a large establishment such a system would rapidly have led to chaos, as some people write too few letters and others too many. The system was rationalised by circulating a weekly summary of all incoming and outgoing letters (except top-secret ones in subjects involving countermeasures or military plans). If you failed to answer a letter or had officiously moved into someone else's territory, you were politely chased, or chastened, as the case might be. Rowe's central office had the good sense to assign the chasing to a lady of considerable tact and charm.

After major contributions to the design of airborne radar in wartime, Sir Alan returned to academic research, becoming a joint Nobel prizewinner for services to medicine. He became President of the Royal Society and received various honours abroad for his contributions to medical research, and was author of numerous publications on the nature of nervous conduction.

Grace Walker (née Dokey), Librarian at TRE

> *'During summer, some of the scientists wore no shoes, and shorts covered only by a long white laboratory smock . . .'*

The arrival of TRE at Swanage must have been welcomed by the landladies and traders who had previously depended so much on visitors. The establishment could be accommodated without recourse to compulsory billeting. But there could be little interchange between the establishment and the local people because of the long working hours: 8.30 a.m. to 6.30 p.m. six days a week, with only Saturday in which to cram all outside activities including shopping.

The outlying villages such as Kingston were even less affected because accommodation there was already taken up by children evacuated from London and Southampton. I was the only person living in Kingston who was directed to work at TRE. (During the war all people of military age were subject to employment direction into the Services or industry.)

I was born in Kingston and had hopes of becoming a teacher initially but the war intervened and in October 1941 I was directed to report for an interview with

A.B. Jones as a result of which I became a laboratory assistant at TRE. My work was in the library at Durnford where scientists would come to consult or take away books or catalogues. The minister of the Congregational church in Swanage, the Revd Atkinson, worked in the library during the week and donated his salary to the church: he was a keen photographer and in their darkroom he developed prints for the Durnford drawing office. Soon, two sub-libraries were formed at Worth and Leeson.

My work at Leeson involved delivering publications around the labs and offices; each person was allowed a publication for forty-eight hours only and I'm sure that because of pressure of work, many publications were returned unread. Some of my customers were unconventional in the matter of dress. During summer some of them wore no shoes, and shorts covered only by a long white laboratory smock. Some of the equipment was stored in an unlit room, so that they'd go in carrying a candle. One day the Superintendent was leading a delegation of high-ranking officers when he saw along the corridor someone who seemed to be dressed in a nightshirt carrying a candle, as if on his way to bed. The following day a Station Order went up announcing that, although the Superintendent did not wish to enforce uniformity, he felt that some reasonable standard of dress should be accepted.[1]

After the war, Grace married Arthur Walker who also worked for TRE. They moved to London and she became a full-time housewife.

E.H. Cooke-Yarborough, MA, F.Inst.P, FIEE, F.Eng.

'Monica was a fully-automatic backwards-looking radar, to be fitted to almost the whole of the bomber force.'

In 1939 I was at Oxford doing the final year of my physics degree. Early in 1940 I was invited to visit a Mr Brundrett at the Admiralty, who explained that physicists with experience of electronics were urgently needed for war research. He had been through the physicists in my year at Oxford, and had concluded that most should stay and take schools in the summer; but because of my amateur radio experience, they could use me at once. He asked if I would be prepared to do this work without waiting for my degree. I said that I would, provided it didn't mean my losing my degree.

Subsequently I was told that if I left Oxford at once I could return in the summer and take my degree. I would only have to sit half of the papers and if I attained the appropriate standard in these, I would, at the end of the war, receive a degree with Unclassified Honours. I agreed to this, so on 4 March 1940 I set off for Dundee where I joined AMRE as an Assistant III at a salary of £195 per annum.

I was first interviewed by W.B. Lewis, Deputy Director, and then handed over to Sidney Jefferson, who told me about the rudiments of RDF and lent me a number of

---

[1] There is a story on record that this self-same Superintendent, A.P. Rowe, when in charge at Bawdsey Manor, tried to instigate 'black tie' dressing for dinner. His suggestion had been met with a near-mutiny since very few of the young scientists possessed a dinner jacket.

pink secret files to read. I was assigned to the Transmitter Laboratory under J.H. Phillips. My first job was to assist Sid England in the development of a pulse power amplifier delivering a peak power output of 1 megawatt at 28 MHz, with a pulse width of twenty microseconds. This power was much greater than that developed by the standard CH transmitter; it was powered by up to 50 Kv DC, so was enclosed in a cubicle for safety. The DC power source was in another similar cubicle at the other end of the laboratory. For test purposes, the radio-frequency load consisted of an array of many 60 watt striplamps in parallel.

I soon found that this work would involve climbing to the tops of the 360 ft steel CH transmitting masts to insert electrical filters in the aerials. Many people climbed these masts without a qualm and some even ate their sandwiches with their feet dangling over into space, but I knew without trying that I would not be one of them. Within a few days, therefore, I was back in W.B. Lewis's office asking for a transfer and he assigned me to airborne radar.

AI

At the time, the work on airborne radar was centred at RAF St Athan in South Wales. The particular equipment which was of interest to Lewis was the Air Interception (AI) Mark III equipment, intended to enable night fighters to find and attack enemy aircraft. This equipment was installed in Blenheims and transmitted pulses at 200 MHz from an aerial in the nose. The four receiving aerials were located above and below the wing, and on either side of the nose. An operator in the rear of the aircraft observed, on two cathode ray displays, the relative sizes of the target echoes received on the four aerials. These gave an indication to the operator of the relative elevation and azimuth of the target aircraft.

A problem was that, as the target was approached, the time interval between the transmitted pulse and the echo became so small that the echo signal merged with the tail of the transmitted pulse and became lost. This was apt to occur at target ranges of 1,000 ft or more and before the pilot could make visual contact with the target, so that contact might be lost.

Lewis had the idea that if the tail of the transmitted pulse could be shortened, the minimum detection range would be reduced. Consequently he arranged for several AI MkIII sets to be delivered from St Athan to Dundee, so that experiments could be carried out.

The transmitter was a push-pull self-oscillator, consisting of a pair of Micropup valves mounted on the ends of hollow tubes which acted as the anode resonant circuit, and which also conveyed cooling air to the valve anodes. A high-voltage DC supply was connected to the anodes via the centre point of the anode resonant circuit.

The transmitter was self-modulated, in that a burst of oscillation would quickly be rectified by the grids of the valves to produce a negative DC grid voltage large enough to cut off the anode current and to stop the oscillation. The negative charge would then leak away to ground through a high-value resistor until the valves again began to conduct. A fresh burst of oscillation would then take place, and the process would repeat. [This is known as 'squegging'.]

Lewis proposed adding a second pair of Micropup valves on the ends of the same anode lines, but connected as diodes, which would be switched on at the end of the transmitter pulse to damp the oscillation. I was given the job of putting this into practice.

The first test flight took place from RAF Leuchars, with Lewis and myself sharing the cramped space in the after part of the Blenheim. This was only the second time I had ever flown. The results were inconclusive, partly because of the difficulty of measuring the range at which the echo signal disappeared.

In May 1940 AMRE moved from Dundee to Worth Matravers. The new site was magnificent, on the top of the cliffs, with its own CH station and shorter-wavelength CHL sets at the cliff edge for detecting low-flying aircraft.

Apart from the Dundee people several other teams collected there, including Donald Fry, Robert Cockburn and others from RAE Farnborough, and Ratcliffe's team from the Cavendish Laboratory at Cambridge. I was happy to find my old Oxford friend Martin Ryle working there on radar aerial design. For a while several of us obtained lodgings together at a house called Windinook and it was here that we heard on the radio Churchill's 'We shall fight them on the beaches . . . we shall *never* surrender' speech. It was very moving and very encouraging.

The weather in the late summer of 1940 was beautiful. We took sandwiches up to the site at Worth and would eat them at the Square and Compass, sitting outside on the stone wall, holding a pint of draught cider and looking over the cliffs to the sea beyond. From time to time an air-raid warden would rush past, wearing a tin hat, blowing a whistle and shouting, 'Take cover!' but we would carry on eating and basking in the sun. Sometimes we saw curving vapour trails in the sky high above and occasionally we heard the scream of an aircraft engine racing out of control, and saw a trail of smoke plunging towards the earth. In our peaceful surroundings it was hard to realise the life-and-death drama which was taking place over our heads. Until France surrendered, Swanage and the Isle of Purbeck retained very much of its holiday resort atmosphere, with the excellent sandy beach and beautiful cliff walks.

My flight trials with the modified MkIII AI installed in the Blenheim were continued at RAF Christchurch – a grass airfield associated with the Airspeed aircraft factory there. I commuted daily from Swanage via the Sandbanks ferry, which involved driving through Bournemouth in my open car. On one of these journeys, soon after Dunkirk, I noticed a peculiar smell in the air. It dawned on me that the streets of Bournemouth were full of French troops brought over from Dunkirk and what I was smelling was Caporal cigarettes.

I was receiving competition from a much more sophisticated AI system devised by A.D. Blumlein of EMI (one of the two companies which had set up the pre-war television service). This used a large and complex delay-line pulse modulator to shape a high-voltage pulse which powered the transmitter. This he was testing in another Blenheim. Blumlein and I would compare notes after our test flights; we both got down to minimum ranges of under 500 ft, but eventually it became clear that EMI were getting better and more consistent results. Their equipment became Mark IV AI and the Mark III system was dropped.

I was given the new job of devising a fully automatic radar range-finder for use with the gyroscopic gunsight in the Hurricane single-seat fighter. So far as I'm aware, this was the first radar required to operate entirely automatically, without an operator. However, this whole project was dropped and I was transferred to the design of a backward-looking radar to warn bomber crews of the approach of a fighter.

Monica

At about this time I first met Robert Hanbury Brown, who had been working at St Athan and who arrived at Worth wearing a white flying suit, having flown by light aircraft from there. He took responsibility for the work which I was doing and soon brought me my first assistant, E.K. Williams.

E.K. Williams.

The backwards-looking radar was officially code-named Monica by the Air Ministry. This choice was from the Latin '*moneo*', I warn; this decision preceded the later policy that code names should not give any inkling of the function of the device. Later code names were prepared in lists by Air Ministry and assigned to projects at random.

Monica was a fully automatic backwards-looking radar, to be fitted to almost the whole of the bomber force. If an aircraft appeared within about a mile to the rear of a bomber equipped with Monica, slowly recurring bleeps would be heard on the intercom by all the crew members. As the distance decreased, the rate of bleeping would increase, until the approaching aircraft was so close that its echo merged with the transmitted pulse, when the bleeps would cease.

Monica operated at 300 MHz (1 m) and used a single folded dipole located just below the tail gun turret for both transmission and reception.

As with AI MkIII, it was important to track the target into as close a range as possible before losing the echo, if only because a steadily rising bleep rate, followed by silence, could be very worrying to the aircrew. I would have liked to use an anode-modulated transmitter, as in AI MkIV; however, Monica was to be manufactured in very large numbers. It had to be cheap and simple so 'squegging' was chosen for the transmitter, as in MkIII AI, but using much lower-power valves, which did not need cooling.

A very important question that we faced early in the development was the possibility of enemy fighter aircraft homing on to the pulse transmission. This question was put to the TRE Mathematics Division who concluded that an individual Monica transmitter would not be distinguishable among many others until the homing aircraft was closer to one target than the mean separation between the aircraft carrying Monica transmitters. This advice proved, much later, to be seriously in error.

As with AI MkIII, the Pulse Recurrence Frequency was determined by the 'squegging' action, which depended on the tolerances of the components in the grid circuit. Consequently no two transmitters ran at identical prfs. Indeed, it was important that they did not, for if two Monicas were almost to synchronise, then the train of pulses sent out by one might appear like an aircraft echo in the receiver of the other.

The fact that the prf was unique to each Monica transmitter turned out to make it possible to distinguish individual transmitters at much greater ranges than the TRE Mathematics Division had predicted. Unfortunately this was exploited by the Germans later in the war.

The early development of Monica took place in the attic of Leeson House where I was assisted by E.K. Williams and Bill Howell, one of the airborne radar team from St Athan. We shared this attic with a number of other people, including F.C. Williams and his team.

The Phantastron

There was a good deal of cross-fertilisation. For example, one experimental Monica circuit contained a special pentode valve with a suppressor grid (between screen grid and anode) which had a high mutual conductance. About 5 volts negative applied to this grid relative to cathode would divert all of the cathode current to the screen grid. The resulting waveforms were unusual and led F.C. Williams, during the same day, to create a new pulse generating circuit which he called the Phantastron. He was fond of christening circuits.

On another occasion, when the warships *Scharnhorst* and *Gneisenau* were holed up in Brest and were expected to make a dash for it up the Channel, F.C. Williams devised an electronic system, literally on a wooden board, which would be capable of timing the release of bombs, blind, through overcast. It was intended to fly this actual breadboard on the mission to bomb these ships but they slipped through the Channel before this system could be used. Nevertheless, this showed how directly and immediately it was possible for us to influence the war.

The 'Boffin Baffler'

Another experimental device produced in the attic of Leeson House was probably the first electronic flight simulator. This was for training pilots in the use of AI MkV. With the earlier marks, an operator had to give verbal directions to the pilot. This caused delays that made it very difficult to follow a target in a stable way, even if it was flying straight and level. MkV put a special cathode ray tube indicator in front of the pilot, so that he could respond instantly to changes in the radar signal.

In AI MkV the up-down and left-right echo signals from the target were sampled using an electronic 'strobe' positioned manually over the echoes by the operator to produce DC up-down and left-right voltages. These were applied to the four beam deflecting plates of the cathode ray tube in front of the pilot, to move the spot to a position on the screen corresponding to the position of the target aircraft. Range was indicated by the length of 'wings' protruding horizontally from both sides of the spot. Thus the apparent movements of the target were indicated directly to the pilot.

The simulator built in Leeson House had a 'joystick', 'rudder' and 'throttle control' mounted in an inverted wooden box. Visiting Air Force officers enjoyed 'flying' this system. At that time we called senior Air Force officers 'boffins' (which later they were to call us), and so the simulator came to be known as the 'Boffin Baffler'.

Monica Flight Trials

As a consequence of the coastal defences, the Sandbanks ferry stopped running and we had to commute to our flight trials via Wareham and the northern edge of

Bournemouth. At about this time the big airfield at Hurn opened and our flying was transferred there from Christchurch.

The first prototype Monica installations were in Wellingtons, the aerial being mounted just below the tail turret. I spent many exhilarating hours in tail turrets testing Monica while a Hurricane or a Spitfire made simulated attacks from various angles, looking for blind spots.

On operations over enemy territory a tail gunner must have felt very isolated and vulnerable. In a safe environment, it was marvellous being able to swing the turret and to see almost all round and up and down, alone out there in one's private world. If one moved the turret about too much one would get a rude remark over the intercom from the pilot because movement of the turret slightly affected the trim of the aircraft.

By the end of 1941 Monica reached the stage of requiring engineering for production in large quantities. At that time the agreed division of responsibility between Government establishments made it necessary to transfer Monica to the RAE at Farnborough. I was sent to RAE to see Monica through this phase.

RAE was very different from TRE. At TRE, most people were under thirty, whereas in the Mess at RAE there were few heads which were not grey or white. Some people who had worked there through the First World War were still only in their fifties. As a place, it differed greatly from Worth Matravers. My memories of RAE are of railway tracks set in cobbles and of buildings of black-painted corrugated iron.

Attitudes were different too. At TRE, if I wanted a multi-way connector made up, I could get it done in a few hours. At RAE I found that the workshop could not make up a connector without an official drawing from the drawing office. The drawing office could not even start to prepare a drawing for six weeks. Since one needed the connector for the next flight trial, one had to make it up oneself. Shortly after I went to RAE, an electronics laboratory was set up at Ambarrow Court, a private house a few miles from Farnborough. Here reasonable electronic services were made available and the situation improved.

Mr Cooke-Yarborough continued working for TRE at Malvern until 1948 when he moved to AERE Harwell where he had a distinguished career, becoming Head of Electronics Division. In 1980 he was appointed Chief Research Scientist, Instrumentation and Applied Physics Division. He retired in 1982.

[Note by Colin Latham – a Personal Memory

I myself recall clearly the move to Ambarrow Court as I was working in the RAE Radio Standards Laboratory at the time. Everyone helped willingly to load up the lorries at Farnborough and unload again when we reached our destination – a lovely old country house near Crowthorne set in wooded grounds, typical of the properties being requisitioned by the Government.

Although the house provided generous accommodation, it was curiously short of lavatories. For our contingent only one was available, at the end of a very long, narrow, straight corridor. The door, which opened outwards, had no lock. Someone had arranged for a stout cord to be attached to the door handle so that whoever was in occupation could achieve some privacy by keeping it taut, thus holding the door shut.

One day the air of peaceful concentration in the laboratory was shattered by a rumpus – the sound of running feet; a woman's terrified shriek and an almighty thud. Those nearest rushed to see what had happened. It seemed that the boss of the department, suffering a most urgent call of nature, had sprinted down the passage and wrenched open the door with gusto. It was a pity that a lady typist, fearful that she might let the cord slip, had wound it tightly round her wrist for better purchase. She was yanked clean off her throne and the impact of her body against his had toppled him backwards. She had landed on top of him – knickerless.

The procurement organisation of the Civil Service was not renowned for fast action; but within minutes a driver was despatched in a fast car to Reading with instructions to find an ironmonger, buy a strong door bolt and not come back without it.]

Roland (Roy) Hodges, MBE

> *'Used as fast torpedo craft and for laying mines, the E-boat*
> *was a constant anxiety for our coastal convoys.'*

A unique airborne experimental 1.5 m radar installation, ACI, was devised in 1941 to provide a facility analogous to GCI for the airborne control of interception of enemy aircraft and E-boats operating beyond the cover of our ground radar stations.

A newly developed transmitter and an ASV MkII receiver were connected to a rotating Yagi aerial above the aircraft fuselage. Airborne and marine targets were displayed as bright arcs by a 9-in Plan Position Indicator unit.

An Outline of ACI Development

After the fall of France, Focke Wulf FW200 long-range, armed, anti-shipping reconnaissance aircraft (Condors) began operating from Bordeaux. Their success caused

An experimental ACI installation in a Wellington bomber, 1941–2. This was the first rotating airborne radar aerial used operationally.

Winston Churchill to issue, on 21 March 1941, a personal minute to the First Lord of the Admiralty and the Secretary of State for Air, beginning: 'The use of aeroplanes, not only to attack our ships but also to direct the U-boats on to them, is largely responsible for our losses in the North Western Approaches. No effort to destroy the Focke Wulfs should be spared. If we could employ radar methods to find their positions and to direct long-range fighters or ship-borne aircraft to the attack, we ought to be able to inflict serious casualties.'

On 6 April, the Condor problem was raised at TRE in a meeting that agreed to fit an aircraft as an experimental flying GCI station. A Liberator aircraft was examined for the purpose and reported on two days later. It was proposed to have a Yagi aerial that could be rotated above the aircraft and install GCI equipment powered by an auxiliary petrol-electric set; the overall weight was estimated to be approximately 1,600 lbs. This proposal was not favourable to the Deputy Chief of Air Staff (DCAS) who ruled that a Liberator was not to be allocated until a lightweight equipment had been developed.

However, a formal request for TRE to investigate the possibility of installing equipment for an experimental ACI was issued by the Director of Communications Development (DCD) on 1 August 1941. By using an ASV MkII receiver together with two new units under development – a high power transmitter (100 Kw peak) and a lightweight PPI – that were expected to become available towards the end of 1941, it was considered possible to conceive an ACI fit that could be powered by the existing aircraft engine-driven generator used for ASV and have an overall installed weight, inclusive of the aerial system, of no more than half the weight of the original proposal using GCI equipment. A range of 50 miles was expected including cover against low-flying aircraft as well as convoy protection.

Aerial System

Until 1941, airborne radar installations employed separate transmitter and receiver aerials to protect the receiver from being damaged by the transmitter. When ACI was proposed, common T and R systems had been developed at TRE for ground CHL stations: a programme of further development for airborne use was due to start. This technique made possible a relatively simple airborne rotating aerial system: it consisted of a Common T & R Unit, an RF Coupling Unit to link the static and rotating elements, a high-gain Yagi aerial with its turning gear, and interconnecting RF cables.

The aerodynamic design, manufacture and installation of a 15 ft aerial blade with mounting and turning gear were the responsibility of RAE, while TRE was responsible for the RF design and performance of the complete aerial system.

Of the limited number of Liberator aircraft that were to have been made available to Coastal Command during 1941, a large proportion were re-allocated for use by Ferry Command. Early in October TRE and RAE agreed that a Wellington would be an acceptable alternative type. On 28 October it was formally confirmed that Wellington MkIc R1629 was to be fitted; this aircraft was delivered to RAE where the aerial was installed. Flight tests to assess the effects of the mounted aerial on the aircraft performance were made in February 1942, prior to the aircraft being transferred to TFU (Telecommunications Flying Unit) Hurn for TRE to install the equipment and to conduct performance trials.

Change of Purpose

During the latter half of 1941, fighter-catapult ships devised specifically for protecting our convoys from air attack were coming into use and proving effective against the Focke-Wulfs and by early 1942 the Condor became of less concern for Coastal Command: of increasing concern were the German E-boats.

Used as fast torpedo craft and for laying mines, the E-boat was a constant anxiety for our coastal convoys: it was difficult to detect and was an elusive target against which our fast craft were not effective in attack. New motor gunboats (MGBs), more suitable in speed and armament for use against the E-boat, started to enter service from April 1941; towards the end of the year they were being organised into flotillas located around the east coast. To deploy these forces efficiently there was a need to obtain early detection of the E-boats on their nocturnal activities and to bring our MGBs into contact with them before they could reach their objective, particularly when this was to lay mines in our coastal convoy lanes.

Trials

The trials were undertaken with the understanding that ACI was to be used for operation against the E-boat. Large and prominent coastal features could be recognised but small detail was obscured by the overlapping paints.[1] [Mainly due to the wide beamwidth of the 1.5 m aerial array.] With ships in a convoy viewed broadside-on, the arcs could coalesce, but viewed at different ranges the paints were separated.

Range tests on a MGB were conducted during May off the east coast. Ranges on other types of shipping and on aircraft were noted as the opportunity arose. The results did not match the performance expected, but they were in keeping with the general performance of a normal long-range ASV installation.

Operational Sortie

On 19 May a signal from Coastal Command ordered Wellington R1629 to be flown to RAF Wick. The captain, Plt Off Jack Ruttledge, was informed that he was to assist in a search for the German battleship *Lutzow*, which was expected to make a dash north to a Norwegian harbour. The ACI equipment worked satisfactorily but no surface target was detected during the line-ahead search that was made off the Norwegian coast. A range of 30 miles could be expected on a battleship out on the open sea but if it hugged the Norwegian coast its echo might be masked by strong coastal returns.

A report by a reconnaissance aircraft that also flew that night led to the opinion that the ship had already reached harbour and the hunt was called off. Wellington R1629 returned south on the afternoon of the 20th to resume trials off the east coast. It is now known that the *Lutzow* joined the *Scheer* at Narvik a week later on 26 May 1942.

---

[1] Paints: the bright arcs produced on the screen of a PPI.

Nevertheless, this incident might be claimed as giving ACI the distinction of being the first all-round-looking airborne radar to be used on an operational sortie.

Termination of Requirement

Rapid strides in the research and development of centimetric equipment led to an experimental 10 cm ASV being flight-tested six weeks before the start of the ACI trials. On 28 May 1942 the Air/Sea Interception Committee formulated specific requirements for ASV equipment. Equipments operating on wavelengths above 10 cm were to be considered obsolescent; production of 10 cm ASV was to be undertaken on the highest priority.

The Committee's decisions were conveyed to the Ministry of Aircraft Production on 5 June and spelt doom for the ACI project. On being asked if the ACI aircraft might assist with any interception problems of theirs, Fighter Command showed an interest and an aircraft was prepared for an air-to-air interception trial at RAF Valley. This was conducted on 22 and 23 September with Sqn Ldr Craig, a very experienced GCI officer, controlling the trial. In his report, he concluded that ACI was practicable but the equipment required considerable technical development before service trials.

[NOTE: although it was intended to perform the function of directing fighter aircraft, as would a Ground Controlled Interception (GCI) station, the concept of ACI was not used in wartime. As the writer explains, the operational requirement changed: further, the expanding and comprehensive range of GCI stations – from the large fixed 'Happidromes' with substantial aerials and multiple displays, to the simpler Type 15 mobiles – eventually met the requirements of Fighter Command.

The sudden ending of ACI work is a good example of how the boffins had swiftly to adapt themselves to new projects as the war situation changed. However, the reader may like to consider the advanced nature of this early but far-reaching concept of ACI radar – an ancestor of modern Airborne Early Warning radar. AEW – with smaller aerials at the much shorter centimetric wavelengths – began service with the RAF in 1951 and has continued to the present day, carried successively by long-range aircraft such as the Shackleton and the Nimrod. The current Boeing E3A AEW1 carries a far more sophisticated American design of microwave radar. ACI may not have seen much active service during the Second World War but it was a brave attempt and a portent of things to come.]

Roy Hodges remained with TRE throughout his career, becoming a Senior Experimental Officer in 1950. He assisted with the development and flight trials of the navigational and bombing radar system for the 'V' aircraft and was responsible for specifying new IFF equipment and the replacement of ageing equipment at RAF ground radar stations. He was particularly involved in resolving operational problems unique to IFF and Secondary Surveillance radar systems.

Sir John Kendrew, CBE, Sc.D., FRS (d. 1997)

> *'During the Battle of Britain, damaged fighters made forced landings at Christchurch and if they leaked petrol we used to fill up our cars.'*

I arrived at TRE in Worth Matravers on 12 May 1940 as a Junior Scientific Officer. Formally speaking I was based at Worth for only three weeks; on 3 June I moved to Christchurch where the experimental flying took place. Only a day after moving to

The Square and Compass at Worth Matravers – a pub that has hardly changed at all since the wartime days when it was TRE's favourite watering hole.

Christchurch I flew as passenger in a Fairey Battle over Worth Matravers, which was having an air-raid practice. This turned out to be more realistic than had been intended because the Battle developed engine trouble and we force-landed in a field outside the establishment. I remember then having lunch at the Square and Compass pub with the pilot – cheese and pickled onions and cider, which I hope is still obtainable there. [It is (1999).]

My job at Christchurch was to carry out flight tests of airborne radar and generally to act as liaison officer between the RAF experimental squadron and TRE. I remember during the Battle of Britain damaged fighters making forced landings at Christchurch; if they leaked petrol – generally the case – we used to fill up our cars in those days of petrol rationing. On sunny afternoons one could sit in a deckchair on Christchurch airfield and watch tremendous air battles going on high overhead, and sometimes in the distance see smoke coming up from Southampton where bombs had been dropped. One evening three German planes came over very low, dropping bombs and machine-gunning as I was walking down a country road. I dived into the nearest ditch and was none the worse, unlike another unfortunate pedestrian who was seriously wounded.

Testing airborne radar was not without its excitements. We used to rendezvous with a 'target' aircraft at 12,000 ft and then test out the radar by homing on the target. On one occasion, after doing this for some time, the pilot remarked that the 'target' was flying steadily south and that we were just over the French coast. Close inspection revealed that the 'target' was in fact a German Heinkel 111 and since our Blenheim was

Charlie Newman, landlord of the
Square and Compass pub during the
Second World War.

unarmed, we rapidly turned tail back to Christchurch. Since airborne radar was at an important stage of development we had a number of VIP visitors: at St Athan, before I moved to Swanage, the King; then at Christchurch, the Air Minister Sir Archibald Sinclair; various air marshals and, in particular, on frequent occasions, AM Joubert de la Ferté (who was responsible for radar in the RAF), among others.

Sir John Kendrew was also involved in operational research in wartime, holding the honorary RAF rank of Wing Commander. As a leading biochemist he became joint Nobel prizewinner for chemistry in 1962 for his work on DNA. He chaired the Defence Scientific Advisory Council and was knighted in 1974. He died in 1997 aged eighty.

Richard Allan Burberry, AMRAeS

> *'While some of the older staff shared real bedrooms,*
> *most of us younger ones were in "horse boxes".'*

I was eighteen when I arrived at TRE Malvern in September 1942. Like many of the new arrivals I'd been to university as a radio bursar, reading natural sciences and radio.

Members of a training course at the monastery, TRE Malvern.

After one or two years, depending on exam results, we were directed into industry, research or into the Forces as signals officers. There were 200 students on my course at Cambridge and probably similar numbers at other universities, so there was a steady influx of young men and women into research establishments.

New entrants at Malvern had to attend an introductory course on radar at the monastery in College Road, for nothing had been published on the subject and there were not many radio text books either. However, TRE did have an excellent library with all the internal reports and American ones too. (A contingent from the Harvard Radio Research Laboratory was based at TRE.)

Many of the single young male staff were accommodated in College Houses 5 and 9. House 5 had the livelier reputation since the Chief Superintendent Jimmy Rowe and his wife had the top flat in House 9. While some of the older staff shared real bedrooms, most of us younger ones were in 'horse boxes'. Corridors in the wings of the houses were divided by wooden partitions on each side into 6 ft by 6 ft cells, with a curtain for door, and just large enough to accommodate a bed, dressing table, wardrobe and chair.

In January 1944 Vera Tweedy (whom I later married) and colleague Jean Brinkworth were transferred from RAE Farnborough when their group leader recognised more scope for 'Empire building' at TRE. At first these two were billeted on a reluctant and niggardly landlady and had a miserable time until Mount Pleasant Hotel opened as a mixed hostel later that year.

Another saviour for staff was the opening of the Piers Plowman war workers' club under Helen Mellor, who created a welcoming atmosphere. Many of us mucked in to help in running the club and it was during washing up on a Saturday night there that I first met Vera; we were married in 1947, as were many other couples from TRE.

After the monastery course, which included a trip to Bawdsey where we all climbed the CH masts, I was assigned to the Rebecca group as an aerial (antenna) engineer. Rebecca was a homing system (the forerunner of DME[1] but with direction capability) to allow an aircraft to home to a ground beacon (Eureka). Its initial use was for dropping supplies, paratroops and gliders, but other uses appeared. My job was to design antennas and to determine their optimum position on all British aircraft except fighters (and later on French and American aircraft also).

While many aircraft could be worked on at Defford, others involved long road journeys in a shooting brake full of equipment to aircraft manufacturers and remote airfields. In those days trips to Stranraer or Prestwick took two days with the inevitable search for cheap overnight accommodation. I was usually accompanied by a Service driver who acted as my assistant on the measuring work.

My base for five years was a 60 ft wooden-framed, tarred-paper walled hut, one of a number alongside a concrete road along the edge of the Aerial Field (the college lower playing field). The road led down to the newly built Engineering Unit. We had electricity, a cold tap and an outside chemical closet. Our equipment was pretty primitive too. Our only bought-out equipment were galvanometers, thermocouples and crystal detectors and the ubiquitous Avo multimeter. Everything else had to be made on site: oscillators, frequency meters, impedance measuring gear. The group workshop could do limited turning and metalwork, but more complicated work had to be done in the Engineering Unit.

Much of my work involved structures including parts of aircraft on which antennas were mounted. If we couldn't get a junk unit from manufacturers or the RAF, we built our own mock-ups in the lab, with the crudest of tools – hacksaw, wood chisel, mallet, tin shears, heavy soldering iron. Our materials were tin plate sheet, telescopic brass tube and what wood and wire netting we could scrounge. With these limited resources we built a Canberra nose and tail mock-up, a Firefly wing section and an 8 ft nose section to go on a Spitfire fuselage to simulate a jet fighter. I also recall building from scrounged materials the first mobile BABS (Beam Approach Beacon System) antenna on a two-wheeler trailer and towing it to Thruxton airfield for flight trials.

Siting antennas on an actual aircraft was also done with simple equipment. The aircraft was positioned on a remote dispersal with flat ground around it. A modified

---

[1]   Distance Measuring Equipment.

version of the antenna under test, mounted on a 3 ft square tin plate sheet, was hoisted into the chosen position on the aircraft and secured with ropes and string to lie flush against the airframe. Some ingenuity was required if the chosen position was under the wing of the aircraft as gravity was distinctly against one. With the antenna position as the centre, a 200 ft radius circle was marked out with stakes at 10 degree intervals: this could be done quickly and accurately with a stretched wire. The heavy oscillator and power unit were hoisted into the aircraft – no easy job in a four-engined bomber – and connected to the antenna.

Initially we had to rely on being near a 240 V mains point as it was some years before petrol-electric sets were sufficiently portable to be carried about. One member of the crew sat underneath it concentrating on a galvanometer, while the other moved a receiving antenna on a wooden stand around the circle, dragging a 200 ft cable between antenna and galvanometer.

On most sites the 200 ft radius took one off the concrete on to the surrounding grass; Defford airfield was built on Defford Marsh so working there could mean plodding round in deep mud all day. No wonder, then, that on the coach ride back to Malvern on a winter evening most people were asleep within a few minutes. One of the joys of working on naval aircraft at Defford was that one could usually rely on the Wrens to brew up hot cocoa. It was on jobs like this that one encountered the joys of trying to coil up 100 yds of heavy, intransigent mains cable, which was invariably cold and wet and muddy.

Able-bodied staff were expected to do fire watching or join the Home Guard. Organised entertainment in Malvern was scarce so we had to make our own. TRE had formed a revue company and a group – the Zenith Players – to perform straight plays. Other members of TRE formed the Piers Plowman Players and there were music groups as well. The college gymnasium was the scene of many activities, presided over by Arthur Wolleter. Home Guard dances were always popular. We worked Sunday to Friday but on Saturdays some of us managed sometimes to get to Stratford to see Shakespeare plays. A colleague and I used to cycle the 36 miles each way; the last 2 miles home were the last straw, being uphill.

Vera Tweedy was working on captured German radio equipment and I soon got drawn into working on the antennas, reassembling heaps of wreckage and measuring the performance. The German radio engineers had a poor rapport with their air force and no attempt was made to reduce the aerodynamic drag of their antennas; whereas we were involved in trying to make flush-mounted antennas. One German array mounted on the nose of a Beaufighter was found to reduce its top speed by 50 m.p.h. Familiarity with German equipment paid off for me many years later when I was able to recognise German influence in many of the designs used by the Russians thirty years on.

I was struck by the wide range of previous careers of some of the older staff. The Rebecca group was headed by biologist J.W.S. Pringle; other colleagues were geologists, schoolmasters and radio amateurs. 'Freddy Lutkin' had been in the photographic section at Bawdsey under Watson-Watt and was to have a long career in antennas at TRE and later at RAE. Of the younger staff two achieved fame as Astronomers Royal: Martin Ryle and Graham Smith.

After the war Allan Burberry continued in the field of work begun at TRE to become a leading specialist and consultant in airborne antenna research at Standard Telephones & Cables. He was responsible for antenna systems on Brabazon, Princess, Britannia and Viscount aircraft and most military aircraft from 1956. In the period 1971–88 he was head of antenna design at British Aerospace. In 1956 he was awarded the Navigation Prize, and the Simms Prize in 1988, for papers presented to the Royal Aeronautical Society.

Joan Ross, Widow of Ken Ross

*'Guilty feelings that we should be doing
more to help the troops to win the war.'*

I arrived in Swanage as a young bride in 1941, just married to a research boffin at TRE. We found our new home covered with tiny typed labels saying 'Just Married' stuck on all the outside doors and windows. Inside, all seemed normal until we went to bed and found dangling brass bells of all kinds knotted with infinite patience on to the wire mattress. We never did find out how the funny men got in!

The Victorian terraced house we rented had an outside WC and we washed in a shallow sink in a tiny kitchen which had a brick-surrounded copper in a corner. Perhaps it was a bath but I have no recollection of using one at all. There was a small back garden with well-used earth, quite unsuitable for 'grow-your-own' vegetables until we double-dug it as recommended by the Ministry of Information. I did the housekeeping with 30s, which included 3s 6d for a sack of coal each week.

I remember eager young men in sports jackets and flannels; their wives and girl friends who shared their leisure time with my new husband and me; walking over Nine Barrow Down to Corfe Castle for tea in a shop where we all thought the fruit cake was made with real eggs and not the deep yellow dried powder from a packet which was in general use for cooking; picnics on the rocks near Durlston Head; queuing for a lemon from the greengrocer after news had quickly gone round the town that a consignment had arrived; having coffee and milk shakes and lively conversation at Forte's Milk Bar in the High Street after going to 'the flicks' at the local cinema; walking in the sunny fields near Langton Matravers and over the cliff paths high above the beaches which were covered in barbed wire. Guilty feelings that we should be doing more to help the troops win the war. Yet all the while our men were closeted away thinking of ways to defeat air attacks and other secret matters. Some of us later did clerical work at the establishment.

Some of our men joined the founding battalion of Home Guards and were issued with minimum uniform that included shoulder insignia printed in black ink, which we then painstakingly embroidered in yellow thread. There was an emergency call-out one dark night when an invasion from the sea was suspected. Wives and children anxiously hid in their homes while our part-time soldiers took up action stations. It appeared to be a false alarm when dawn broke.

Canadian troops were billeted in the town for a time and we were all begged to find them each a room with a bed. One called Leon Wendt came to us. He enjoyed our home comforts and a party at which we had pancakes served with lemon and sugar – a dish unknown to him.

Tip and run raids had begun, mostly on the area around Worth but strings of bombs hit the town once or twice and at night we felt safer in the cupboard under the stairs. Quite soon a decision was made to move the research station and we were all packing our bags and heading for Malvern in Worcestershire.

E.K. Williams, ISO, B.Sc. (Physics), MIEE (d. 1997)

'The Eureka sets were rather bulky (some disguised as Huntley & Palmer biscuit tins) but the partisans in France were able to operate the system successfully.'

The Swanage Years

'Report to AMRE Worth Matravers' read the message from the Ministry of Aircraft Production. It was June 1940 and this was my call-up for National Service from a Ph.D. course in physics at King's College, London (evacuated to Bristol University).

Notwithstanding the urgency of the summons, AMRE had not been advised of my coming nor that of two other graduates who arrived later in the same week. So the first ten days were spent in the library reading the limited literature about CH radar. On the Monday we three were taken before three wise men for allocation to suitable posts, for the princely sum of £240 p.a. On the following day I was collected by Dr John Pringle (a Cambridge biologist) and told I was to work in his section on airborne radar. Several years later I learned that I went to the airborne section because my research at University had been on a 200 MHz project, and I had admitted to a 5s trip in an aeroplane. For the other two, one went to the transmitter section because he had built a ham radio set; the other to an aerial section because his hobbies were climbing and surveying. By such vagaries were our futures decided!

My first task was to work with E.H. Cooke-Yarborough, a radio ham from Oxford University who owned a green MG sports car; each trip with him to the airfield was a hair-raising experience. Our task was to build and flight-test a radar range-finder for eventual use in a Hurricane fighter. Professor Jones at the Gunnery Research Unit (GRU) in Exeter was running a project to design a predictor gunsight for the Hurricane, in order to improve accuracy in attacking aircraft crossing abeam.

Today it is difficult to convey a clear picture of the great urgency of solving problems with the limitations on the design and manufacture of equipment. Radio valves and components were rationed and restricted to a limited range of 'preferred valves' that had been determined by RAE at Farnborough; and a restricted list of components set up by a consortium of the Components Industry and MAP. In principle the need to restrict production to a limited range of electronic components was correct, but the lists were based on the design of old pre-war radio communication sets and were largely irrelevant to the 'pulse' working of radar. Most of the AMRE sections had to rely on ingenuity in designing circuits with what was available from cannibalisation of damaged radio sets, re-use of earlier 'breadboards', and the few components that could be obtained from the stores. With the use of some parts of an old MkI AI radar and other bits scrounged, the first 'RDF range-finder' breadboard was ready for test late in 1940.

In our case 'breadboard' was not a misnomer: the parts were screwed down on to a sheet of 7-ply wood supplied by the aircraft engineer at Christchurch for installation in an Anson aircraft of such considerable vintage that the undercarriage had to be manually wound up and down by the 'boffin' during the trial. The tests mainly consisted of flying to and fro across Boscombe Bay chasing another Anson to evaluate the consistency of acquiring 'range' from various aspects.

The Anson trials looked promising so it was decided to build a prototype model for installation in the Hurricane. As space would be limited it was necessary to reduce the number of valves by means of more rigorous circuit design. None of the valves on the 'preferred' list offered much hope so we had a search through old valve catalogues, although such action was officially '*verboten*'. But the radio hams had a good supply of literature and perhaps with more luck than judgement I spotted an obsolete pentode valve made by Ediswan that appeared to offer the potential of doubling up for several valves used in our ranging circuits, by virtue of the fact that it had a short suppressor grid-base combined with a useful screen wattage suitable for pulse working.

A telephone call to Ediswan resulted in an invitation to visit one of their storehouses to see if I could find any of this type of valve. I was lucky and found a box containing a dozen and they proved to be exactly what was needed. Moreover, once we had alerted our colleagues to the special virtues of the valve, there was such a demand for it that Ediswan had to make a small production run. It was designated VRl16 and used in a number of projects.

Together with several others, our section moved to an evacuated girls' school, Leeson House. We worked in a dormitory with a message on the wall that read 'Ring the bell for your mistress', which was carefully preserved throughout our stay. At Leeson we began to appreciate the opportunity to exchange ideas with other sections in the same building.

Our prototype rangefinder was soon built in a more engineered and compact form to be installed in the radio compartment aft of the wing of the Hurricane, which was flown to Christchurch ready for trials in the summer of 1941. Unfortunately the trials proved to be one disaster after another. On the second day an RAF mechanic ducked under the aircraft wing and speared his head on the radar aerial, damaging his skull and breaking off the aerial blade. Christchurch promised to make another front section of the aerial within a day, so the GRU sent one of its Defiant aircraft to collect it. On the way home, the air gunner decided to engage in some gun practice over the sea. Where had they put the new aerial? On the floor of the turret! The mangled remains were not a pretty sight, nor was the face of the Wing Commander. Yet another aerial had to be made, this time collected safely late in the evening, ready for installation the following day. That night there was an air raid on Exeter and all electricity was cut off, making it impossible to solder the aerial blades to the radio frequency cable.

But eventually we were ready and the next three days were spent on trials against another Hurricane with photographic recording of the range as seen by the radar. Although the radar locked on and tracked in range in a chasing and overtaking mode, range lock was intermittent when the aircraft was banked towards a crossing target. It was suspected that due to large variations in aircraft engine speed, the regulator controlling the special 80 V a.c. supply to the radar was not coping. Tests on the ground indicated that if the regulated voltage fell below 75 V the transmitter power was much reduced. As there was no immediate prospect of stabilising the aircraft power supply, the trial was abandoned and the equipment taken back to Swanage for a rethink.

The Birth and Demise of Monica

Co-incidentally there was at that time a major change in RAF policy and priority was switched from Fighter Command to Bomber Command. The GRU project was cancelled and a decision taken to modify our RDF rangefinder to operate as a warning aid to the rear gunner in bombers against approaching enemy fighters. Fortunately the special aircraft supplies were better regulated in bomber aircraft so that only relatively minor changes were needed to the radar design to overcome the problems that had been encountered with the Hurricane. The equipment had to be repackaged to suit bomber aircraft with the range meter display replaced by an audio tone injected into the rear gunner's headset. The tone varied in frequency, rising as the attacking fighter closed in range. The new system was code-named MONICA and for reasons not clear at the time, the project was transferred to Radio Department at RAE Farnborough. So Cooke-Yarborough went with it to oversee development, production and introduction into service. Although fairly successful initially with Mks I, II and III, the concept was cancelled after about a year as enemy fighter aircraft were provided with equipment that enabled them to detect the Monica transmission and home in on the bomber.

Rebecca/Eureka

Meanwhile a new task had arisen that was to occupy most of my time for the rest of the war. In 1940 Pringle and Hanbury Brown had demonstrated to the War Office an experimental airborne/ground beacon system that would enable army aircraft to drop supplies at night to a beleaguered force. The aircraft radar sent out an interrogation pulse which, on receipt at the beacon, caused the latter to send back a pulse reply on a different frequency. A CRT display in the aircraft could show the range of the beacon from the aircraft and, by means of special receiving aerials, how far to the left or right of the aircraft's track the beacon was. The Army didn't take up the idea, but SOE (Special Operations Executive) got to hear of it and thought it might be suitable for dropping supplies to their agents in France. A few airborne sets (REBECCA MkI) and some beacons (EUREKA MkI) were hand built at TRE and given to RAF Tempsford from where the SOE aircraft were controlled. Although the Eureka sets were rather bulky (some disguised as Huntley and Palmer biscuit tins), the partisans were able to operate the system successfully. So successfully, in fact, that it was decided to develop both prototype and production versions for use by airborne forces for the delivery of supplies, paratroops, gliders etc. into Europe in a future invasion, as well as supporting SOE.

The contract was placed with Murphy Radio at Welwyn Garden City; I was responsible for the airborne project (Rebecca II) and B.D. White for the beacon (Eureka II). In order to provide for flexibility in future design changes and operational mobility, it was decided that Rebecca would be built in modular form on a mounting

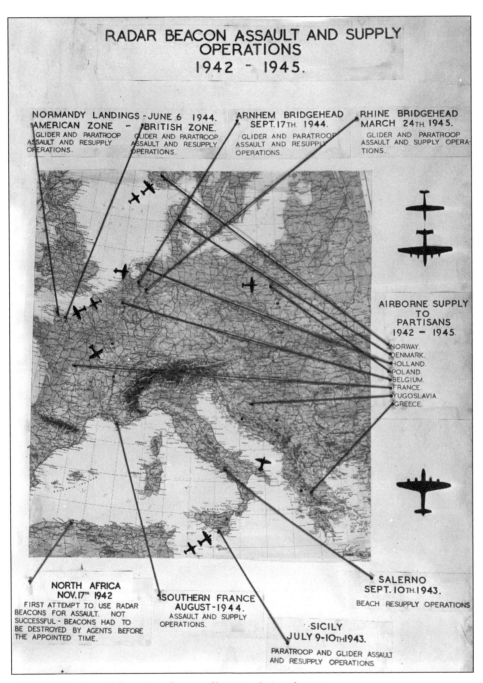

RADAR BEACON ASSAULT AND SUPPLY OPERATIONS 1942 - 1945.

NORMANDY LANDINGS - JUNE 6 1944.
AMERICAN ZONE - BRITISH ZONE.
GLIDER AND PARATROOP GLIDER AND PARATROOP
ASSAULT AND RESUPPLY ASSAULT AND RESUPPLY
OPERATIONS. OPERATIONS.

ARNHEM BRIDGEHEAD
SEPT. 17TH. 1944.
GLIDER AND PARATROOP
ASSAULT AND RESUPPLY
OPERATIONS.

RHINE BRIDGEHEAD
MARCH 24TH. 1945.
GLIDER AND PARATROOP
ASSAULT AND SUPPLY OPERA-
TIONS.

AIRBORNE SUPPLY
TO
PARTISANS
1942 - 1945.
NORWAY.
DENMARK.
HOLLAND.
POLAND.
BELGIUM.
FRANCE.
YUGOSLAVIA.
GREECE.

NORTH AFRICA
NOV. 17TH 1942
FIRST ATTEMPT TO USE RADAR
BEACONS FOR ASSAULT. NOT
SUCCESSFUL - BEACONS HAD TO
BE DESTROYED BY AGENTS BEFORE
THE APPOINTED TIME.

SOUTHERN FRANCE
AUGUST - 1944.
ASSAULT AND SUPPLY
OPERATIONS.

SICILY
JULY 9-10TH 1943.
PARATROOP AND GLIDER ASSAULT
AND RESUPPLY OPERATIONS.

SALERNO
SEPT. 10TH. 1943.
BEACH RESUPPLY OPERATIONS

A TRE display board illustrating the use of beacons during the war.

Rebecca II aerials installed on aircraft (above) enabled it to home on to a ground-based Eureka beacon (below).

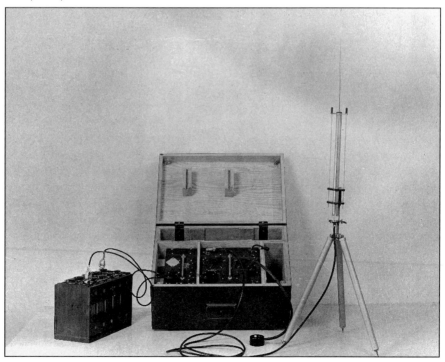

frame with facility to select five transmit and receive frequencies in flight. The aircraft display was not developed by Murphy but by Bush Radio because there was a policy that displays should be standardised, as far as possible, around a basic framework to ease aircraft installation problems, and to avoid total system disclosure to any one firm.

In May 1942 the project was partially set back by the decision to evacuate TRE from Swanage to Great Malvern. One evening early in May, Pringle told me to pack up all my equipment and go to Malvern the next day with a Pickfords van crew and supervise the construction of his working laboratory, which was to be in House 2 in Malvern College.

Malvern

For security reasons few of the Malvern residents could be told the purpose of TRE nor why it had been evacuated to Malvern. Some were upset by the rather heavy handed approach of the Regional Billeting Officer demanding that every spare bedroom be made available at short notice for us. For the princely sum of 5s a week they had to offer a room with bed (supplied if necessary by TRE) and access to WC/water, but no meals. For a guinea they could additionally offer breakfast and evening meal.

The eventual layout at Malvern became:

House 1:	Administration
House 2:	Navaids, Rebecca/Eureka
House 3:	Aerials and Receivers
House 4:	RAF Liaison
House 5:	Hostel
House 6:	Post Design Services
House 7 (at The Lees):	Electronic Countermeasures
House 8 and Preston Lab:	Centimetric devices
House 9:	Hostel
School House:	Ground radar
Big School:	Trainers for Service Demonstration
Pavilion:	Circuit design
Memorial Library:	Drawing Office
Monastery:	Lecture School
Rackets Court:	Environmental Test Chambers
Gymnasium:	Stores

In April 1942 the Free French were occupying House 5, with parts of HMS *Duke* in Houses 1 and 2 but new accommodation was found for both by mid-May. The electrical power required by TRE was more than the local Malvern supply could cope with so a special power line was laid all the way from Gloucester, which in due course was used to power the American wartime hospitals built in 1943–4.

Most of the senior staff had been able to visit Malvern and arrange their own accommodation. The others, arriving late in the afternoon, tired and hungry, were given a crude map of Malvern and the address of a billet, only to be often rejected by the householder. House 5, and later House 9, was organised as a hostel to take in the rejected; in due course chaos subsided and TRE was at work again.

We were continuing to support SOE with beacons for use with the partisans. A particularly noteworthy effort was that of a Norwegian, trained in the UK, who operated a Eureka I for over two years despite having to hide the units under the snow during winter. The set was last used for a SAS landing for the heavy water factory demolition and brought back to TRE for display at the press release of radar on 15 August 1945. (Unfortunately for history, somebody stole it from the exhibition.)

In June 1942 TRE suffered the tragic air disaster when a Halifax aircraft engine caught fire over Ross-on-Wye while on an early H$_2$S flight, with Blumlein and other EMI staff, TRE staff and RAF liaison officers on board. Before the pilot could make an emergency landing near the Severn Estuary the wing fell off and all eleven on board were killed. Later, in the 1990s, a memorial window to all the RAF and civilian aircrew attached to TRE who were killed on duty was unveiled in Goodrich Castle, close to the site of the Halifax accident. (See Epilogue, p. 249).

By June 1942 Murphy Radio had completed the first two prototypes of Rebecca II for delivery to Malvern. In those days test gear to evaluate radar performance was pretty crude such that test and evaluation was laborious and intuitive. We had to try to ensure that operational performance was acceptable, that the design of sets would lend themselves to the normal tolerances in production and that they were suitable for carriage in the designated aircraft.

Tests in the laboratory showed up a few problems that could be cured, but although flight test results from Defford were acceptable at moderate altitude (5,000 ft) there appeared to be problems at higher altitude due to corona[1] in the transmitter. The set was installed in a Wellington to reach 10,000 ft, and one had to climb over the main spar to get to the rear of the aircraft from the cabin and carry out quick observations – quick because of the lack of an oxygen mask in that part of the aircraft. Unfortunately there was quite a severe corona problem in the transmitter which could not be resolved with local design changes and repeated airborne tests.

[E.K. Williams has provided further information not included here but lodged in CHiDE archives. He describes problems encountered during the development of Rebecca/Eureka; how they were tackled by TRE and its contractors; the evolution of BABS (Beam Approach Beacon System) and gives examples of military campaigns in which beacon systems were used. He also writes about TRE at Malvern after the war was over. We conclude his reminiscences with these words:]

It is appropriate to pay tribute to the firms working on airborne radar in the heavily bombed areas of the bigger cities and ports; for their efforts to keep the projects going despite personal and logistic disasters. One felt almost ashamed to come back to the relative peace and quiet of Malvern after visits to firms who were clearing up chaos of the previous night; to ride on the Underground having to pass through lines of people

---

[1] Corona: an electrical discharge between conductors, aggravated by the lower air pressure at high altitudes.

sleeping out night after night on the platforms; to listen with others to the 'phut-phut' of the V1 missile hoping that it did not cut out before it passed overhead, and when it did, to shrug off the noise and smoke that arose maybe a few streets away. In the fourth to fifth years of the war one could not but see that the population of the larger towns had aged, but despite their exhaustion, everyone seemed determined to keep going; to keep the shops open, the works open and the railways running.

[NOTE: Beacons: pulsed beacon systems such as Rebecca/Eureka are often classed as radar because of their similarity in circuit techniques and in form of display to radar equipments. However, there is a clear difference in their mode of operation. The interrogating transmitter (e.g. in the airborne Rebecca) does not have to rely upon the vagary of reflection for the signal returned to its receiver because it triggers a positive transmission from the beacon (e.g. Eureka on the ground). The strength of the returned signal reduces much less with distance than with radar (only as the inverse square rather than the fourth power): thus strong and consistent return signals can be obtained over operationally useful ranges with transmitters of only modest power. Also, the beacon's reply to an interrogation can be completely free of interfering echoes if – as is usually the case – separate frequencies are used for interrogation and reply. Further, the pulsed nature of the beacon's reply readily permits coding for the purpose of identification.]

After the war E.K. Williams stayed on at TRE and continued working on airborne radar until he retired in 1978. His last project – Blue Fox for the Hawker Harrier – was ready just in time for the Falklands War. In 1972 he was awarded the Imperial Service Order for services to the country. A notable part of his career was the welfare work he did for the IPCS and Whitley Council. Following retirement he worked for some years as radar consultant for Ferranti.

Dr Harry Sutcliffe, MA, Ph.D.

'Senior people were helpful with explanations. I was surrounded by more and better tutors than those of the average Ph.D. student.'

When the war began in 1939 I had completed the first year of a degree course in general engineering (mechanical sciences at Cambridge) and was working as a vacation apprentice at the GEC plant at Witton in Birmingham. I volunteered to join the armed forces but was rather pleased when letters came back advising me to finish my course. This I did, and stayed at Cambridge throughout the 'phoney war' and the bombing raids, apart from the summer vacation of 1940 during which I was a vacation apprentice at the then Metropolitan Vickers plant in Trafford Park in Manchester.[1]

Before the final examinations in June 1941 I was summoned to a breakfast-time interview with C.P. Snow at Christ's College. It was like a scene from one of his novels. He was urbane and donnish and asked searching personal and technical questions such as 'Have you used an oscilloscope?' I suspected that over-modesty would not be much in demand so I replied in the emphatic affirmative. After all, we'd had 'The Full

[1] Metropolitan Vickers Electrical Company Ltd ('Metrovick') produced a vast range of first-rate technical equipment for the armed services in wartime. The company was widely respected in the field of radar for the excellent design and construction of its transmitters used in many systems including CH, CHL, GCI and GEE.

Wave Rectifier' as a laboratory experiment and had looked at the waveform across the resistive load on a Cossor Cathode Ray oscilloscope. I presume that he set the wheels turning for my appointment, as an Assistant Experimental Officer, I think, to TRE in the summer of 1941.

It was a long, hot journey from the north of England to Swanage. At about 7 p.m. in the evening I emerged from Swanage station with my bicycle and pushed it along the promenade towards my digs. There was an astonishing sight: behind the barbed wire on the beach were hundreds of swim-suited men and women, playing in and out of the sea and giving me the impression that they were all members of the same set or tribe. It seemed that the enemy was not expected to invade that evening and the local military had decided that it would be good for morale to let the overstressed workers of the area have a frolic on the sands. I was seeing my new colleagues en masse for the first time. Alas, it was too late for me to join them and so far as I know the event never took place again.

Up at Worth Matravers on the following morning I was photographed and issued with a pass. I expected to start right away devising potent radars (at that period Radiolocation Equipment). But in fact I was sent at once on a short course at Petersham near Richmond Park.[2] There, a group of us were instructed in the art of designing multivibrator circuits and suchlike by one Corporal Dr Jones; and in the versatility of the Fourier Transform by J.A. Ratcliffe. Equipped with these powerful skills I returned in a few days to Swanage and reported to my allocated group at Leeson House.

The small group, with John Clegg as leader, had three R & D projects on hand. These were: a blind landing beacon for operation with AI MkIV; a Terrain Clearance Indicator using a frequency modulated Heil Tube;[3] and, as principal project, a Homing Beacon for 10 cm AI Marks VII and VIII. I became the most junior of three on the homing beacon project and was most fortunate in having S.W. (Spencer) Noble as section leader.

Spencer had a kindly and encouraging disposition and a delight in the art of applied electronics. I remember well his successful design of the main amplifier in the beacon receiver. It was not a simple problem because of the requirement for high gain and wide bandwidth; the bandwidth being determined by the spread of frequencies of the individual transmitter magnetrons in the airborne radars. Spencer opted for a 'video type' amplifier. The best valve to use would have been the Mullard EF50 but they were in short supply and reserved for airborne equipment, so we had to use the older Mazda SP41 with its top-cap grid and its annoyingly non-standard octal base. Spencer devised an elegant interstage network, stray capacitance and inductance being minimised by mounting the valves alternately up and down to keep grids close to preceding anodes. My own role in all this was tin-bashing, wiring and testing. It was a joy when the prototype had 15 MHz of flat frequency response.

---

[2] Instruction on the Army's GL (Gun Laying) radars was given in the Anti-Aircraft Command Radio Wing Wireless School at Elm Lodge and All Saint's Church (newly built but not consecrated) at Petersham, near Richmond.

[3] Heil Tube: a generator of microwaves, an early form of Klystron.

High voltage condensers were in short supply too, so in the mains power supply for the transmitter we had about 10 kV of low voltage electrolytics in series. They stood in rows mounted on insulating board, the aluminium cans looking as if they were grounded and safe to touch. There were some very narrow escapes![4]

The aerial of course had to be all-round looking and fairly narrow-beamed vertically. Eric Pickup designed it, as a biconical horn. Fortunately the radars were vertically polarised which eased the aerial-to-cable transforming. My range of understanding now extended to standing waves, Smith charts, double stubs and the like. Senior people were helpful with explanations. I was surrounded by more and better tutors than those of the average Ph.D. student.

An interesting very short trip of 'outside duty' was in a period of bitter weather in the winter of 1941–2. A small microwave responder had been assembled with the aim of testing it on small Royal Naval launches in the Channel near Dover, to make them identifiable on the shore-based radar. We travelled by establishment car to within a few miles of Dover; then we skidded on ice and turned over in the ditch. The car was towed out by a passing tank and along to a nearby pub where Eric Pickup worked wonders on the telephone. For the next few days we worked at the radar station. Digs were in Folkestone, full of entertaining linguists working in propaganda broadcasting. One evening we went to a Christmas pantomime and learned later that the *Scharnhorst*, *Prinz Eugen* and *Gneisenau* had chosen that night (11–12 February) to slip up the Channel.

EF50s and capacitors were not the only items in short supply. Cigarettes were scarce and many of us were addicted in those days. We gathered on Saturdays in Swanage outside one particular shop which opened at about 10.30 a.m. and was sold out within a half hour. It was quite a social occasion. Another social activity as the winter nights came along was the weekly dance at the hotel near the pier. We civilians did get an occasional dance or two despite the presence of dashing types in uniform. (Did we *really* go over to a table of young women and bravely ask one of them: 'May I have the pleasure?'.)

But the more vivid memories of our scarce leisure hours are of rambles or cycle rides in the afternoons. Ballard Down, for example, or over to the Agglestone, were acceptable substitutes for my northern hills. I and my companions were aware that we were fortunate to be in pleasant surroundings, cared for by competent and caring landladies, and working alongside stimulating people in the fascinating field of applied electronics. All this when the war was bringing terror and misery to millions.

I was home on a short leave in 1942 and there met my Uncle Fred. A Londoner, he worked in an office at St Pancras station. 'Here Harry – why do you lot down in Dorset want to hire fifty of our big removal vans?' I hadn't a clue what he was talking about.

---

[4] Condenser: the term used until well after the war for components having electrical capacitance – now superseded by CAPACITOR. Electrolytic condensers – more compact than other types, though often less reliable – were available for working up to some 300–450 V maximum. Thus a cumbersome string of perhaps thirty, more or less, was needed for 10 kV.

Some weeks later it was revealed that we were to pack everything up and travel more or less in convoy to Malvern.

We loaded the gear of my section into a big van (one of Uncle Fred's?) and on the appointed day, started out down the drive of Leeson House. The driver was my friend and colleague Willie Wilmot. He had driven before, but not much, and only in a small car. It was in the region of Wareham that he found out how to get us into third gear. Then it was plan sailing all the way to Malvern.

After the war, Dr Sutcliffe remained with TRE (RRE) at Malvern until 1951, then spent the rest of his working life in research and teaching at University College, Dundee, Smith's Aircraft Instruments, Bristol University, Salford University (of which he became Emeritus Professor) and University College, Galway.

Sir Robert Cockburn, KBE, CB (d. 1994)

'Air Marshal Sir Philip Joubert must have given our work a huge priority because my team began to grow.'

I was recruited into the Scientific Civil Service in 1937 but did not join TRE until 1940. I was instead posted to the Royal Aircraft Establishment Radio Department, Farnborough, as part of a team to design a new communication system for the RAF operating on a new VHF band 100–120 MHz to replace the inefficient old HF system.[1] The team was led by a rather eccentric electronics engineer called Bartlett, with Holt-Smith as his deputy. We found the Radio Department hopelessly out of date and we had to start from scratch. I was responsible for designing a 100 W ground transmitter. We saw this into production at BTH at Rugby and then installed the first ground equipment in the aerodromes round London – I did Hornchurch and Duxford. By 1939 all the southern and east coast squadrons were equipped. I remember seeing my first Spitfire land at Duxford at what seemed to me a quite incredible speed – it was a close-run thing.

With the VHF system fully operational, we were posted down to TRE at Worth Matravers in the spring of 1940. The Battle of Britain was in full swing. I found the labs in temporary huts grouped around the transmitter towers of the early warning radar station at Renscombe Farm. As soon as I arrived I was assigned to the job of countering the Knickebein bombing aid, which the Germans were using to guide their raids on ports and production centres in the Midlands. I stayed with this kind of work for the rest of the war.

All through that summer the air battles continued. One morning there was one right over the top of the site and we all came out to watch this warfare in the sky, until we

---

[1] The ground-to-air link, which permitted direct speech in both directions, was a significant step forward in R/T technology. It worked in the VHF band (about 120 MHz) and gave solid cover throughout and beyond the GCI region. Without such fast and reliable communication, GCI would not have been possible.

realised that the pattering all round us was spent bullets falling from 20,000 ft; we dashed for the comparative safety of our huts! By early June the last of our Army had been evacuated from Dunkirk and many people felt a sense of relief to realise that we were now on our own. There was talk of Hitler collecting masses of flat-bottomed barges in all the French and Dutch ports ready for an invasion of Britain. At the bottom of our little lane in Corfe, an old naval pensioner, Mr Coombs, lived in a little hut and cultivated a smallholding. He was utterly scornful of the story: 'Flat-bottomed barges – bah! The Navy would soon blow them out of the water!'

AM Sir Philip Joubert was organising resources to counter the German navigational beams and on 14 June I was able to explain how this could best be done. He was impressed and must have given our work a huge priority because my team began to grow. During the following year we designed various jammers to counter the three successive systems which the Germans brought into use. We were also trying to locate all their transmitting sites and we had an isolated hut on the cliff edge where Cyril Banthorpe with one or two RAF personnel, was getting accurate bearings on the German transmitters. I used to visit him during the night and getting enough sleep became quite a problem. The unit was moved to Durnford House and finally to Leeson, where we began to build up our staff and facilities.

I set about looking for a house for my family, whom I'd had to leave in Farnborough, and eventually found a little bungalow on the outskirts of Corfe Castle. During those early weeks I often had a ploughman's lunch at the Square and Compass pub in Worth. The only other people living at Corfe were the Superintendent of TRE, A.P. Rowe, and his wife, who had a flat over a shop in the main square.

At TRE we had designed a jammer code-named Aspirin to deal with the Knickebein beams and I went off to Diss in Norfolk to try it out. Early in September 1940 I had installed a very powerful jammer on top of Beacon Hill to the north of Salisbury. This was intended to mask the Cherbourg transmitter over the whole of the country. I would work all day in the labs, grab a meal and drive off to operate the jammer as night fell. The raids would continue until about 3 a.m. I was billeted in a nearby great house, where the chatelaine, an Army wife, still lived in grand style. Her husband had gone missing at St Valéry; she hoped he was a prisoner but had had no reliable news. I would return home during the afternoon after snatching a few hours' sleep; this demanding routine continued for several weeks and I became absolutely exhausted and had to take a few days' sick leave to recover.

The staff at TRE and their wives were now integrating into a community. Our closest friends were Margery and Cyril Banthorpe and Sam and Joan Curran. Another very hospitable home was Craiglands where a number of the younger men shared a communal life and were helped out with their housekeeping by several of the sympathetic wives. Our garden provided us with a steady supply of fresh vegetables and despite the rationing we never seemed to go short. This was largely because so many of us were travelling round the country to various places and rarely failed to pick up some farming surpluses. I remember picking up a load of tomatoes at a greenhouse in Wimborne and on another occasion George Thorne returned from Wales with a large basket of eggs – all these extras were shared out. We were once given a duck by an RAF corporal who lived in Aylesbury.

By the summer of 1941 the heavy night bomber raids had diminished, partly because of the countering of the German navigation aids; partly due to the improvement in our night fighter defences; but mainly because Hitler was withdrawing most of his bombers to the Eastern Front ready for his invasion of Russia in June 1941. But sporadic night bombing continued even into 1942, though mainly of southerly targets – Bristol and Poole were attacked several times and we spent several evenings during April sitting under the kitchen table. My wife remembers an elderly lady showing with great pride to her cronies in the Rose Café a spent bullet which she had found in her bedroom. I can remember one morning seeing a German raider shot down into Swanage Bay.

Quite an active social life developed in the town. There were public dances, a choral society, visits to the cinema and numerous private parties. We were still able to bathe from the beach at Studland and often went for long walks on Ballard Down. I also went horse-riding on the Downs and even played a little golf. At Christmas a few of us organised a Christmas dinner at the Grosvenor Hotel – a modest affair but quite an event for our wives.

However, despite this pleasant social life, the laboratories were under increasing pressure. In February 1942 the *Scharnhorst* and *Gneisenau* escaped from Brest and came up the Channel and safely to Germany. We were caught completely by surprise. The passage of these two battleships had very heavy air cover from the French airfields and all our radars were heavily jammed. We had been urging the RAF for many months to carry protective jammers but the policy was against taking the initiative since it was assumed that we ourselves would be very vulnerable. But the escape of the two ships showed that the Germans were already prepared and willing to use jamming. This changed our policy almost overnight and the radio counter-measures group now came under immense pressure to produce a whole range of airborne jammers.

The other significant event in February 1942 was our Commando raid on Bruneval and the capture of a German Würzburg. This showed how very vulnerable we were on the south coast where all our scientific effort on radar was concentrated. After the war the Germans told us that it never occurred to them that we could be so foolhardy and they never proposed an attack; however, the powers that be were really alarmed and in May 1942 a huge convoy of removal vans descended upon the town and within a week the labs, with all their equipment and a little later all the staff and their families and furniture, had departed from Swanage and been deposited at Malvern. Our pleasant existence in the lovely country on the Isle of Purbeck had suddenly come to an end.

D-Day

During 1943 we were heavily involved in designing a range of specialised airborne equipments to protect the bomber force from the increasingly sophisticated German defences. But we were well aware that there was to be a full-scale invasion of Europe during the following year, and had given a lot of thought to how we could contribute. We soon decided that we should be able to construct a 'spoof' invasion.

This would depend on the use of Window and on a device we had used earlier in the war, codenamed Moonshine. It was a device which expanded and modulated the single received pulse so that it appeared on the German radar as if it came from a large group of aircraft. This caused them to take off a number of their fighters to meet the threat. Eventually these had to land back to refuel, and then we would launch our real attack. It was only useable for a short time because the Germans soon found out how to recognise the decoy pulses.

Window was the code name chosen at random by the Superintendent A.P. Rowe because it bore no relation to its real purpose. It had been developed by Joan Curran early in 1942 and consisted of bundles of metalised strips cut to a half wavelength. She demonstrated that two or three such bundles produced on the radar screens an echo equal to a four-engined bomber. Its operational use was immediately banned because it was feared that if the Germans were to use it against us, we were – if anything – more vulnerable than they were.

After the war we discovered that at almost exactly the same time, the Germans had carried out the same experiments, reached the same conclusion and banned its use for the same reason. Incidentally, the German code name was 'Düppel' because the experiments were carried out on an estate of this name; but it also suggested the word dipole in English. The Americans called it 'chaff' from the start and we adopted the new name because by then there was no point in concealment when we had used it with such devastating effect in the summer of 1943 during the holocaust we inflicted on Hamburg.

Early in 1944 we put forward our plans for a spoof invasion and these were eagerly accepted by the planners. In the spring of 1944 I was formally 'bigoted'. This was a Top Secret clearance which allowed me to know the exact date of the invasion and the positions anticipated during the first week of the fighting. I recall vividly the day I was invited up to Norfolk House, headquarters of the planning staff. I was led into the map room and a Colonel unfolded two panels under which was a map illustrating the entire invasion plan. I was frightened out of my life that I might inadvertently let slip some vital fact, or even talk in my sleep.

In May 1944 I was given control of two key Squadrons: 617 Squadron of Lancasters led by Group Captain Leonard Cheshire (the 'Dambusters'), who used the Gee-system for navigation; and 218 Squadron of Stirlings using the Gee-H system for navigation. I visited 617 Squadron at lunchtime to brief them. All the air crews knew by now that they had been given some special task in the invasion and the mess was tense with anticipation. The Group Captain and I walked out to the middle of a cornfield and I explained what I wanted. They would have to fly an orbit 6 miles long over a front of 6 miles, progressing at an apparent speed of 6 knots, and they would have to drop bundles of Window. He agreed that the Squadron could manage the task; he insisted that he would have to relieve the crews half way through but he guaranteed that there would be no break in the Window cloud.

Meanwhile we had moved some captured German Freya, Seetakt and Würzburg radars up to Tantallon Castle on the Firth of Forth, well away from any German monitoring stations; and here we rehearsed the complicated flight patterns. They were found to be completely successful. Finally we flew a full-scale trial round Flamborough Head against one of our Type 11 radars, the nearest equivalent to the German Würzburg. The WAAF operators were not briefed on what to expect. They all agreed that the blips on their screens must come from a very large convoy, larger than they had ever seen before. I was now confident that the 'ghost' fleet would deceive all the German radars.

We then concentrated on preparing the second component of the 'spoof' against any airborne radars. Four Air-Sea Rescue launches had been allocated to us but they only arrived at Tewkesbury on the River Severn during the last week in May. (This was the nearest they could get to Malvern.) Allen-Williams fitted them up with the Moonshine equipment. Time was so short that the launches could only arrive at Newhaven on the actual day of the invasion. We nearly missed it as the launches were delayed a day by bad weather. Fortunately the operation had been put back a day for the same reason, so by the skin of our teeth we managed to arrive in time.

We had had one piece of extraordinarily good luck. An American Signals Group stationed in Iceland had been overlooked by their planners and were posted to Malvern to be trained to operate the Moonshine launches. They were very expert professionals who rapidly learned their new job. We had rigged up in the laboratory a test programme so that they would recognise any airborne radar characteristics and tune the Moonshines to them.

It must have been a thoroughly uncomfortable trip, puttering along at 6 knots in the quite rough English Channel. But they performed their task admirably. They Moonshined eight radars and also found one more which we had not previously detected. The Navy supported this operation with fourteen pinnaces, each towing two balloons carrying a corner reflector, giving an echo equal to a 10,000 ton ship. When these 'fleets' had arrived at their stop line, they laid a smoke screen and broadcast the noises made by a number of ships dropping anchor. Their job completed, they all cleared out of the area.

As a diversion, Bomber Command launched an attack down the Somme and jammed all the German fighter communications supported by powerful jammers back in England. During the previous weeks, our fighter-bombers had systematically attacked all the radars along the stretch of coast which we planned to invade; but for every radar attacked in this area, two were attacked elsewhere. We had developed a system which could fix their position to within about 100 ft. So successful was this softening up operation that I became seriously worried that no radars would have survived to detect our 'ghost' fleets.

The 'spoof' directed towards Boulogne was detected and radar-controlled artillery aimed at it. E-boats were also instructed to approach the area. The Cherbourg 'spoof' attracted little attention, either because there were no radars able to operate or because it was too close to the real invasion force. The latter remained undetected until 2 a.m. on 6 June, when the noise of the ships' engines were heard off the east coast of the peninsula. But it was not until the afternoon that the German High Command finally committed its armour to the battle and by that time we had firmly established our bridgehead.

Looking back on it all now, one of my outstanding memories is of the mounting excitement as we saw the signs of some great venture in preparation. On the way to London for one of my many meetings, I saw all the copses and woods along the road filling up with masses of armoured vehicles. The whole of southern England was an immense armed camp. In the Beaulieu River enormous

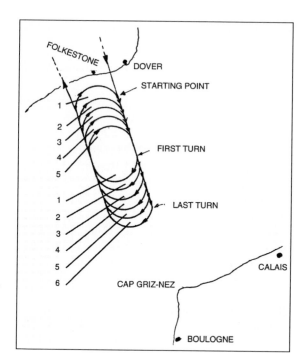

The phantom invasion fleet was created by aircraft dropping Window in a series of turns, gradually advancing towards the French coast. (For simplicity, only a few turns are shown.)

concrete constructions were ready to be towed over to France to form a complete harbour. Yet our absolute command of the air and the strict security prevented the Germans getting any clear warning of the Sword of Damocles hanging over their heads.

In retrospect, we could no doubt in the inevitable fog of war have got away with a much less sophisticated diversion. But there was no point in taking unnecessary risks. About a month later I was asked to create a similar spoof for the landing at Ciotat in the South of France. We had none of the facilities which were available for the main invasion. We cobbled up the Window-dropping operation, using Coastal Command aircraft keeping station on a beacon carried in a ship well away from the invasion fleet. The officer commanding this operation was Douglas Fairbanks Jnr. The landing was made without any great resistance and the spoof was reported to have been successful.

At the end of the war the USA recognised Sir Robert's contribution to countermeasures by the award of the United States Medal for Merit. His postwar career embraced many senior appointments in the fields of science and engineering including such posts as Scientific Adviser to the Air Ministry; Chief Scientist, Ministry of Aviation; Director, RAE Farnborough and chairmanship of official committees on television, computing and communications. He died in 1994, aged eighty-four.

Sir Samuel Curran, D.Sc., FRS, FRSE (d. 1998)

'It was urgently necessary to have a means of delivering big power in pulse form to this amazing British discovery – the magnetron.'

More than fifty years on, clear images of Swanage come to my mind. I first saw it on 10 November 1940. I was married on 7 November and both my wife and I had worked very hard for RAE at Exeter since the first day of September 1939. Before that we had both been Cambridge scientists working on atomic research in the Cavendish Laboratory. We were asked to consult with Government scientists just before war broke out so when it did, in September 1939, we stayed in Government work and soon found ourselves devising and testing a most successful fuse. This fuse worked when the shell or rocket or bomb came into the vicinity of a target, so that the destructive power of the weapon was always used to some extent, even without a direct hit. Explosion was automatic when the device reached the closest point of approach to the target. For this reason it was known as the proximity fuse;[1] it turned out to be a marvellous tool when German V1 rockets were giving London a trying time in 1944. I myself was often in London overnight at that time and was happy to know the proximity fuse ensured that most V1 rockets were destroyed before they could damage the City (and not to mention me).

I had had in the Cavendish Laboratory a young Cambridge graduate, Joan Strothers, as my assistant in 1938–9. Both of us went from there to RAE at Farnborough. As soon as war broke out we were evacuated to Exeter and there started work on the proximity fuse. By October 1940, the main scientific problems of the fuse were solved and we wanted a fresh challenge: we decided to get married. Given four days' leave, we headed for Sidmouth on honeymoon to be greeted on arrival by a telegram telling me to report to Worth Matravers near Swanage immediately. So our honeymoon lasted one day!

As a married woman, Joan was freed from her post but I transferred officially to TRE. But as soon as we were settled in, she volunteered again for scientific work and was asked to be a member of the Countermeasures Division, then beginning to grow in an exciting way under Robert (later Sir Robert) Cockburn.

One of the two cottages we rented was leased by us to a young scientist of my own group, Geoff Hensby, who was later killed when the Halifax test bomber crashed near Ross-on-Wye during a flight test with H2S – the blind bombing centimetre radar. Eleven valuable lives were lost that day – seven RAF, three from EMI and one TRE.

From the start of my research work at Glasgow University, I had taken a close interest in gas discharge studies, so that I could solve really substantial problems in making Gieger counters operate properly. When I began in 1933, people talked of Geiger tubes and the wonderful way they detected every ray that reached them from radioactive material. I found they were erratic and very slow – to be used only with weak

---

[1] The early British work on the proximity fuse was one of the secret subjects disclosed to the USA during the Tizard Mission of 1940. Very considerable further developments took place in America, where the fuse was eventually manufactured in vast numbers and used in Britain against the V1.

substances. It appeared that I was right because Rutherford wanted me in Cambridge as I was able to build fast Geiger tubes and make a wide variety of new types of counter that had not been devised previously.

It was evident to me in November 1940 that with the possible advent of the miracle device – the magnetron invented at Birmingham University which might give big power at centimetre wavelengths – it was urgently necessary to have a means of delivering big power in pulse form to this amazing British discovery. I found soon that none of the established modulator tubes would do the job as they stood. I decided within weeks to construct a new triggered spark gap as it was evident to me that to have currents of 10 to 100 amps at voltages of about 10 kV we needed to forget existing radio tubes and go for gas-filled devices, of which I had gained a good deal of experience in my university research.

Soon I built pyrex bulbs with two stout tungsten rods of around 5 mm diameter mounted opposite each other and with their tips between 5 and 10 mm apart. Close to the tip of one of them, at about 1 mm separation, I mounted the triggering electrode to which I could apply a series of pulses of over 1,000 volts at a rate of up to 2,500 per second. Each pulse was very short in duration, say less than one microsecond.

I evacuated the bulbs with a simple rotary pump which did not give a truly low pressure and filled the bulbs to some centimetres of pressure with argon gas. It is useful to anticipate later studies of what proved to be excellent modulator tubes by saying the tubes were much better in performance if the gas was not really pure but was really argon with a little nitrogen. In practice, the sparkgaps[2] were well suited to the task of driving the magnetrons and more than able to reach the high pulse rate of 2.5 k per second, delivering 100 kW or so of pulse power. So the new wonderful magnetron could be used to its capacity and sparkgaps went into operation as natural partners to the novel device which proved so vital in such applications as ASV and H_2S.

I felt that we were now in a position to defy German offensive planes with AI and enemy defensive devices of all kinds. Although we had many setbacks after this time, I felt entirely sure then that we could win the war. This conviction continued with me to the time of successful participation of some British scientists, including my wife and myself, in the research and development in the USA of the atom bomb. With it in our hands, nothing could hinder our final victory and in fact it came extremely rapidly.

Of the experimental work on Window done at Christchurch by my wife, Professor R.V. Jones in his book, *Most Secret War*, says that she did the definitive work on this highly successful countermeasure.

In 1944, Sir Samuel Curran went to America to work on the development of the atom bomb. After the war, he worked at Glasgow University with Philip Dee where he invented the scintillation counter for measuring radioactivity. In 1955 he moved to Aldermaston where he helped to develop the hydrogen bomb. Later he became Principal of the Royal College of Science and Technology in Glasgow, and in 1964 established Strathclyde University. From 1967–77 he was Chief Scientific Adviser to the Secretary of State for Scotland.

---

2   Generally known as trigatrons.

Lady Curran, BA (Cantab), MA (Cantab)

'The guard on the gate shouted, "Get down,
get down!" and I shouted back, "Where?"'

I worked first at Leeson House and then at the other school, Durnford. On one occasion I walked to the Worth site and had just arrived at the gate when the guard shouted 'Get down! Get down!' I shouted back, 'Where?' but at that moment a German plane flew over very low with machine-guns firing. No damage, fortunately, but I expect it was photographing the site and the aerials. Another time there was a night raid when we took shelter under the stairs: it was really noisy since the bombs were setting off mines laid on the beach. The Downs collected a few holes too. One morning the town was machine-gunned at about 7 a.m. and I dived under the bed – Sam hardly bothered to wake up!

I worked on the early development of Window. I cut up copper foil and made strings or ladders of the bits and the first trial was carried out one Saturday morning at Sturminster Marshall GCI station. The results of this primitive experiment were quite spectacular, the whole baseline of the display unit being deflected. We later used condenser paper and the whole thing became more sophisticated, with the strips of paper getting thinner and thinner, and effort being concentrated on how to package and drop them rather than just throwing them over the side of the aircraft. After the move to Malvern, larger scale trials were held on the east coast over the North Sea, and a final big trial took place at Drem; this last one I did see in company with the then Dr Cockburn.

At Swanage it was not possible to make many expeditions to the surrounding countryside; lack of petrol restricted us and we often used bicycles. We did enjoy the walk along Nine Barrow Down to Corfe Castle, and we went as far as Lulworth, but of course one could never get near a beach, as they were all wired off and mined. We were able to visit Bournemouth occasionally and Sam recalls a few games of golf somewhere in that area, but our leisure time was really very limited.

A few memories linger regarding the fire-watching stints at Leeson accompanied by literally hoards of mice – I've never seen so many. I did wonder sometimes just what we'd do anyway if there was a fire. I remember, too, when the heavy hearth of the fireplace in the room above us came crashing through the ceiling one day, nearly on top of one of our precious magnetrons.

[NOTE: Window ('Chaff' in USA) referred to the notion, which had been dormant since Bawdsey days, of confusing radar by dropping reflective strips of metal foil. It was revived at TRE under the codename Window. By March 1942 Joan Curran was able to report the results of trials which showed it to be highly effective against various British radars at wavelengths of 1.5 m and below. It would therefore act against German 50 cm radars.

Whether, however, it would be advisable to use it at that stage of the war soon became a matter of top-level contention. Those in favour argued that it must be to the advantage of Bomber Command since a bombing force dropping window should be at reduced risk from fighters directed by ground-based radars; from radar-equipped nightfighters and from radar-controlled anti-aircraft guns. But others disagreed: evidently it was not accepted that the control of fighters from ground-based radar stations – coupled with the use of airborne radar – had in Germany reached the stage where it was a significant factor accounting for the loss of our bombers. Also, it was reported that the losses from ground-based gunfire were known to be low; and of that small amount only a fraction was attributable to radar-controlled guns. Thus, jamming the radar of those guns would not make much overall difference.

Consequently it was maintained by the anti-Window lobby that to use it against German radar would not necessarily have a worthwhile effect in reducing our bomber losses: it was not worth the risk that if we did so the enemy would soon copy us, thus spoiling our sophisticated GCI and AI capabilities and jeopardising Fighter Command's ability to respond to any further attacks upon us. A renewal of Window trials against our own radars was demanded, the object being to seek ways of working through it should the necessity arise.

In retrospect it may perhaps be concluded that one reason for this argument becoming heated and protracted was the lack of positive information about the extent to which the loss of our bombers was attributable to enemy radar. However, by July 1943 with more known about the subject and with Winston Churchill involved, it was agreed that since the balance of the opposing air forces had by then swung in favour of the Allies, the use of Window was justified. Following its first success in a massed raid on Hamburg on 23/24 July 1943, when the bomber loss rate was significantly below the norm, it continued to be used extensively for the rest of the war.

Although the original intention of Window was to prevent radars from detecting targets, it was by the creation of false targets – the 'Phantom Fleet' on D-Day – that it may be most enduringly remembered in history.

It transpired that Germany had experimented with a similar scheme but, for reasons akin to ours, had been reluctant to introduce it too soon. It was called Düppel after the district where trials were held.

(For a full description of the issues involved in the use of Window, see R.V. Jones, *Most Secret War*, Chapter 33.)]

After her work on radar and later on the Manhattan Project, Joan Curran settled down to a life as a full-time mother and as wife of Sir Samuel, whose job as Principal of Strathclyde University kept them both fully occupied.

H.C. Spencer, MIEE, C.Eng., FRTS

> 'He dumped his wireless set on the table: "Her don't play," he said, "thee knows about wireless."'

I was sent to Worth Matravers with Dr A.C. Bartlett's group from RAE towards the end of May 1940. We were not the earliest arrivals by a long way and I was advised to take my tent – good advice as it turned out. The actual journey was in company with Dr R. Cockburn by car, arriving in time for a quick snack at the Square and Compass pub. Enquiries as to lodgings produced no replies but on asking about a site to pitch a tent, I was told to 'see Charlie Hardy' whose family ran the café on the Kingston Road; they found me a place in their garden. Later on, when the weather changed, it was suggested that I put my bed up in the café each night – a very welcome suggestion.

One evening in June, transport called for me quite unexpectedly and I was whisked off to a meeting in Whitehall together with Reggie Neale, Vic Russell and Bob Light. It was a wrangling sort of meeting, R.V. Jones[1] in the chair, to discuss ways and means of dealing with some intelligence reports of 30 MHz Lorenz beams [German navaid]. I remember having an argument with T.L. Eckersley who was clearly out of touch with

---

[1] Professor R.V. Jones, Head of Scientific Intelligence in the war and, later, author of *Most Secret War*.

30 MHz propagation. For that I was sent with Wing Commander Blucke[2] in an Anson to prospect for these enemy transmissions, which we found without difficulty.

After another meeting, Bob Light and I were sent off to Ottercops Moss (CH station) to monitor these beams. It was so hush-hush that we were not told our destination, but were given a warrant for Newcastle-upon-Tyne and told that we would be met by RAF transport. Arriving early evening, we were met by a smart WAAF driver who appeared from nowhere and took us to Usworth, a Fighter Command station. We did not get a courteous reception but were clapped in jug as impostors until we got it sorted out at high level. Meanwhile two more 'imposters' were doing the same thing at Ottercops Moss.

So we started our watch. We had a tiny garden shed tied to the 360 ft transmitter tower with string, with a mains supply sufficient for a receiver and light. A Hallicrafters S-10[3] had been obtained for us: we managed to get an aerial rigged and it was working by nightfall, which was fortunately quite late. 'Signals' had already installed a tele-F (field telephone) and we reported the beam characteristics to Filter Room as soon as it was heard. We were there for some time and must have beaten the pole-squatting record, which was at that time about three weeks.

The investigatory work on the beams was codenamed 'Headache' and appropriately the work on countering them was 'Aspirin'. One line of approach, which I remember trying, was to use the radiating properties of a superregenerative detector as a transmitter which would have the effect of widening the 'twilight' zone[4] and so apparently bend the beam.

I got on with the locals at Worth extremely well. I managed to track down the owner of a holiday bungalow and had moved in about a week or so when our neighbour walked in with a Pye portable set. He dumped it on the table with: 'Her don't play – thee knows about wireless,' and walked out. After repair I took it to his kitchen, switched on and said: 'She plays,' and came out. A week or more later we were given a colossal hare.

Time scales were astonishingly short. This was due to some real team work. At Leeson House we were working on H_2S with D.W. Fry's group and castings were needed for the Plan Position Indicator. These were unobtainable from the usual sources so Callick and I decided to produce them 'in house'. Our lab was the vegetable scullery and we had two sinks with taps etc. One sink was turned into a hearth; somebody lost a vacuum cleaner, which was used for air supply up the waste pipe; we found both coke and anthracite in an outhouse – we were in business.

Patterns were made of most unlikely materials, Plasticine featuring prominently. Preston's sister from the chemistry laboratory knitted a pair of gloves from asbestos string

---

[2] Blucke flew the Heyford in the Daventry experiment of 1935. Other attempts had, it appears, been made previously to locate the Lorenz beams, without success.

[3] An American commercial communications receiver of excellent performance.

[4] The Germans used dots and dashes to indicate either side of the correct path, merging at the centre. The 'twilight zone' was an area where the demarcation was not clear; 'Aspirin' widened this and thereby reduced the accuracy of the system.

for us overnight – a most noble act and they made everything that much more possible. There was a lack of moulding sand, but there was a supply of ARP sand. There were no horses so cow manure had to do. I remember A.T. Starr coming in while I was mixing this and on being told what it was, he went a ghastly shade of green. The metal had to be obtained from scrap and we sent Ernie Cattle to forage for duff HT batteries and all sorts of dry cells for their zinc content, and old aluminium chassis or panels, also copper scraps. I can't remember where our first crucible came from; it was very small and only just held enough metal for the largest casting.

On the first run, we barely obtained sufficient heat when someone said: 'What about injecting water vapour?' No sooner said than done: the tap was turned, with a thumb to make a spray, and we poured the first mould. We knocked off the riser and when cold it rang like a bell, with no visible blow holes.

Apart from surprising everyone with the products, the sequel was to me quite hilarious. The people in the room above had noticed an unpleasant smell and complained to Works and Bricks that the drains were faulty; they arrived complete with rods and paraphernalia!

While at Leeson I was working on a waveguide switch which had to be positive in action and take a minimum of time to operate. I made a mechanically operated lab model to prove the system, which successfully worked with the aid of a pair of elliptical gear wheels. Workshops, not surprisingly, were unhelpful so we cast the blanks, I made the cutters and then cut the wheels, all on a Myford ML7 lathe we had in our lab. It was the only time in my life that I ever had a need for elliptical gearing. A Maltese cross mechanism was ruled out because of backlash. This was again a team effort because of the urgency demanded. I doubt very much if these were isolated instances; I quote them in support of my contention that versatility was the name of the game during the war.

Another unusual device we made was a differential capacitor of some 100 pF having a straight-line-frequency law. Again, we made press tools and pressed out the vanes using a vice. Callick, Cattle and I took turns at this arm-aching job.

I remember Bill Harris whose workshop was the conservatory at Leeson. He needed a small micrometer, a virtually unobtainable item at the time, and he spent two fire-watching nights making one – a beautiful instrument. More mundanely, I made our first 10 cm signal generator, opting for a piston attenuator. This used one of the first Sutton klystrons from Bristol. The bolometer used for level-setting came from HIVAC[5] where they worked from a sketch of ours. This was used by Garfit on receiver development. I enjoyed making that – all brass and covered with Aquadag inside to minimise leakage.

After the war, Mr Spencer returned to EMI before moving to Mervyn Sound and Vision where he worked on the development of radio and factory test sets. He ended his career working for BTR at Taplow where he was Head of Radio Division under Sir Archibald Gill and where he developed solar power supplies and sets.

---

[5] Trade name of a British valve manufacturer.

Peter Hall, OBE, B.Sc., C.Eng., FIEE

'I was only concerned with putting everything together;
clever people like Martin Ryle did all the brainy bits.'

Final examinations during the evacuation of Dunkirk felt odd, if not pointless, and when battle-scarred soldiers appeared overnight on the hallowed lawns of King's (where students were strictly forbidden) we all realised what a desperate situation the country was in. I learned that I'd achieved a First and was speedily directed to mysterious, secret work with TRE at Worth Matravers.

My first assignment was on the somewhat crazy invention called the Long Aerial Mine. This proved a dead end, so I moved to GCI, where my job was to visit the early stations as they were set up, to help the Controller get used to his job. I worked at Sopley, Sturminster Marshall, Durrington and Langtoft in the Midlands. During my time on this work we improved the systems significantly: common transmitter and receiver aerial arrays, continuous rotation and better height-finding.

We were having trouble with a rather sophisticated German radar called Würzburg. The boss of the RCM team, Bob Cockburn, was supposed to do something but we had far too little information to go on. In a rash moment, at a meeting with Service chiefs, he said that it would be easier if we could examine the crucial bits of the radar in our laboratory. Mountbatten was looking for an excuse to try out his new Commandos, so off they went to Bruneval and brought back some of the Würzburg radar. In order to make sure they brought back the right bits, a TRE chap, Don Preist, was dressed up as an RAF officer and went over on the raid. He was obviously chosen for this exercise because of his dare-devil nature (he was interested in very fast cars etc.). He was an eccentric: he used to put people off at meetings by tapping his glass eye with a pencil.

In due course, as the German night-bombing offensive tailed off, I moved on to a new job with the Radio Countermeasures (RCM) Division, which was responsible for jamming enemy radio transmissions. And at about this time, TRE moved from Worth to Malvern.

The RCM Division was organised in groups and I was number two to our group leader Martin Ryle. Our job, in simple terms, was to do all we could to protect the bomber force. Our bombers were suffering heavy losses and the German successes depended on their radar, which – in spite of our propaganda – was good, in fact at this time, probably better than ours. The task therefore was to neutralise their radar by whatever means, particularly jamming.

My first job was to try and improve an airborne jammer called Jostle 2, which was meant to block out the radio communication between the ground controller and the fighter. (Obviously if the fighter pilot could not hear directions, the ground radar was useless, however good it was.) The problem with the jammer was that it operated over a very narrow spread of frequencies. Bob Cockburn used to tell the tale of how I solved the problem by the simple trick of hanging a bit of tin near a tuning condenser, which shook with the vibrations from the aircraft's engines. It worked, but I don't think the idea was all mine.

The Germans had a very fine ground radar called Freya on to which we put a lot of jamming effort. Our principal jammer for Freya was Mandrel, which was where most of my effort went. While the night bombers could not fly in formation, they were reasonably concentrated, and it was therefore possible for a Mandrel in, say, 10 to 20 per cent of the bombers to 'screen' the whole bomber force. So the job was firstly to design the jammer, its aerial system and its installation in the various types of bomber: Lancaster, Halifax, Stirling, and later the American Fortresses, Liberators and Mitchells. I was only concerned with putting everything together; clever people like Martin Ryle did all the brainy bits.

Mandrel was used right up to the end of the war, continually being modified to cover the ever-widening band of frequencies used by the Germans to try to counter it. Mandrel was a 'noise' jammer, i.e. the signal radiated from the Mandrel transmitter was white noise. To keep the amount of amplification of the noise signal to a minimum, we needed a very noisy electronic source. We found one in the RCA 931 tube (an electron multiplier) which we proceeded to import in large numbers from the States. All of a sudden we found that new deliveries did not work. Panic! The Americans, noting that we were using a lot of these tubes, decided that they would do us a good turn by improving them. For normal purposes, the lower the noise the better. After a lot of effort, they produced this much improved tube, except of course it was no use to us at all and we had to ask them to put their research into reverse.

I spent a lot of my time testing new installations of various devices in the aircraft and making sure the equipment worked properly. I checked lots of Mandrel installations, but sometimes also helped others in our group to test theirs. David Allen-Williams developed a device which was codenamed Boozer, which set off a warning signal whenever an enemy fighter's radar locked on to one of our bombers. This was installed in every bomber and made the crews feel much safer. Ted Cooke-Yarborough invented a backward-looking radar, code-named Monica, which alerted crews to nearby fighters. But the Germans discovered these devices and started homing in on the transmitted signal, so it became dangerous to use. This was a very simple example of the continuous electronic war that went on between us and the Germans.

As the size and sophistication of our efforts grew, a dedicated RAF group – 100 Group – was set up to concentrate on countermeasures. Apart from jamming, 100 Group had squadrons whose job was to neutralise the enemy night fighters by attacking their bases, and indeed clobbering them in any way possible.

When we began attacking in daylight, with sweeps over enemy territory using fighter bombers like the Mosquito, we often suffered significant losses from enemy fighters. They had good radar, and in spite of our jamming seemed to get good warning of our planes' approach. As soon as our massed squadrons began to form, the German fighters were alerted and had assumed their position by the time we arrived. Someone had a cunning idea: what if we could install some electronics in one aircraft which would make it appear like perhaps fifty planes on the enemy radar? Then we could send this plane over and he would think there was a big raid and get his fighters airborne. Then, when they ran out of fuel, we could send over the real raiders. The beauty of this idea was that even when the Germans realised what we were up to, it would still work. They would see a raid coming but wouldn't know if it was real or not, so they'd have to put fighters up in case. We could ring the changes: sometimes it would be real, sometimes not. This device was code-named Moonshine.

I had a great time getting Moonshine going. Several of us played a part in making the airborne electronics; David Allen-Williams played a major role. We had to build a receiver which would receive the enemy radar signal then amplify – stretch it, and put on a beating signal to simulate the beating echoes of a massed formation. To test it, we had to build a radar as similar to a German one as possible and on the frequency used by the Germans. In order to keep our testing secret, we set up our simulated German radar (Freya) as far away as possible from enemy territory – at Drem near Edinburgh.

We used Defiants for our tests, and when the day for action arrived we flew them south and tried a dummy run towards the French coast. I watched in the main Fighter Command control room at Bentley Priory. As our Moonshine raid approached the enemy coast, we were amazed to see from our radar reports a massive build-up of enemy fighters: squadron after squadron appeared on the plotting table. We decided that discretion was the better part of valour and told our Defiants to dive down to sea level and run for home. Moonshine worked! After that the RAF were left to get on with it. They had great fun spoofing the enemy and undoubtedly saved many lives and aircraft. Moonshine was to find another use later too.

Our group's most important contribution to D-Day was the spoof invasion of the Pas de Calais. Bob Cockburn was involved at the highest level in planning this operation, which was a great success – the enemy were fooled for long enough. In fact they held back an armoured division from the actual invasion beaches to meet what was expected to be the real invasion in the Pas de Calais. [For more on this operation, see Sir Robert Cockburn, p. 191.]

After the invasion, we were faced with the threat of the V1 and V2 rockets. Our group could do little about the V1 – the pilotless aircraft or Doodlebug – but the V2 was a different matter. This was a supersonic rocket and therefore exploded on its target before it was heard coming. The powers that be knew that a massive bombardment of London was planned and the German production and launch sites were repeatedly bombed. What is more, parts of the radio guidance system had been 'acquired' by our intelligence people and I had them in my lab. Unfortunately some clever German operator had stolen a vital bit on the way. Martin Ryle did some brilliant detective work, following some extensive listening to the radio signals being transmitted from the German rocket experimental station. To confuse us, the Germans were transmitting masses of signals in the frequency bands we suspected they would be using for real. Only a few of the signals would actually be controlling the rockets, but which ones? Martin's brilliant analysis led to the conclusion that two frequency bands would be used – something like 40–44 MHz and 80–90 MHz. These bands would be idled with lots of signals popping up and disappearing continuously. However, amidst all these signals, when a missile was to be launched and controlled, there would be two signals related by the formula 'f and 2f+4'. When signals related in this way came up – watch out! – a missile was on its way and would arrive in a minute or two. We therefore had very little time to detect the signal and set up a jammer. Even if we could do so, we could not stop the rocket coming, but we could ruin its navigation system and so reduce the risk of it hitting vital targets. That is exactly what we did, and after the first day or so the Germans found out and replaced the radio guidance system with a much less accurate inertia system.

Our V2 jamming was really quite clever. We equipped a squadron of Flying Fortresses with a sophisticated receiver and a very powerful transmitter, which I think we called Jostle 4. The receiver had a screen that showed up all the signals in two bands, one above the other (X axis frequency, Y axis signal strength) in such a way that any two signals related 'f and 2f+4' would be directly one above the other, and could be highlighted by a strobe (a brightening of the signal). Setting the strobe would automatically fix the transmitter to the right frequency. An operational signal would therefore be very quickly detected and the transmitter switched on. The Germans had done their best to 'hide' the system, and to confuse us, but we had our jammers in the air twenty-four hours a day within about twelve hours of the first V2s arriving. To give them credit, though, they had their fallback system (inertia) up and running within twenty-four hours or so of us starting to jam. We kept our jammers going, however, just in case they reverted back to the more accurate radio system.

After the war was over, one of the strange things was interrogating captured German scientists. It was fascinating to hear their side of the radio war: how they had struggled to discover what we were up to, and how they countered our moves. It was also scary to hear of the new weapons that were on the way. We won the war only just in time.

Peter Hall's postwar career began at AERE and led on to directorships in major industrial concerns in the fields of semiconductor manufacture and computer technology.

John E.N. Hooper, B.Sc. Physics, University College, London

'. . . it was discovered that 49 per cent of our bombs were falling in open country . . .'

[Oboe was the most accurate of the wartime bombing systems. Calculations made carefully in advance of a raid determined precisely the point in the sky from which a bomber at 30,000 ft, flying a predetermined course close to a specified speed (about 300 m.p.h), should release a bomb (whose falling characteristics were known) in order to hit the required target. After navigating (usually by GEE) to a position some 50 miles from the predicted bomb release point, the bomber would come under control, for ten minutes, from a pair of Oboe ground stations which each measured accurately its range from them. Typical ground station sites for targets in Germany were on the English east and south coasts.

One station (the 'Cat') sent a stream of control data to maintain the aircraft at constant range so that it flew on a slightly curved course towards the release point. Simultaneously the other station ('Mouse') monitored the aircraft's range from it and sent successive updates of the aircraft's diminishing distance from the release point and, finally, the release signal itself. After 'bombs away' Oboe control ceased and the bomber returned to base.

While the principle of defining a distant position by range cuts from two widely spaced known positions was sound and simple, its practical realisation with great accuracy was only achieved as a result of close teamwork and exceptionally ingenious electronic circuit design. Oboe set new standards of precision and stability for pulsed systems.

The following contribution from John Hooper is based upon his lecture at the CHiDE 1997 Navaids Colloquium, Bournemouth University.]

In 1940 when I was at TRE we were approached by the RAF at Boscombe Down who wanted to know if we could help them. Their task was to locate the beams of the

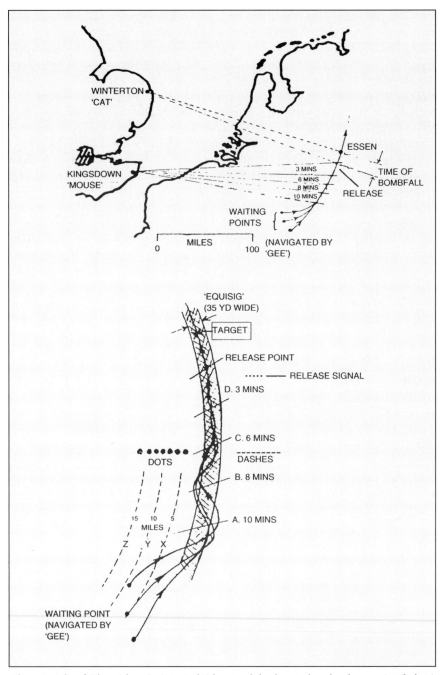

The principle of Oboe (above). A typical Oboe track leading to bomb release point (below).

German navigation system which their pathfinder squadron used to locate targets in Britain. It was the job of one of the crews at Boscombe Down to fly in the afternoon to determine where these beams were laid so that an intelligent guess as to the targets could be made.

When they weren't engaged in that, they thought they would fly down the German beam towards its source – and there was such a source on the Cherbourg Peninsula – and drop a bomb on it. Unfortunately, as they approached the transmitter they ran into a cone of silence and were at a loss as to when to release the bomb. Could TRE help them? TRE tried, with such equipment as was to hand, but it was not adequate for the job; although I think a little damage was done to these stations they were not put off the air.

Lord Cherwell arranged an examination of photographs taken by Bomber Command's aircraft; and it was discovered that 49 per cent of bombs were falling in open country and only 25 per cent of the aircraft located even the target area. So Bomber Command was not being terribly effective up to this time.

Alec Reeves came along to discover what we were doing with the Boscombe Down people trying to bomb the Cherbourg transmitter. He didn't think very much of it but put his mind to helping Bomber Command with offensive radar, because up to that time radar had been invented and developed primarily and almost solely for defensive purposes. Reeves came up with various trial systems, among them 'Howler Chaser'. I mention this only because the tone that was being transmitted to the pilot was said, by one of our young team members, to sound like an oboe. The name stuck and that's how Oboe got its name – nothing to do with the system that ultimately developed except that the name stuck.

Reeves's first idea was a couple of ground stations separated widely but linked with a land line, so that they could send out their pulses, simultaneously perhaps. Any aircraft that received the two pulses coincidentally would be flying along a straight line, but if there was a delay between the two pulses the aircraft would be flying on a hyperbola. The principal pilot of the Boscombe Down flight was Flt Lt Hal Bufton, who didn't think it was a very clever idea to fly out from this country in what was virtually a straight line, or at worst a slowly curving hyperbola. He thought that this would be giving the game away from the beginning.

So Reeves went back to the drawing board and came up with the system that was finally adopted. The idea was that a tracking station would send out pulses to the aircraft which would carry a transponder, so that it got a strong signal back and the aircraft would be controlled to fly at constant range from this 'Cat' station. If the pilot strayed a little too far, he got in his phones a dash signal; if he came too near, a dot signal. He would endeavour to fly on the equi-signal and that was at such a range that it would take him to the bomb release point eventually.

Now another station, the 'Mouse', was sending out pulses on the same radio frequency but at a different repetition rate and was measuring both the range of the aircraft (which was changing continually) and its velocity, and from knowing the height of the aircraft which was pre-arranged, and the ballistics of the bomb, a release signal could be given to the navigator to drop the bomb in the correct position. This was the system that was finally adopted.

Long before even a soldering iron was heated, Reeves had written a series of papers about Mark I Oboe, Mark II Oboe, Mark III Oboe and so on. There were difficulties concerning the range: you could only work with an aircraft within optical range, or very little beyond the optical range, so Reeves proposed a system of repeater aircraft whereby you could transmit the pulses on to the bomber at much greater ranges. He wrote a series of papers that found their way to Headquarters, where a certain gentleman wrote to DCD:

> I regret having to do this, but I'm sure it is true to say quite bluntly that these disquisitions from TRE on Oboe are becoming ridiculous. If they came as inventions from the outside public and not from official sources, they would be rejected without hesitation. No notice is taken of the very serious criticisms which have been made of the system generally, indeed whole Mark numbers are announced, although none of them, not even the first, exist otherwise than in the imagination. Yet if those responsible for bombing operations see this screed they would probably conclude, with some justification, that several tested systems are ready and on offer to Bomber Command. I see with grave concern that TRE proposes to incorporate Gee with Oboe. . . . It would be disastrous to permit the protagonists of this fantastic Oboe the chance of causing a sensible and practical system like Gee to share the disrepute into which Oboe, even if raised to Mark XX, would inevitably fall.

But it was Reeves who in 1937 had the patents for PCM (Pulse Code Modulation), which is now the basis of most modern communication systems although it had to await at least the invention of solid state devices before it could be readily incorporated. Reeves was a genius.

In May 1941 a small group of six, of which I had the honour to be a member, was formed under Dr F.E. Jones to take this scheme further. The group soon multiplied. We worked with the flight at Boscombe Down because they were used to the dot–dash method; they had originally been a blind landing unit and had become involved with the German beam locations. They were known as the 'Wireless Investigation Development Unit' (WIDU).

We arranged a demonstration for an aircraft to fly over a camera obscura, the aircraft being controlled from a Cat station at Swanage and a Mouse station at West Prawle. Instead of giving a bomb release, it gave a signal to the navigator to press a flashlight in the bomb bays and the obscura noticed this. On the strength of this demonstration we were given permission to drop bombs on a bombing range in South Wales. Again the two controlling stations were Worth Matravers and West Prawle in Devon, and we were to drop bombs when the weather was fine. But after two days when the bomb splashes were almost on top of each other, we were allowed to drop them through cloud if necessary. The WAAFs who were plotting the bomb splashes couldn't believe their eyes that bombs were appearing through the clouds in exactly the same position as they had on the previous two days. This was a demonstration to prove a system which we hoped to develop on 10 cm because we were pretty sure that it would soon be jammed off the air on 1.5 m. But the Air Ministry said that even if it only lasted for a month they must have it because Bomber Command's efforts without it were so depressing.

So stations were sited at Trimingham near Cromer in Norfolk and at Walmer in Kent with a view to attacking targets in the Ruhr. We got sidetracked in December 1941 because there was a requirement that the *Scharnhorst* and the *Gneisenau*, which were in Brest harbour, should be attacked.

Oboe had not developed sufficiently to be used for this job, but we had some experience of measuring ground speed etc.; so guidance was laid on from Helston in Cornwall, across the Brest peninsula, to lie over the harbour at Brest, and from our West Prawle station we would measure the aircraft's speed and give him a height and a release signal. The aircraft were to be Stirling bombers, flown from East Anglia. When they arrived in Devon one of the Boscombe Down pilots took over and flew the aircraft across the Brest peninsula. This went on over Christmas 1941 and damage was inflicted; in fact I don't think the battleships ever went to sea for any other reason than to creep up, unfortunately, through the English Channel to return to Germany for repairs.

The operation had some benefit for Oboe because one of the limitations of the Oboe system was that it would take ten minutes for the pilot to settle down on to the dot–dash circular track, and it was thought to be dangerous to fly on a very nearly straight line for ten minutes. But these Stirlings had flown over the Brest peninsula on a constant track at 15,000 ft or higher and suffered no damage, and that was one of the most heavily defended parts of France at the time. So some of the critics were silenced, and we had a lot of them. However, this exercise set the Oboe programme back a bit because Frank Jones himself was manning the station down at West Prawle and some of us were out in the Stirling squadrons or at 80 Wing HQ.

In March and April of 1942 we did bombing trials which were so successful that Air Ministry called for operational stations on the east coast. We could only operate pretty well at line of sight. There was some refraction of radio waves in the atmosphere which meant that at 250 miles – which was about the distance from our shores to the Ruhr – an aircraft would have to fly at 30,000 ft in order to receive our signals and retransmit them. We had 'put our money' on the Wellington MkVI, which was a pressurised aircraft. But unfortunately the prototype of the Wellington MkVI came to grief; what could we do? Hal Bufton learned of an aircraft called the Mosquito. It could certainly fly high and it could fly fast; but could such a small, two-seater aircraft take the equipment? The C.O. of 109 Squadron (previously called the WIDU) attended a meeting at the Air Ministry at which he was given one week to ensure that the equipment could be fitted into a Mosquito. Happily it was proved possible.

Oboe in Action

The first raid was not on Essen but on a coking plant in Holland at Lutterade, which was chosen because it was supposed to be a virgin target. But when the PRU came back the next day with photographs, the whole place was plastered with bombs. Bomber Command must have dropped their spare bombs on it on their way home. So we couldn't detect which were the Oboe bombs or with what accuracy they had fallen.

So a second target was chosen by Dr R.V. Jones (Chief Intelligence Officer at the Air Ministry). He chose a fighter station near Florennes and had alerted his agents over there to watch out for where the bombs fell. I think this is the only occasion on which the agents were forewarned of the target; F.E. Jones was told to go out into the country somewhere near Malvern to a particular public telephone box at 10 a.m. one morning, where he would hear the results: the bombs had fallen within the target area.

Oboe raids were then launched officially and I think Essen was hit the first time. But very soon it was decided to use Oboe as a target marking device; instead of dropping bombs the Mosquitos dropped markers for the thousand bombers which followed them. This was very nearly over Reeve's dead body because he thought it was like using a micrometer to crack a nut: here he had a precision instrument and the precision was not really being used. However, on the eve of D-Day, Oboe aircraft marked ten gun emplacements on the Normandy coast for attacks by the 'heavies'; all but one was silenced.

Oboe MkI on 200 MHz had a life of over a year before there was any serious interference from the Germans. They heard the signals but the story goes that they thought these were associated with some naval activity: torpedo boats or something of that nature, and it was quite a long time before they got round to tying it up with the Oboe aircraft at 30,000 ft. Once the bomb or target marker had gone, the pilot just put his nose down and he was home very quickly – no one was going to chase him at those speeds – and the losses were less than 0.1 per cent of all sorties.

The 10 cm equipment was further developed and installed in GL MkIII trailers. The Americans had joined us at TRE and were interested in what we were doing. We were having trouble in preventing our high-power transmitters arcing at heights of 30,000 ft, where the atmospheric pressure was down to half. The Americans offered us a pressurised transmitter with a tuneable magnetron, for which we were very grateful. We put it into all the aircraft and into the ground stations too. And so we were able to carry on Oboe's work at 10 cm; and the trailers went overseas after D-Day in support of our advancing armies.

After the war, John Hooper remained until 1967 with TRE at Malvern (rechristened RRE – Royal Radar Establishment) working first on radar meteorology and later as Head of Training. In 1967 he became Assistant Director of Professional Staff Management at the Ministry of Technology in London.

Denis Bolesworth, Flight Lieutenant, Navigator/Bomb Aimer, 105 Mosquito Pathfinder Squadron

> *'Alec Reeves was recognised as a genius in his own lifetime.'*

Back in 1941, the only navaids we had (apart from wetting one's index finger) were radio bearings and the Astrograph. But in September 1944 I joined 105 Squadron at Bourn and began working with Oboe. I remember some of the scientists well, especially Robinson, Jones and Hooper, who were not infrequent visitors to Bourn. Then there was Blanchard, who seemed to be Alex Reeves's nuts-and-bolts man and who put his dreams into wire, solder and valves to make them work. He came to the Squadron frequently with some secret bit of kit that he attached to a spare aircraft and got a pilot to fly him around to test it. He was something of a navigator himself, which was useful as there was no room for three in a Mosquito, the cockpit being about the size of a Mini car.

Alec Reeves was recognised as a genius in his own lifetime. He always reminded me of a cartoon of a mad scientist, with protruding forehead, bulging eyes and a sallow, pock-marked, bloodless complexion. He dreamed of nothing else but radar and electronics and they said he couldn't boil an egg. If Reeves was presented with valid objections to the viability of a scheme, he would merely say, 'Well, we'll get over it another way.'

Blanchard said he would be called into Reeves's office and on arriving would find him gazing at the ceiling, on another planet. After some minutes he would come to and ask Blanchard what he wanted, to be reminded that he had been sent for. Then Reeves would come back to earth. Reeves had already invented – some thirty years before it was used – the modern pulse telephone system (before the final piece of the jigsaw, the transistor, was invented.)

There was a Sqn Ldr Barton at TRE whom I met. I think this was an honorary rank bestowed upon him and Reeves when they went to Germany at the end of the war to question the scientists there. One of the people they quizzed was Gen Martini who had been head of German Signals, directly under Goering. It was reported that in 1940, just before the blitz started, Martini warned Goering that he had better bomb some of the masts on the English south coast which had sprung up from Kent to the Isle of Wight. He did not know their exact purpose but supposed it was something to do with radar. On 12 August 1940 they did send over some Stukas that certainly damaged a few stations, but these were very soon repaired and the Chain continued throughout the Battle of Britain and for the rest of the war.

Martini, according to Barton, also said that he knew we had an accurate bombing device which could see through clouds (as he put it) but didn't know how it worked. He knew that it was used on Essen on 11 March 1945 when the part of Krupps still able to work was flattened through cloud by Oboe. He said that Hitler was hopping mad and had Goering on the mat at Berchtesgarten and tore him off a strip and said that they too *must* have a device which could see through cloud. Goering said that a hole had appeared in the cloud over Essen and Krupps was bombed through the hole. He told Martini to say the same thing or else he would be in trouble. When Hitler asked Martini whether we had a device that could see through cloud, he had to say no, but whether he was believed or not is not known. Barton said there was a marked difference between the structure of the Signals Group in Germany and TRE, as theirs was directly under Goering and what he said or thought went. By comparison, TRE had their 'Sunday Soviets' and often a problem in one department was solved by a boffin in another offering a suggestion.

Oboe was the most accurate bombing device used during the war. Our maximum error was about 65 yds and we operated at 30–40,000 ft, which led to arcing between high voltage components in the MkI versions, but was rectified in later sets. Aircrew didn't use the names 'Cat' and 'Mouse' but 'Tracking' and 'Releasing'. Trimingham, on the north coast of Norfolk, was our Tracking station and Winterton, further south, the Releasing station. We just listened and dropped bombs and markers by our ears! The 'beam' on which the pilot flew was actually an exact distance from the tracking station to the target in miles, yards and feet. We flew on a track with dots on one side and dashes on the other with a steady note in between which made a noise like an Oboe. The average reaction time of a navigator, from hearing the release signal to pressing his thumb on the button, was 0.3 seconds. This was taken into account in the timing of the release signal sent from the ground station. The code letters A, B, C and D were passed to the pilot by the navigator by the scientific method of using the forefinger of the left hand on the windscreen. The only failure we had was Berchtesgarten on 25 April 1945. We were foiled by a peak – the closest to heaven I have ever been – as yet!

After the war Denis Bolesworth returned to his family's hosiery manufacturing business at Hinckley in Leicestershire.

Dr J.R. Robinson, Ph.D., M.Sc.A

'Ours was the first mobile Oboe to set up in
continental Europe, in August 1944.'

Although a member of the RCAF,[1] in 1942 I was 'loaned' to the RAF and trained at No. 31 Radio School, Clinton, Ontario as a radio mechanic (RDF). I was commissioned and sent to the UK where I commanded several radar stations – mostly administrative work – and became completely bored. I desperately wanted practical work with a soldering iron, to use my training in electronics, the job for which I'd joined up.

After five months in the Faroe Islands, I invaded the sacred sanctum of Wg Cdr Edward Fennessy at 60 Group, Leighton Buzzard, and my fortunes improved at once. He told me 'there is a laboratory in Worcestershire which should satisfy your needs'. He was right, although at the time I did not know that (1) Wg Cdr Fennessy was responsible for 60 Group's programme in radionavigational aids; (2) TRE in Malvern was the centre for the Air Ministry's research and development of all types of radar equipment, and (3) the 60 Group radio technicians detachment at TRE was badly in need of trained hands.

By the time I arrived at Malvern, the atmosphere and general perception was akin to that of any small university town. To me it seemed like Eden after the bleak and windswept Faroes. The Malvern Hills sheltered the town and provided trails for recreational hikes to historic monuments such as the British Camp and the Worcestershire Beacon. More than one crucial radar problem was resolved during a contemplative walk over those ancient granite hills which had nurtured defending forces of Britain in Roman times and now, with 'high tech', were doing so again.

I reported on arrival to Squadron Leader Truscott, CO of the 60 Group Detachment (RAF Malvern). This unit consisted of radio mechanics of all ranks having adequate

[1] Royal Canadian Air Force.

skills to be useful to the boffins in the laboratories. Officers and airmen of the detachment were privileged to work as equals with the civilian scientists, without regard to uniform or rank: on the job, only technical ability counted and, apart from the pressure of wartime urgencies, it was a truly academic research atmosphere. Outside the laboratories, of course, normal RAF procedures prevailed, although these were administered with reasonable consideration: there were formal parades for church, roll-call etc., but I never saw the entire unit together at any one time. Airmen were quartered around the town and officers in a well-run and comfortable Mess in the Abbey Hotel.

Among the latter were many who made incalculable contributions in their own fields of radar, such as Wg Cdr Derek Jackson, DFC, AFC (of AI and Window fame), and Flg Off Joe Richards, RCAF, the tireless Canadian who, in Lovell's group at Defford, was crucial in getting H2S installed and working in the air. Because of the 'need-to-know' security principle, I was unaware at the time of the details of their work, as they were of mine, but there were pleasant mealtime encounters. Like bird-watchers we were treated to occasional and fleeting glimpses of very highly placed visitors as they were accommodated in the Mess while attending TRE for the 'Sunday Soviets' or equipment demonstrations.

My initial interview was with Dr J.A. Ratcliffe who had been a very distinguished professor of upper-atmosphere physics and electrical engineering at Cambridge, and was from 1941 to 1945 Director of both the Educational and Post-Design Services at TRE. These functions ran the gamut from getting equipment prototypes into commercial production; assignment of personnel and installation in the field; arranging for all necessary test equipment, technical manuals, courses and demonstrations to senior commanders. By 1945, Ratcliffe was in charge of more than 1,000 of TRE's 3,000 staff.

As with all the great men whom I met at Malvern, I was at the time naïvely ignorant of Ratcliffe's importance and eventual fame in the annals of British radar history. One of his many earlier contributions had been his elucidation, in 1940, of the 'anomalous propagation' of radio waves caused by temperature inversion. This phenomenon was reported by E.G. Bowen at Orfordness in 1935, when he observed RDF echoes from hundreds of miles beyond the assumed range of the equipment. These 'over-the-horizon' responses, fleeting and unpredictable, had been a particular plague at CHL stations until Ratcliffe, based on theory, explained the problem and relieved the nuisance through antenna adjustments and siting improvements.

Busy as they were, all the scientists received me with courtesy and appeared to have a genuine interest in my training, in my views and in what I would like to do. Most had been teachers, so I suppose they knew best how to extract whatever was available from callow youth. I came to full knowledge only later of their pre-eminent roles in radio and RDF history, and of how very privileged I was to have met them.

Ratcliffe apparently decided that I should work with the Oboe group and he sent me to the office of Dr A.H. Reeves. A very quiet, thoughtful personality, Reeves received me most graciously and enquired about my radar experience. He was a prolific and far-sighted inventor – a man given to contemplative daydreams. He was not an academic like Ratcliffe but he held a doctorate in electrical engineering and was a leader in industrial communications research, having been with Standard Telephones & Cables Ltd for seventeen years before the war. He had pioneered in transatlantic high frequency radio telephony and in microwave communications between England and France. In 1940 Reeves had turned his thoughts to the needs of the RAF for radionavigational aids, particularly for use in accurate bombing, and he proposed the system which, after much refinement, became known as Oboe.

Much of the working of blind bombing was explained to me that day by Dr Reeves when he welcomed me to 'our Oboe family' and sent me to meet his deputy, Dr F.E. Jones. While Reeves was, by nature of his personality and his position, rather remote and seldom seen at our level, 'F.E.' was very actively one of us. At university he had worked on the absorption of microwaves in liquids and, later on, pulsed wave propagation in cables.

'F.E.' was the ideal role model for us: vibrantly active, tall, blonde and athletically handsome, and at only twenty-nine years of age he was definitely one of our generation. Although far excelling us in mental brilliance and authority, he treated everyone with an open friendliness, a genuine interest and mutual respect. By personal example he set the pace and standard of work expected of us and because of his attitude we all, at every level, did our best for the Oboe project.

The Oboe section working on the development of the MkII Mobile, to which I was assigned, was at the end of a long row of huts. The hut next to us housed Dr Robert Dippy's group working on Gee improvements, and in the Preston building facing us was Professor Lovell's H2S group. Each hut held a unit engaged in research into particular aspects of radar and all were extended by satellite groups at TFU[2] Defford or at RAF operational bases or with an associated industrial laboratory.

F.E. Jones was frequently absent from the lab, pursuing the interests of Oboe at every level of the ministries (Air, Aircraft Production, Supply etc.); with the Air Marshals, officials in the electronics industries; with circuitry wizards at universities, and among both civilian and military authorities from the USA. Jones had a special regard for the men of the Oboe Pathfinder squadrons and he spent as much time as possible with 105 and 109 Mosquito squadrons and later with the Oboe-equipped strategic bombers of the US 9th Army Air Force.

On his return to the labs, with his youthful enthusiasm he would fascinate us with stories of test-flying Oboe equipment in the 'Mossies' and Marauders and of Oboe operational successes. His stories had a highly positive effect on our morale and made us feel very much a part of the war effort.

The on-site manager of the Oboe development team at TRE was John Hooper. One of the original group of six convened by Jones in May 1941, Hooper had already been involved in all the earlier, pre-Oboe blind-bombing experiments: use of the Bailie (Lorenz-type) beam; the 'Broody Hen'; 'Howler-Chaser' and, later, operations 'BBC' and 'Trinity'. Like 'F.E.', John Hooper was youthful, enthusiastic and very capable of organising and inspiring others by example.

In early January 1944 I received instructions to set up our hand-built prototype MkII Mobile Ground Station at RAF Marham where the two Pathfinder Oboe squadrons

---

[2] Telecommunications Flying Unit.

were based. Our equipment was installed in a heavy trailer fitted with twin parabolic dish antennas, originally designed for MkII Gun Laying use. It was a severe test of the system's mobility, towing the trailer from Worcestershire right across central England to the Wash in Norfolk. Our crew consisted of myself and two other Air Force technicians.

At Marham we worked closely with Gp Capt H.E. Bufton the CO of 109 Squadron, who had been deeply involved with radar navigation in pre-Oboe days. He had been the first to hunt down and identify the Luftwaffe's Knickebein beams in 1940 and later, working with Reeves, Jones and Hooper, had suggested many useful technical improvements for Oboe based upon the user's point of view. Now, in nightly operations, he was putting the system's target-marking techniques to the test over the Ruhr. We were soon on the air and starting to perform calibration tests, using a ground station at Tilly Whim (Swanage) as 'Cat', aircraft from 109 Squadron and an inland bombing range. Very soon we found the power output of our klystron-based transmitter completely inadequate, and were supplied with equipment to substitute a magnetron as the power oscillator.

In March 1944 we moved the equipment from Marham to RAF Beachy Head – another long, cross-country journey – and set up for pre-invasion operations. Our crew was enlarged to include a Unit CO, Adjutant, four Oboe controllers from 8 Group (Pathfinder Force), and four complete watches of mechanics and operators supplied by 60 Group. We were soon engaged in guiding the Pathfinders to mark targets selected to disrupt enemy troop concentrations, flying bomb sites, factory production and road and rail infrastructure in France, Belgium and Germany. During this period we had a number of distinguished visitors from Invasion Headquarters and the Air Ministry, including Robert Watson-Watt.

On the night of 5/6 June we were heavily involved in marking the enemy's coastal batteries covering the invasion beaches on D-Day. Early on the morning of 13 June we had a front row seat to watch the first salvos of V1s attacking England.

Some time during this transition from an experimental prototype development to a fully operational station, my personal status of being 'on loan to TRE' disappeared and I was once again back in the RAF, on the strength of 75 Wing, 60 Group. This return to full service 'formalities' was quite a shock after the intellectual freedom of TRE. Shortly after D-Day another posting, this time to 72 Wing of 60 Group but operating under the Allied Expeditionary Air Force. A completely new crew was formed with all new, factory built equipment; it was strange to see our familiar old hand-made prototypes transformed into shiny new components – but it functioned in the same way.

This was the first mobile Oboe to set up in continental Europe, in August 1944. We were approaching Paris before its liberation and were able to visit the city while shooting was still taking place in the back streets. A long way from quiet, peaceful Malvern.

After the war Dr Robinson worked as research scientist at the Canadian Department of Agriculture and was engaged in the synthesis and use of radioactively labelled pesticides to study their biochemistry. He published scientific papers on his research and gave instruction to university graduate students on the subject.

Albert Shorrock, Airframe Fitter at RAF Defford

*'We have come a long, long way since those
early Defford days of tinfoil and piano wires.'*

It was in February 1942 that I arrived at Hurn airfield near Bournemouth to begin working closely with the TRE boffins. But soon afterwards, they decided to uproot the whole establishment and for safety's sake move it to Malvern. In early April I and nineteen other bods were instructed to get down to the airfield with our full kit and were immediately loaded on to a Wellington full of bell tents: destination Defford near Malvern. We took off and climbed to about 150 ft when the cowlings fell off the port engine. The pilot, with a shrug of his shoulders, carried on but unfortunately about five minutes later the starboard engine cowlings started flapping about in the breeze. The speedometer was reading zero, so he decided to return to base. We landed safely and transferred to a Lockheed Hudson, then we were away again.

Our first sighting of Defford was when the pilot announced 'There's your new home lads', but all we could see were three landing strips slap in the middle of a vast area of utter desolation – the only sign of life down there as we descended was a lot of what looked like yellow ants scuttling to and fro. As we came in to land, these became recognisable as bulldozers, diggers, graders, earth movers, rollers etc. It was W. Wimpey's Travelling Roadshow. Runways were being extended and buildings were in all stages of construction – there was mud, mud, MUD everywhere!

I was assigned to Servicing Wing to service incoming aircraft and we were certainly kept busy; the early arrivals were a veritable 'Heath Robinson' collection: Anson, Oxford, Wellington, Lysander, Hurricane and Swordfish. Our greatest problem was we didn't have any starter batteries; it was all hand-swinging or cranking for contact. We had no idea of our geographical position, or what lay beyond the boundaries of the airfield in the outside world: no signposts, no maps, no transport, no road lighting – just miles of unknown countryside. There followed six weeks of complete isolation, until the rest of the station personnel arrived. Slowly but surely, Wimpey's Travelling Roadshow were doing a grand job and eventually we had comfortable billets, cookhouse, NAAFI and cinema.

During the four years I was at Defford we equipped and maintained almost every type of operational aircraft in service during the war. Our job was top secret – no careless talk, no cameras, no diaries. We knew we were something to do with radar (whatever that was) but that was all we were aware of, so when our boffins dreamed up their weird and wonderful ideas, then told us to 'stick this here' and 'stick that there', we just did it. The result was that aircraft would fly in, displaying their sleek, clean lines, but when they flew out again they would be bristling with all kinds of appendages protruding all over the place – wings, tail, fuselage. On one occasion I had the privilege of carrying out an interior decorating job on an Airspeed Oxford with rolls of tin foil stuck on with fish glue (the most obnoxious, evil-smelling concoction imaginable). What the foil was for I knew not, but the smell alone would have kept an enemy attacker at bay. The 'heavies' came in next: Halifaxes, Stirlings, Lancasters, Fortresses etc. – huge and majestic. However, when they left us they had developed boils, carbuncles and great big blisters, sticking out from their noses, their backs or their bellies.

In due course I found out that we were situated in the centre of the most beautiful part of England – miles and miles of glorious countryside surrounded by the marvellous Bredon and Malvern Hills. Off duty we could cycle off into the Worcestershire countryside in any direction we chose: Upton – Worcester and the River Severn; or Pershore – Evesham and the River Avon to Stratford. The whole 'Garden of England' was at our disposal.

The scientists had settled down in peaceful surroundings, undisturbed and able to invent and develop their technical skills as part of a huge co-operative team. We installed and tested out their ideas and brainstorms. Radar was to become a household word for war and peace, as today's technology will verify. We have come a long, long way since those early Defford days of tinfoil and piano wires.

After the war, Mr Shorrock became District Inspector of South Staffordshire Waterworks Co. and then Head Groundsman/Assistant Superintendent of the District Borough Council Sports Ground and Parks Department. Later he became a department manager in a bonded distribution warehouse.

Squadron Leader P.J.S. Boggis, DFC, RAF (retired)

[Boggis was one of the pilots stationed at RAF Defford, near Malvern, flying experimental radars as requested by the TRE scientists.]

> *'Occasionally TRE showed us a film about radar,*
> *and one of these made a big impression on me.'*

I think there is a fairly widespread ignorance about wartime radar: apart from those involved with TRE or stationed at Defford I've never come across anyone who had any idea of what went on there. I myself was at Defford from January 1943 to March 1944. There were two wings, Offensive and Defensive, and I was a pilot in the former, with an assortment of twin- and four-engined aircraft in my flight. Mostly I was working with H$_2$S stuff, with all sorts of other boffinry from time to time.

The boffins didn't discuss their work with us very much – after flights they usually disappeared to their laboratories and what information we gathered came mostly from RAF sources. The senior boffins were members of the Officers' Mess but I don't remember any 'shop' being talked there. We greatly admired the boffins for their dedication and for risking their lives in the air, without flying pay I believe. They in turn had experienced crews to fly with, which must have reassured them a bit, though fortunately they may not have realised at the time that conversion from one type of aircraft to another usually involved only a couple of demonstration circuits and landings. Having parachutes must have been a bit irksome, and baling out in an emergency would have had its problems, especially with scientists sometimes separated from their 'chutes in different parts of the aircraft.

During my time at Defford there was only one accident with boffins on board, which involved a Lancaster taking off with 'George' (the automatic pilot) in. Unable to

Throughout the early history of radar experimentation and development it was essential for the scientists to have aircraft, crew and ground crew permanently at their disposal to try their ideas out in the strictest secrecy. Flight trials of radar equipment – an integral part of Bawdsey's work - began at Martlesham in 1937 with Heyfords, Battles and Ansons. From Dundee use was made, with difficulty, of Scone and St Athan airfields; then from Worth Matravers, Christchurch. After the move to Malvern, TFU (Telecommunications Flying Unit) was established at nearby Defford, where this picture was taken of 'B' Flight in front of a Warwick bomber equipped with radar aerials. Gp Capt Frank Griffiths – one of the pilots on the Bruneval raid – is seated front row centre. Many of TFU's pilots were 'resting' after a tour of operational duties.

overpower 'George', the pilot aborted the take-off and ended up going through the fence that surrounded the Station Headquarters, coming to rest near the Station Commander's office. The CO dashed out and into the aircraft, tackled the first person he saw (who happened to be a boffin) and asked him what happened. This fellow, despite being a little shaken, replied with commendable sang-froid: 'I don't know. Why don't you ask the pilot?' No one was injured and the damage to the aircraft was not serious, but we heard afterwards that this Lancaster was due to fly to the USA with various demonstration radars fitted and the accident caused embarrassment at all levels. (This is probably why the pilot was dealt with more severely than otherwise might have been the case.)

Occasionally TRE showed us a film about radar and one of these made a big impression on me. It was a radar picture of one of the large raids by the German Air Force during the Battle of Britain and displayed on the screen the massive build-up of hundreds of bombers and their subsequent movements with fighter escorts across the

Channel – the various blobs on the cathode ray tube showing up quite distinctly. It was a remarkable recording of history being made.

Peter Boggis remained in the RAF after the war and in 1947 commanded 207 Squadron, Bomber Command. He flew until 1954 when he was transferred to Air Traffic Control until retirement in 1967.

Gurney Thomas, MA (Cantab.)

'The young staff at TRE were given responsibility and opportunities far beyond anything I have seen elsewhere.'

Early in 1941 I received a summons to attend Dr C.P. Snow's[1] rooms at Christ's College for interview. At that time he was heavily involved in the recruitment of scientific manpower and was acting for the Cambridge University Joint Recruiting Board. I was told that of the three main options (the technical branches of the services, industry or research) I was to be directed to research.

On 19 May I received a letter from the Ministry of Aircraft Production offering me a temporary appointment as an Assistant III (the lowest grade for a graduate) at a fixed salary of £200 p.a. plus £13 1s 0d Civil Service War Bonus. I took my finals in May 1941 and a week after the end of term I reported to the Establishment Officer at TRE Worth Matravers. It was just a few weeks since my twentieth birthday; looking back now I realise that I was a very green product of the technical education system. I was somewhat thrown to be told that I could forget about the lodgings I had arranged and was to go to the Army Anti-Aircraft Gunnery School, Petersham, to be indoctrinated into the subject of radiolocation. This school had been set up when it was found that the introduction of gun-laying radiolocation sets had not had the required effect on firing accuracy and an intake of technically qualified people had been commissioned into the Army to correct this. The school took in the TRE recruits as a sideline and I had a feeling that our easygoing civilian ways didn't fit in too well with the Army's ideas.

The instruction was excellent. For us TRE people, J.A. Ratcliffe was the outstanding instructor. He dealt mainly with aerials and propagation, then key aspects in deciding the feasibility or otherwise of radiolocation systems. He had a difficult task since his audience included physicists whose study of advanced optics made radio propagation little more than a branch of a familiar subject but he also had to contend with a wide range of mathematical competence. These differing abilities must have been noted because when we returned to Swanage, we were all allocated to work for which we were well suited.

I was allocated to Group 17 under Robert J. Dippy to work on the circuit design of Gee airborne sets. The airborne equipment section was under Frank H. Wells at

---

[1] Scientist, and well-known novelist.

The Gee group with leader R.J. Dippy in the centre of the picture.

Durnford. The Gee system had above average reliability for the times, and for this much credit is due to Wells, the circuit designer. He, more than anyone else, taught me what being an engineer should be. He never looked for short cuts, never took chances and never employed an elaborate solution to a problem if, by additional hard work and investigation, a simpler one could be found. His designs had a style about them which was clearly recognisable.

When I joined the group, the rush was on to complete a dozen or so airborne Gee sets for field trials by the RAF. The ground equipment must by then have been largely in place. It was a case of each member of the team assisting with assembly and wiring. Wells was a little unhappy about asking newly qualified graduates to do this work, thinking (quite wrongly) that its routine nature might sap our enthusiasm. In fact it was excellent training. We were familiarised with the smallest detail of the sets (useful when we were sent out trouble-shooting). And in my case at least, I never forgot what sustained attention to detail is required if reliable electronic equipment is to be produced.

The field trials were successful and a production run of Gee Mark I sets was produced for introduction into service in 1942. Only a limited number of MkI sets could be made because by this time the rapid growth of RDF systems had produced a shortage of Mullard EF50 valves around which many of them were designed. The decision was taken to redesign the Gee airborne sets around the Mazda SP61 valve, similar in characteristics but quite different in shape. At the time this was a matter of concern but the opportunity to redesign was taken, to produce much-improved sets which came into service early in 1943.

It is perhaps not surprising that we regarded TRE as an outstanding place to work; it was after all for many of us our first job. Nevertheless, the young staff were given responsibility and opportunities far beyond anything I have seen elsewhere. There was a remarkable openness among staff and between departments which provided a fertile ground for new ideas. Even the most junior were listened to if they had a well-intentioned idea to put forward, and there was little recrimination if misplaced enthusiasm resulted in one exceeding one's brief. And we always knew that our work was needed and that it fulfilled pressing Service requirements.

That this was the case was in large measure a result of the attitude of the Chief Superintendent, A.P. Rowe. I remember him as a genius – a view reinforced by working in other establishments later. He organised regular visits by Chiefs of Staff who told us themselves of their Service needs, and attendance at their talks extended to quite junior people. He defended us from Civil Service and Armed Service bureaucracy and restrictions. But most important of all, he let us know what he expected of us. For us juniors he was a man to be held in considerable awe; I never heard of anyone trying to take advantage of relaxed working conditions. And he mixed the carrot and the stick with skill.

Both the carrot and stick were demonstrated at one of the evening seminars that he arranged to enable us to keep abreast of new developments in other groups. This was a particularly stimulating one but A.P. Rowe introduced it with a personal talk about the war situation and the need for us to work all the hours there were, subject only to not becoming stale and ineffective. With superb timing he added: 'I cannot understand those who leave work at 5.30 as if there were no war on.' At that moment a group of these gentlemen were seen walking past the window of the lecture room on their way to catch the bus home. 'There they go,' he said.

In 1946 Mr Thomas joined Harwell Electronics Division, then in 1951 the Coal Board Research Establishment. At Dowty's, where he worked from 1956 to 1983, he was engaged as a mechanical engineer on the design and manufacture of mine roof supports.

G.W.A. Dummer, MBE, C.Eng., FIEE

> *'Our laboratory was in the laundry of the College*
> *and conditions were fairly cramped.'*

In September 1939 I was working at the GEC High Frequency Laboratories of Salford Electrical Instruments when I saw an advertisement in the *Daily Express* for electronics engineers at a research establishment in the Air Ministry. I applied and a week later received a letter inviting me to an interview in London. There I put forward my experience on CRTs during four years with A.C. Cossor Ltd and four years valve testing work at the Mullard Valve Co. as well as my design experience with GEC. I was offered an appointment as Technical Officer at £275 a year and told to report to Bawdsey Research Station, Suffolk.

Before I had time to go to Bawdsey I received an urgent message to report to Dundee College, to where BRS had been evacuated. On arrival I was met by

A.P. Rowe, who explained he was very busy, gave me a copy of the 'bible' and left me to study it all day. John Mercer then took me in hand and introduced me to Sid Jefferson, Robert Dippy and others. I was put to work with A.W. Eva on time bases and we made up a 'gain to range' time base circuit to reduce the effect of the transmitter pulse on the CRT. My wife and I arranged digs with Eva and his wife, sharing a flat with them.

Our laboratory was in the laundry of the college and was organised in three groups: Jefferson in charge of receiver design; Dippy of time base design and Dr England in charge of transmitters. In the time base group there were Dippy, myself, Dr E. Franklin, A.W. Eva, C.D. Florida and one or two lab assistants. Eva and I designed an IJAJ (Intentional Jitter Anti-Jamming) device, and Franklin and I designed the first electrostatic PPI, using magslips and, later, a magnetic deflection PPI with mechanical rotation.

The development of the PPI enabled the existing CHL equipment to be converted to the GCI of night bombers. Later, in Swanage, six emergency PPIs were constructed by Florida, Franklin and me working all day and most nights to complete six GCI stations in two weeks. These were installed at Sopley and other areas, enabling Group Captain Cunningham and Squadron Leader Rawnsey to shoot down several enemy bombers at night.

Conditions in the laundry were fairly cramped and we were glad to move to Worth Matravers after ten months in Dundee. At Worth we were allocated two large Nissen huts with Dippy in charge of one and I of the other.

Training Devices

Early in 1942 a new group was formed to design training devices for operators to learn to operate the rapidly expanding radar systems in the RAF. Because of our circuit design experience, Dippy and I headed this new group, but Dippy decided to work full time on Gee navigation and I was given charge of it.

There were at the time only two ways to train operators in the new radars which were being introduced: either in actual operation, using real aircraft taken off operational requirements; or to use synthetic echoes produced by circuits designed to simulate the moving picture which would be seen by the operator.

The first synthetic trainer was designed to simulate the first early warning radar – CH – and it used mechanical cams to control the realistic movement of the echoes. As each new radar came on stream, a synthetic device was produced to duplicate the real operational presentation. Some seventy-three different types of synthetic radar trainers were developed and produced by a small group of about twenty of us in about five years. Among these, and following the initial CH early warning system, came many others: CHL, GCI, AI, ASV, GEE, GEE-H, BABS, IFF, Rebecca/Eureka, H2S, Oboe, AGLT, Air Cigar, Bodyline, Monica, Rugger Scrum, Big Ben, Ash, Fishpond, ACR. For every one of these a synthetic trainer was designed and built.

When TRE moved to Malvern in 1942, the group continued to design, manufacture and install many ingenious devices which were used to train over 55,000 operators, navigators and controllers, avoiding wasting the use of operational aircraft, petrol and time – estimated to have saved the country £65 million.

Following wartime design work on radar equipment and trainers at TRE and MIT, Geoffrey Dummer was awarded the MBE in 1946, and was later awarded the USA Medal of Freedom (with Bronze Palm). He became known internationally for his scientific approach to reliability in electronic equipment. His leadership of technical committees and numerous specialised publications has established new accepted procedures and standards for assessing reliability in components and system design.

The laboratory at Malvern where radar trainers of many kinds were developed. One of the first – a CH trainer with receiver – can be seen in the top left-hand corner of the picture. (Courtesy G.W.A. Dummer.)

Squadron Officer A.L. Rundle, MBE

'I heard the well-known voice: "Fly with a woman?
In my aircraft? Absolutely preposterous!"'

In 1940, although recently married, I applied for a job which turned out to be in the research and development of radar and was very pleased to be interviewed by that great but unassuming genius Sir Robert Watson-Watt. Selected for a direct entry commission, together with a dozen other graduates, I embarked on a lengthy and arduous course of instruction.

First we went to Cranwell where we were trained for our commission. Next, we moved to various CH stations to learn the job, and later on to train as radar mechanics. In due course I went to a CHL station and then to Bawdsey for a GCI course. After all this I eventually arrived at TRE Worth Matravers for the most technical part of the course. Head of the proceedings was Dr Leonard Huxley, brother of the more famous Julian. After eighteen months of continuous study, there were lengthy written papers and interviews, at the end of which I was asked by Dr Huxley to accept an appointment with the aim of co-ordinating the production of AI trainers for use of night-fighter navigators and pilots. I was first attached to Dr Lovell's group under the direction of G.W. Dummer, to familiarise myself with the trainers. I sought the expertise of Wg Cdr John Cunningham and his navigator Jimmy Rawnsley – the most outstandingly successful team of night fighters. I was much encouraged by their genuine approval of the trainer on display and their obvious enthusiasm for production to be stepped up.

Under Dummer's surveyance I became a reasonable authority on my subject and duly reported to Gp Capt Carter in the Directorate of Technical Training at the Air Ministry. I was given an office, all information pertaining to AI trainers and the title of T.Sigs.2A. I found my main suppliers, the Hacker brothers of Maidenhead (later Dynatron), to be real craftsmen – ready to work all hours and with tremendous pride in the performance of their product.

The more I got involved in the job, the more it came home to me that with the tremendous shortage of components for all types of radar, manufacture should be co-ordinated by one governing body, and I wrote to the Director of Radar to that effect. In reply came a summons to Whitehall and to my relief, the Director himself, Air Cdre C.P. Brown, was in agreement. He took over the AI trainers forthwith and I became assistant to Sqn Ldr Gilfillan within the Directorate of Radar, liaising with Bomber Command in respect of all their radar requirements.

Some months later Gilfillan accomplished his dream and flew with Lancaster ED 604 from Defford carrying 10 cm H_2S, tail warning and other devices, to demonstrate to the Americans so as to enable them to copy and, more important, to set up production. He was later posted to Washington and I took over his job. I assisted in AI training at 62 OTU Usworth and in the introduction of AI MkVIII in Beaufighters of 85 Squadron, Hunsdon.

On one memorable occasion I was in charge of a Monica (tail warning) trial at Defford and was allocated the tail of a Wellington – the nose being used by Wg Cdr Derek Jackson (of Grand National and *News of the World* fame). He was not in the best of moods, having been banned from visiting his wife, due to the presence in their home of Sir Oswald Mosley. As I approached with two NCOs, I heard in the distance the well-known voice: 'Fly with a woman? In my aircraft? Absolutely preposterous!' I made my presence known, hopped in the tail and with no further ado we were airborne. There followed a slight setback – my sergeant reported that the transmitter had inadvertently been omitted. Somewhat crushed, I announced this predicament to Wg Cdr Jackson. Happily for me there was a big smile on his face as he admitted that he had failed to locate his target. The flight, while a complete flop experimentally, created a friendship between us that was to last throughout the war.

I became heavily involved in equipping the Lancasters of 8 Group (Pathfinders) with 10 cm H_2S. BTH had to be kept under constant pressure to produce the magnetrons for this and the crews needed to be familiarised with its use.

In the Directorate of Radar we welcomed the boffins and were eager to hear of their latest schemes. One morning a charming, rather slight fellow walked into my office and made a startling suggestion. 'Hang on a moment,' I said, 'I think the Group Captain would like to be in on this one.'

'Sir,' I said to Gp Capt Walter Pretty, 'I've got a chap in my office who wants us to throw silver paper out of our aircraft!'

'Heavens – what will they think of next! What's his name?'

'Cockcroft,' I said, 'John Cockcroft.'

'Oh, I think we'd better listen to this one; he's the chap who split the atom!'

And so Window was introduced, with which, by confusing the enemy ack-ack and fighters, our bomber losses were cut by 30 per cent. Cockcroft could have demanded an interview with the Director General of Signals, but he chose to saunter into my office – no fuss and bother; just get the job done. That was the way the scientists worked and that was the way Directorate of Radar co-operated.

H2S was still in very short supply. We had only two and a half squadrons fitted with it when I received a call from Pat Hansford of Admiralty Research at Haslemere. He wanted a few sets for the Navy. Doubtful that ships could make use of it, since our aircraft had to fly at 15,000 ft, I was not being very helpful when he offered to prove his point by showing me a set in operation.

I loaned him one, and within a week I took the train to Portsmouth where a smart Wren boat crew conveyed me to the Isle of Wight to join a small ship with the H2S set attached to its 30 ft mast. We sailed around the island and every small cove was pictured most clearly on the screen. I could visualise what real assistance this would give to night landing operations. 'Right!' I said, 'you're on!' (H2S had earlier been used, under the direction of Lovell, for the invasion of Sicily. The future, and more extensive use, on which Hansford was working, would be for the Normandy landings in 1944.)

Coastal Command were next in the queue for H2S [ASV MkIII] and had great success in their hunt for U-boats in Wellingtons flying from Chivenor in North Devon. Eventually Coastal Command practically annihilated the U-boats from the Atlantic.

With Fighter, Bomber and Coastal Commands, the Navy and the Fleet Air Arm all in desperate need of radar, a top-level co-ordinator was required to determine their respective priorities. Overall responsibility became one of the tasks of Sir Robert Renwick, Deputy Controller of Communications at the Air Ministry. He held frequent high-power meetings with all interested parties and I was present at all the meetings involving Bomber Command. Neither AVM Bennett nor Dr Lovell ever attended, being justifiably too busy.

Owen Jaques, FCIPA, JP, Patenting Agent with the Ministry of Aircraft Production

> *'Sir Stafford Cripps, who replaced Lord Beaverbrook as Minister of Aircraft Production, gave instructions that something must be done about getting patent protection for radar developments.'*

For some years before the war my activities in the patent profession involved me in electrical subjects generally and electronics when I joined EMI in 1936. In their research department intensive work had been proceeding on the development of television and even before going to EMI I had to study numerous basic patents on cathode ray tubes and circuitry. Isaac Schoenberg, Head of EMI research and patent departments, wanted to ensure that in the event of litigation the company would be represented by Sir Stafford Cripps who, at the time, was the most eminent patents KC at the Bar.

I was a technical assistant to H.A. Gill who acted as an expert witness in many patent actions and Schoenberg asked him to get Sir Stafford's opinion on the strength and validity of the basic patents which EMI either owned or were licensed to use. So I had to prepare thirty cases for Counsel's opinion. The inventions included amplifying circuits, waveform generators, electronic and electromagnetic focusing for electron beams and so on. There were many conferences with Sir Stafford and I was amazed at his brilliance. This happened before the mid-1930s so by the time I joined EMI in 1936 I was fairly familiar with television.

Before the war started, the research department's programme changed as a result of the Spanish Civil War. The old sound locators used in the First World War were still being employed to detect raiding aircraft, so the German bombers would switch off their engines to avoid detection. Someone found that by placing a bolometer or radiation heat detector at the focal point of the dishes instead of a microphone, the heat from the engines of the incoming aircraft was enough to provide a fix. Fantastic. So, outside the research laboratories at Hayes there were experimental dishes and an old school friend of mine, Harry Clarke, among others, was assigned to develop the technique. It was soon abandoned because others were already working on radar. Several EMI research workers, Alan Blumlein in particular, were making valuable contributions to its development and the Government granted contracts to a number of firms to make and supply radar equipment.

Because the research and patent departments at EMI were Top Secret, the staff were not called up for any of the Services, but the time came when I felt I wanted to do more towards the war effort. Schoenberg called me in and he also saw other people in the patent department to ask if they felt the same. MAP needed a patent agent and someone had told them about me and in due course I left EMI to join MAP, which is why I found myself from time to time visiting TRE at Malvern.

In 1940 Sir Henry Tizard, with a team of scientists, had gone to the USA and provided the Government there *and their contractors* with details of our radar developments. No major patent protection had been sought on the radar inventions and because they obviously had peacetime applications, Sir Stafford Cripps, who replaced Lord Beaverbrook as Minister of Aircraft Production, gave instructions that something should be done about getting patent protection.

The Ministry of Supply equipped the Army with gunnery radar and the Admiralty Research Department with radar for the Navy. Both had patent agents qualified to deal with getting patent protection, but the really basic inventions were made by TRE in developing the work started by Watson-Watt. Through the Government department that he worked for, long before he was knighted, Watson-Watt filed a secret patent application in *1935* on the original radar invention. He followed it in 1936 with another patent application covering the invention of IFF. Corresponding patent applications were filed in USA but little else was done and Watson-Watt was instructed to develop the heat-detecting [infra-red] technique. However, he persuaded his bosses that radar was the right route to follow and IR was dropped.

MAP had a few qualified patent agents who dealt with inventions in the mechanical and chemical fields, but not in electronics so I was taken on. However, I soon realised the task was so vast that I would need help. Barristers in the various Inns of Court tend to specialise in subjects they choose and there has always been a rather select Patents Bar composed of barristers with a background in one technology or another but usually, like Sir Stafford, capable of quickly absorbing knowledge enabling them to understand quite difficult inventions.

There were difficulties with the USA Patent Office in connection with the IFF patent application and I had to meet Watson-Watt to discuss it and also the patenting programme I was attempting to cope with. Apart from the job of gathering the technical details, plus visits to TRE at Malvern, RAE at Farnborough and bomber stations, I was up against Civil Service bureaucracy.

I have referred above to the vastness of the problem of attempting to retrieve the lost opportunity to protect the radar developments as they arose. The simplest example concerned the cathode ray tube itself. Although well developed for television purposes, there was a fundamental difference in its use in radar requirement. In the case of a TV tube, the materials on the inner surface of the screen that respond to impact by an electron beam must be such that the brilliant spot produced will fade quickly enough to follow the changes in intensity of the picture signal: otherwise a blurred picture would result. By contrast, the image resulting from received radar signals should persist rather longer for best observation. A Professor Merton was responsible for developing the composition of materials which gave the necessary time delay before fading ('afterglow') and I visited him to get his signature to a patent application form.

The CH chain was installed to detect incoming aircraft but TRE had to develop much more radar and navigational equipment. Not only were there navigational schemes like Gee and Oboe but airborne equipment for bombers using those systems as well as airborne equipment for fighters seeking out and attacking hostile aircraft. New developments would entail a succession of Marks (e.g. airborne radar very soon reached AI Mark VIII).

Development and supply contracts were granted to firms like Ferranti, Cossor, GEC, BTH and of course my old employers EMI. So I found myself visiting research people in the laboratories of EMI who were already known to me and who had made individual inventive contributions to merit being included as co-inventors in some of the applications for patents.

From Defford airfield, not far from Malvern, aircraft flew to test airborne equipment. During tests on H_2S in a Halifax an engine caught fire; tragically the aircraft crashed killing the crew, several TRE men and three from EMI including Alan Blumlein. I knew the EMI men very well from pre-war days and all those on the Halifax represented a wealth of talent. [The circumstances of the crash of Halifax V9977 are described in Chapter 13 of Sir Bernard Lovell's *Echoes of War*.]

Early on in the war when some of our aircraft picked out by our searchlights were brought down, I suggested as a way of preventing such mistakes that our aircraft be fitted with a photocell and amplifier so that when a searchlight impinged on the

The Halifax bomber which, carrying prototype H₂S equipment, crashed near the Wye Valley in 1942 killing eleven members of TRE, EMI and the RAF.

photocell a signal would be immediately transmitted identifying the aircraft as British. My memo went to the EMI research department and Blumlein told me that while my idea was a good one, it meant involving 'another window that would have to be cleaned' etc. However, what he did not tell me at the time, because I had not then become involved in radar, was that IFF was already being developed.

H₂S depended on a magnetron having a copper anode so substantial – despite a number of drillings through it – that it was difficult to destroy by the kind of explosive charge built into radar equipments for activation should they fall into enemy hands. Because of its relative indestructibility, Churchill refused to let H₂S be used at first, in spite of pleading by those who needed it, because he had heard that as a test some H₂S equipment had been installed in a Junkers aircraft and the explosive triggered. It blew a 10 ft-wide hole in the aircraft but the magnetron had remained intact. Churchill gave way in the end and H₂S proved its worth on bombing raids. We filed a secret patent application on H₂S but of course by now the patent and all of them would have expired many years ago.

After the war, Owen Jaques served for three years with Parnall Aircraft as resident patent agent, then in 1950 he became a partner in Abel & Imray, a founder firm of the Chartered Institute of Patent Agents, of which he was President in 1970.

Douglas Fisher, FRPS, official wartime photographer at TRE

'Yer carn avit – specially you, young Doug!'

[An important supporting service to the radar scientists and the RAF was provided by the photographic and film unit which, after beginning life in the Bawdsey days, was expanded further at TRE at Worth Matravers and Malvern. Staffed by experienced photographers and later by film makers, script writers, animation artists, cameramen, film editors etc., it gradually became well equipped for a complete range of filming and photographic techniques, including some filming in colour and later experimental stereoscopic filming.

The work ranged from the mundane security pass photos of TRE staff through to highly detailed still and movie records of radar systems during development, to full-blown technical training sound films on radar systems produced for the RAF.]

It was a hot day in July 1939 and I was sweltering on the LNER train from Kelvedon to Liverpool Street, on my way to attend an interview at Adastral House in Kingsway. I was seventeen at the time and had responded to an advertisement in the *Daily Telegraph* calling for assistants at the Air Ministry Research Establishment.

From a small child, my obsession had been with the cinema. From my early teenage years I had had my own movie cameras and projectors and by the time I was fifteen I was presenting regular film shows, for profit, in three Essex village halls, with my own sound-film projectors. Great stuff and happy days.

At Adastral House I was ushered into a stark room with three stern-looking men seated at a table whom I later learned were A.F. Wilkins, J.E. Airey and A.B. Jones. At the end of the interview they offered me a job as laboratory assistant, but they wouldn't tell me what AMRE was about, nor could they give me a starting date. It all seemed very odd. They told me to go home and wait until called – that call didn't come until some *nine* anxious months later, May 1940 in fact.

AMRE at Worth Matravers came as a tremendous surprise to me – all those high-tech masts and rows of odd-looking huts in a sea of mud, and nearby an old farmhouse and cows. Three or four of us youngsters were ushered in to one of the huts and introduced to A.B. Jones, who frightened us rigid with the Official Secrets Act. He then told us what AMRE was about. 'Fisher,' he said, 'you have two options. You can join Mr Seiger's Skyatron team or his photographic unit.' I opted for the latter.

There I met Dennis Segaller (films), Keith 'Jock' Russell, Tony Brinkley (stills) and 'Ossy' Osborne, general assistant. I soon settled in and took to the situation like a duck to water. The movie and stills equipment in the unit were so antiquated I was horrified at first, but dear old Jock Russell was a gem – he was a great Leica enthusiast and instantly converted me. He had worked out the film/developer combinations for best possible speed, grain and sharpness from what were then quite modest 35 mm film emulsions. I can see him now, hand outstretched with his beloved Leica IIIa sitting on his palm, saying, 'Doug, even if it couldn't take a picture it'd still be the most beautiful instrument to have, wouldn't it?' It didn't take me long to sell my movie projector and buy my own Leica. It was a IIIb with f/2 Summar lens and it became my constant companion for the next few years. I subsequently bought additional lenses and gadgets for the Leica, thanks to subsidies from home.

Demand for our photographic services grew and grew. I was usually the one sent off on airborne assignments to shoot both stills and movies. I enjoyed working with our scientists and with the RAF aircrews at Christchurch. For filming airborne CRT sequences for our 1941 film *AI Mk.IV* the engineers at Christchurch built me an anti-vibration mount to support an AI MkIV indicator unit and a 35 mm Newman-Sinclair movie camera. This was set up in the blacked-out mid section of a long-nose Blenheim; the small round perspex window in the floor was also blacked out.

My radar operator was Dennis Holdsworth, with Cliff Wright our pilot. We took off with high hopes. To reduce ground returns to a minimum, we climbed and climbed. I can't remember our operational height but even with our padded flying suits we were freezing. Condensation dripped off my face mask and as it hit the metal case of the Newman-Sinclair, it froze into little buttons of ice. Fortunately our equipment worked well and the exercise went according to plan. In our very cramped quarters Dennis and I were totally engrossed in the filming when suddenly there was a loud crack. A blast of freezing air came up at us as Dennis shot downwards. I instinctively grabbed him. He had been standing on the little blacked-out perspex window and it had had enough! Fortunately, only one leg was dangling below the aircraft and we soon rectified the situation and decided to return to base. I'm glad to say that the films looked well and are still available.

During the two years we were at Worth, new faces joined the photo unit. One of them, Dennis Segaller, made the film *How Many Aircraft?*. He collected all the pre-war CH/CRT films shot by Jock Russell and was editing them with newsreel shots of military aircraft in flight, a few simple diagrams, and a terrible commentary talking down to WAAF CH operators. I shot some additional CH/CRT material for *How Many Aircraft?* at Worth. The camera was a Williamson which could have come from Billy Blitzer who shot *Birth of a Nation* in 1913: it was a wooden box housing a simple hand-cranked mechanism, lens and two wooden film boxes. Its 180 degree shutter 'broke out' through the side of the box and was covered by a metal cover. A powerful synchronous motor had been fitted to the drive shaft (to drive the film at exactly twenty-five frames per second) and a half-inch hole had been drilled in the shutter cover.

When the camera was set to view the CH cathode ray tube, with all lights out and the camera running, the trace was viewed through the hole in the shutter cover and the phase-shift knob on the CH turned until no trace could be seen through the hole. The film in the camera was then 'seeing' and recording a perfectly synchronised CRT image. This was Jock's idea.

For our equipment needs we were restricted mainly to the photographic items listed in the RAF Stores catalogue Group 14, Section A: capital equipment, e.g. cameras, tripods, enlargers, lenses etc. Section B: items that could wear out, e.g. cases. Section C: consumables, e.g. films, developers, bromide papers, lamps etc. The Stores Manager at Worth was one Sam Soppit (cruelly known as Sam Stoppit) and his favourite reply to any request was: 'Yer carn avit – specially you, young Doug!.'

We had endless trouble getting anything from Stores, and when we did we sometimes faced further problems. One day a delivery of bromide paper for photographic printing together with a box of flash bulbs arrived, and I went to collect them, only to find the storeman with opened boxes of bromide paper counting the sheets in broad daylight, and another of them testing the flash bulbs (to destruction) with a car battery.

Sam Soppit.

At Worth and Christchurch, each day seemed to bring a new event. One was the return of Donald Preist after the Bruneval Raid. He brought in several interesting items grabbed from the German radar site, which we photographed. And at about this time, a high-quality Telefunken ¼-in tape recorder came into the unit – from Bruneval?

In time I got to know several of TRE's leading figures. I can remember an occasion when Dr Bowden came into our hut and said, 'Fisher, come over and look at this!' He had rigged up a sheet of glass about 2 ft square with a shallow rim, filled it with water and placed a small electric bell mechanism at one side, with its 'hammer' in the water producing ripples. There was a small spot-lamp on the floor under the rig which cast a shadow of the ripples on to the ceiling. When he placed a matchbox in the water, the ripples were reflected, and with this simple setup, Dr Bowden demonstrated the basic principles of RDF to his students. I subsequently photographed a series of his ripple patterns from the ceiling, which he then used as slides for lectures.

After the war, Dr Bowden became Lord Bowden of Chesterfield, Principal of Manchester University and Science Minister in the Wilson Government. One weekend at Worth I had tea with the Bowdens and their new baby. Leica in hand, I managed to get some super shots of Baby B. Forty years on, at a TRE reunion, I packed a couple of the prints to show him. We chatted for a few moments then I pulled them out, and Lord Bowden said: 'Sorry, Fisher, I can't see them. I'm blind.' I was terribly upset.

Only one laboratory in the country could process Kodachrome – Kodak at Wealdstone. We had the lab cleared for security and I regularly took batches of our Kodachrome films there for processing. Ronnie Anderson was experimenting with and duplicating Kodachrome, which was very new at the time, having only been launched in 1938. Ronnie was a great problem solver. I asked how I could shoot CRT traces on Kodachrome. 'You can't,' said he, 'it's too slow. But if you shoot them on high-speed black and white film, I'll dye it green so that you can cut it into your Kodachrome.' Results of our efforts can be seen in several TRE Flying Unit films: *Rebecca-Eureka*, *Monica*, *Village Inn* and *AGLT*.

To Malvern

In 1942 TRE moved inland from Worth Matravers to Malvern. (Our moving traumas are well documented elsewhere.) By then our film unit had grown dramatically to meet the ever-growing needs of TRE. Magnetic recording was on the horizon. We'd acquired a couple of primitive magnetic wire recorders from the USA but it was the arrival of the Telefunken tape recorder mentioned earlier that made everyone sit up. It was the first tape recorder any of us had seen and its sound quality was excellent. Soon Alec Tutchings had dismantled it and was producing circuit diagrams.

At first we were a little cramped at Malvern, but when we eventually moved to our special huts it was sheer luxury. We had a studio, film theatre, drawing office for the artists, animation camera rooms, offices and darkrooms. Also a photostat room, which housed an enormous copy camera which took rolls of bromide paper around 14 in wide. The paper was exposed, chopped off and wound into a covered dish of developer and then placed in a fixing bath. Having been removed, it was put into a sink to wash, then pegged on a washing line to dry. Molly, wife of TRE's Chief Superintendent A.P. Rowe, offered her services as photostat operator. She soon got the hang of it and was popular with all of us.

In 1943 the TRE aircrew trainers unit was asked by Coastal Command to produce a special trainer to help improve aircrew accuracy in bombing U-boats. This special trainer was devised by Dr A.M. 'Pete' Uttley, of TRE's Vision Lab, and I was co-opted to make films for it. This involved filming a real submarine diving repeatedly in the

Atlantic. Filming from the air in January 1943, it took us about two weeks and was bitterly cold.

For the exercise, the Royal Navy was persuaded to lend us one of their 'H' class submarines complete with its Commander, Lt M.H. Jupp, DSC, and crew. For filming we used two aircraft from TRE's naval section at RAF Defford – a Walrus amphibian and a Swordfish. I filmed the action from an open hatch in the nose of the Walrus as we dived on to the submarine. The dives were repeated from many angles and at varying speeds, with the submarine diving and on the surface.

Pete Uttley took over the processed films and selected about twenty different dives. These were assembled in sequence and from the film images he calculated the precise point of release of the depth charge to hit the submarine. He then notched the edge of the films which were projected by a modified 16 mm machine and viewed by up to six trainees, each of whom was provided with a 'bomb release'. Instruments on the instructor's panel enabled him to assess each trainee's accuracy by comparison with the ideal as marked by the notches.

At dinner one evening in House 9 at Malvern, I was told that Mr and Mrs Rowe would like me to have coffee with them. It turned out that A.P. was a Leica fan and wanted to chat to me about photography. I enjoyed that and asked if I could come again to take some portraits of them both – I particularly wanted to try out my new 14.5 cm lens. I was happy with the shots of Molly but not of him, so I persuaded him

Doug Fisher filming in a Lancaster bomber.

to let me take some more in his office a few days later and one of them is reproduced on p. 31.

After the war, Douglas Fisher joined the Wellcome Foundation to make medical teaching films. In 1957 he moved to Granada TV to make TV films on animal behaviour. Then in 1959 he formed Douglas Fisher Productions Ltd to make natural history programmes for television and corporate films for multinational companies. This work took him abroad to many different countries and today (1999) he is still producing video documentaries.

Joshua Sieger, OBE, CBE (d. 1993)

*'Most of us would take sandwiches and eat them either at the
Square and Compass pub at Worth Matravers or sitting
in our cars or out in the bright sunshine on the cliffs.'*

[NOTE: the broad and popular conception of TRE is one of a group of highly qualified scientists and engineers (boffins) continually generating new ideas and producing magic boxes. That was so, but only part of the story: the boffins depended upon the support of drawing offices and workshops as well as a stores/supply system for the provision of essential components and materials.

In the following extracts from the reminiscences of Joshua Sieger we read how these services were set up at Worth Matravers for the two years that TRE was there and how the Research Prototype Unit was established at Bournemouth for the remainder of the war.

It is part of the nature of the job that the person in charge of any manufacturing unit invariably faces problems; but where prototypes of complex products are concerned, the difficulties are greatly magnified and for Sieger the additional pressures of wartime must have been enormous. There can surely be no doubt that much of the success of TRE stemmed from his efforts.

Money

Where costs and wages/salaries are indicated – not only in this section but throughout the book – it is helpful to reflect upon what a £ was worth in the period just before and during the Second World War. A pre-war pound would buy 400 good cigarettes or about 15 gallons of petrol. It would buy 30 lbs of pork sausages; 20 medium-priced seats at a good cinema or 120 Mars Bars. Small cars (Austins, Fords, Morrises) cost little more than £100 brand new and decent 3-bedroomed semi-detached houses were available in many areas for upwards of £400; detached from about £500. Many semi-skilled workers ran families on £2 10s a week; at twice that a young professional engineer, skilled worker or experienced draughtsman would be comfortable; a man on £1,000 a year was well into the upper income class and would have enjoyed a superior lifestyle.

Engineering Development

When ideas are generated for a novel piece of electronic equipment – such as an airborne radar – it is usual for the engineer or scientist to produce a laboratory model for basic feasibility trials. If successful, the next stage is models for more extensive flying tests, to be followed – usually after modifications – by manufacture in quantity. It is unusual for the first model to be made in such a way that it can be copied exactly for manufacture because hand-made laboratory methods are essentially different from those of a production unit. In industry today, this point is recognised and tackled in various ways. In some companies the original designers see the job through to production; in others they hand it over to technically qualified production engineers who, while preserving the concept and performance of the original, have authority to modify the

design to suit the manufacturing facilities at their disposal. In Sieger's account we read of 'productionising' –
an ugly word certainly – but it describes the essential process outlined above.

Joshua Sieger joined AMRE Dundee from Scophony Ltd, pioneers of large-screen electro-mechanical
television systems for public viewing, and after the move to Worth became involved with electro-acoustic
techniques for radar displays and countermeasures. However, his principal contribution to TRE was the
setting up and running of the factory at Bournemouth as the following extracts from his memoirs illustrate.]

The head of the engineering drawing offices at Worth Matravers was W.G.N. Chew, a
Principal Scientific Officer and ex-Post Office engineer. The workshops were run by
J. Morley, a very practical all-round engineer. We were all working a five-and-a-half-
day week and I, with a group of others, went to see A.P. Rowe to suggest that it would
be more efficient if we did a five-day week and cut out Saturday morning. This meeting
coincided with the Germans over-running the Maginot Line and arriving at Cherbourg
on the same day. We decided to do a seven-day week with one day's rest!

Towards the end of summer 1940, Rowe said he would like me to take over the
workshops and drawing offices, the library, the training film area and the engineering
and drawing offices at Christchurch and Hurn Aerodromes. I was given an assistant and
deputy, Robert Munroe, a Scottish engineer with a tremendous imagination. Soon
after, I became Divisional Leader of Engineering.

I appreciated the full responsibility and it gave me an opportunity of talking to all the
scientific staff and knowing in general what was going on throughout the establishment,
which was expanding very rapidly. With the considerable influx of new people and new
ideas, particularly the work on centimetre radar, Leeson House at Langton Matravers
was requisitioned. This, however, was not enough and Durnford House on the main
road to Swanage outside Langton Matravers was also taken over and I had my office
there with a personal secretary, Miss Wareham. My librarian was the vicar of Langton
Matravers, the Revd H.A. Atkinson. Not content with the three areas we also acquired
Forres School just outside Swanage.

Spread as we were over that area, most of us in the first few months would take
sandwiches and eat them either at the Square and Compass (Worth Matravers's famous
pub) or sitting in our cars or out in the bright sunshine on the cliffs. There was
obviously a need for some form of canteen and my wife suggested to Rowe that she
would be quite prepared to organise this with other wives, which she did and it was
very successful.

RPU is Born

We were aware of a number of projects that had been flown experimentally from
Christchurch or Hurn and which could be given to commercial companies for
'productionising' and manufacturing. The delay time between the prototype and a
tested production unit was anything from a year or more. Munroe and I decided that
what we needed was a Research Prototype Unit which would have all the facilities
available in various commercial companies. This would mean that we could produce
prototypes for Project Leaders to see their ideas fulfilled. Munroe and I looked around
for an adequate area to build a unit; we felt this should be about 20,000 sq ft and in the
Bournemouth area, to be convenient for Hurn and Christchurch aerodromes.

We found a 16 acre site in Francis Avenue, Wallisdown, Bournemouth and approached the council to discuss requisition. They told us in no uncertain terms that this was to be a residential site and they didn't want any factories in that area. This was despite the fact that the Whitehead Torpedo Engineering Division was manufacturing torpedoes in the building opposite Francis Avenue. An important individual came down from London and had a word with the council but he got nowhere either. He had his last meeting with them on a Friday afternoon: the following Sunday a German Me110 was returning from a raid with a few bombs left; saw a nice town below him and dropped the lot. One fell on the Metropole Hotel; one on Beale's department store and six were straddled through Westbourne. The war had come to Bournemouth. The council granted permission immediately for us to build on the site we had chosen.

We arranged with that well-known Government organisation called 'Works and Bricks' to draw up plans for a building. It is interesting to note that from an empty field, eighteen months later an audit carried out at RPU in September 1942 showed there were 270 industrial employees, 33 civilian technical corps, 45 weekly paid staff, 20 salaried monthly staff: a total of 369 on the site.

Component procurement was covered by a radio amateur named Parkinson. When we had the prototypes of H$_2$S equipments on a small production run of 150 units for Dr P.I. Dee, the complete shortage of components was more than the manufacturers could make up. I had a word with Rowe and then with O.F. Brown, the DCD (Director of Communications Development), telling him that if I had £5,000 in cash, Parkinson could help, since he knew all the back streets in Soho where components were sold, as well as most of the radio shops in the country, having been a travelling salesman in that field before the war. He would buy all the components we needed wherever he could, even if they were not approved to the right specifications. I got the £5,000 and within ten days Parkinson brought back everything we needed and some change. That money was called the 'bag of gold' – never heard of in the Civil Service or the Treasury before.

With the enthusiastic labour force our production of laboratory equipment was quite rapid and the project people found it extremely valuable for them to have working equipment in a relatively short time ready to be put into an aircraft and test-flown. To reach our production unit we used the Sandbanks ferry crossing the entrance to Poole Harbour, which ran daily. We would sign a paper on boarding and cross either to Hurn, Christchurch or RPU and we never knew who paid the bill but none of us ever paid anything.

One day an Me109 came over, fired a few shots at the huts at Worth and a few more at me. I ran across a field full of rabbit holes – how many times I fell I do not know – but he zoomed over and with a lot of spluttering his engine failed and he landed a few fields away. He had missed me, thank heaven, but a belt drive to one of the lathes in the workshop was cut completely in half by a stray bullet. Of course we all rushed over to have a look at the plane, but the RAF and the Police were there almost immediately and we couldn't help ourselves to any spare parts.

One Saturday morning in 1942, Rowe called us together and said that the invasion of France had happened so quickly that Swanage was now an undesirable place for a research organisation, with the Germans just 63 miles away across the Channel. We would have to find accommodation more in the centre of the country and move

Joshua Sieger's Lagonda was well known at TRE and Donald Preist's also. Models varied, but all were superbly made and of distinctive appearance. This 1932 '16/80' (6-cylinder, 1991 cc) Crossley-engined version, in use in 1998 and owned by Dr C.S. Hobbins of Anglesey, is representative of the marque.

everything out before the next full moon. (The moon played an important part in life during those days when the full moon made bombing easier.)

To Malvern

Rowe asked me to go with him and Dr Dee to find a suitable building which we could requisition for the whole establishment. We set off in my Lagonda and went first to Marlborough College, one of the two places recommended by headquarters. It wasn't big enough to accommodate some 1,000 people, so we went on to Great Malvern and there saw the college, set in beautiful grounds and absolutely ideal for our needs.

I was instructed to co-operate with Sir Alan Gordon-Smith, Chairman of S. Smith & Sons (later Smith's Industries) to organise the move from Swanage to Malvern immediately. Sir Alan provided well over a hundred Pickford's pantechnicons; I arranged with all the laboratories and their Project Leaders to load everything into one pantechnicon per laboratory – or two if necessary – and drive straight to Malvern. The entire move was organised and completed with a few days to spare before the full moon. Munroe was down at RPU and I was at Malvern but thereafter I would spend some days at RPU and some at Malvern until I became Superintendent full-time at RPU for the rest of my time with TRE.

[Joshua Sieger had his labour problems like any other factory manager. In wartime the Ministry of Labour directed workers to factories across the country as needed, and Sieger found himself in a hornet's nest when men drafted in from London firms were paid up to 99s per week against 89s for local staff. Only his quick and positive response in introducing an equalising merit pay scheme averted either a strike or the case escalating to become a national issue with its inevitable time-wasting deliberations with unions, ministries and the Employers' Federation].

From 1944–6 Joshua Sieger was Production and Works Director at Hamworthy Engineering Co., Poole. He moved to the USA to become Vice-President and Director of Engineering & Research at Freed Radio Corp., New York. From 1951–3 he was President and Chairman of J.H. Bunnell in New York, then returned to Poole as Consulting Engineer with his own R. & D. labs. He became Chairman and Managing Director of J. & S. Sieger Ltd, and was the inventor of gas analysis and detection systems. From 1980–92 he acted as a consultant advising start-up companies.

Stanley Ratcliffe, B.Sc., FRAeS, FRIN

*'I was given a circuit diagram
and told to "build that"!'*

In January 1940 I applied for a post as laboratory assistant at an Air Ministry Research Establishment in Dundee. After an interview at Air Ministry, Kingsway, conducted by A.B. Jones, head of Administration, and Joe Airey of the same establishment ('Can you use a soldering iron? Have you built a radio set? Could you, if you could afford the components, build a television receiver?'), I eventually found myself appointed to work at Worth Matravers at £2 per week. I rode my 98cc motor bike to Worth, arriving at about 4 p.m. on the day before work was to start.

Next morning, after they had sworn me to secrecy, it was revealed to me that it had proved possible to detect aircraft by means of radio waves. As one who had worked on television at EMI Hayes, this was no surprise to me.[1] After deciding that to send anyone called Ratcliffe to work for J.A. of that ilk was only to court confusion, they directed me to work for C.P. Fogg on the receiver side, nearest to Renscombe Farm. I was handed over to Harry Grayson who proved a good man from whom to learn electronics, but he clearly didn't intend to waste time on me until I'd demonstrated some competence. I was given a circuit diagram and told to 'build that'. With some interruptions to help unpack boxes from Dundee, I did so. I was being asked to build a fixed tuned radio receiver with no provision for input of any kind; together with other

---

[1] Many who worked on early experimental TV systems, using wavelengths of less than 10 m, reported visual interference from passing aircraft. Though frequently observed, it was regarded merely as a nuisance rather than as a clue to understanding a defence system.

unfamiliar features. 'What frequency do you want to receive?' I asked. 'Anything you like!' It transpired that I was measuring receiver noise, a task that was to occupy me for nearly half the war.

The station at that time was working a slightly stretched version of peacetime Civil Service hours: five-and-a-half days a week, Saturday morning counting as a whole day. The pace of work rapidly quickened as we realised the problems that lay ahead. Germany could, and soon did, install jammers along the French coast to damage the performance of our radars. They also installed novel radio devices for guiding their bombers in night raids on Britain. Remedial steps were initiated, with mixed success.

A significant part of the establishment was engaged not in defending Britain, but in preparing to win the war by bombing Germany, with the aid of night navigation systems of our own. The working week soon lengthened to six days, staff being allowed to choose – work permitting – their own day off; but it was not unknown for rest days, annual leave and even sleep at night to be sacrificed to complete some vital task.

My most important task in 1940 was, it emerged, to scrounge or otherwise acquire such components as I or my colleagues needed for our work; all of which were in very short supply. I came to have a great confidence in C.P. Fogg as a man to work for. I was once sent out to find twenty-four 6BA nuts – 'I don't care how you do it but get them!' Stores, Mr S. Soppit in charge (sometimes unfairly, perhaps, known as Sam Stoppit), hadn't got any, and if they had they'd all go to Main Workshops (J. Morley in charge, A. Bullard foreman). The latter spent some time trying to get rid of me, then consulted the boss, returning with the message 'he says you and Fogg can go to hell!'.

Feeling rather a failure, I returned to Mr Fogg (not remarkable for his good temper) and delivered this message verbatim. I was bundled out of the office by his second-in-command, W.S. Robertson, as Mr Fogg was asking to speak to the Superintendent of the station, A.P. Rowe. A little while later, still breathing heavily, Fogg informed me that if I went back to workshops, they would give me the nuts. Never by word or deed was it suggested that I had overstepped my brief, although I was never again sent out with such an instruction.

One of the more persuasive scientists was Dr Kinsey. There was an autogyro which he often used for measuring the performance of modified radar aerials. One day he despatched it after instructing the pilot to circle the church spire in nearby Kingston at a height of a few hundred feet. The church was at the desired distance; it gave the pilot a convenient landmark and was at a known position.

In the words of an official letter that set out the circumstances of an incident that resulted from this instruction: 'It had apparently escaped the attention of the officer in charge of the experiment that, the day being Sunday, a church service would be in progress.' Even from my slight knowledge of Dr Kinsey it seemed unlikely that he would willingly abandon his experiment for the Day of Judgement, let alone the sabbath. The official account went on to report that the vicar directed his congregation to lay out various items of laundry outside the church, spelling out a request to the pilot to 'go, in the name of God!', whereupon the pilot left to consult Dr Kinsey. He returned at speed to resume his circular flight round the church. The report then referred to somebody with a shotgun opening fire on the autogyro, but the pilot – the 'intrepid pilot' the report called him – apparently preferred to face shotgun fire rather than Dr Kinsey in his wrath. The experiment was concluded without bloodshed.

Our numbers grew rapidly, with the result that many of us were unknown to others including, as it turned out, Mr Rowe. One evening he, who strongly approved of staff working very long hours, walked into a hut at about 9.30 p.m. to find a man still at work. 'How's it going?' he asked, with the reply, 'Well, it'd go better if people didn't come in asking silly questions.'

I have memories of going to the cinema in Station Road and afterwards – on the few occasions when I felt affluent – getting egg and chips at Forte's Café across the road. Those of my colleagues who lived nearer to Worth Matravers sometimes chose to spend evenings in the Square and Compass inn (known to the scientific staff as the 'Sine and Cosine').

The TRE Home Guard were rather flattered by an invitation to join in an exercise with a unit of Commandos – the South Wales Borderers. They were to 'attack' TRE Worth. We were a little surprised on our first encounter with a group of men who systematically broke the agreement that the main gate (used by vehicles bringing the RAF radar team on and off watch) was out of bounds as were the RAF radar personnel and the huts in which they were working. In the event, most of the raiding party arrived in a highjacked RAF vehicle which drove in through the gate past a sentry who did not obey his orders to shoot. The rest of the raiders came over the officially unclimbable fence on ladders which they had 'liberated' in Worth village. They had little trouble in seizing the objective marked out for them with a red hurricane lamp. This proved to be the firewatcher's hut.

The Home Guard had been trained to point rifles at people and say 'Bang, you're dead'. Our Commando friends, it turned out, had a habit of hitting people on the head with pickaxe handles: 'Thud, you're unconscious!'. The exercise did, however, briefly raise the Home Guard's status in Swanage when we were seen to have emerged relatively unscathed, whereas many of our Commando friends were walking around heavily bandaged with arms in slings etc. This was not in fact a tribute to our prowess at all, but to an Army lorry overturning on the way back to the billets.

A certain light dawned later when it was discovered that the Commandos had been training for a raid on a German radar station at Bruneval. We had the comfort of learning that the Wehrmacht did not seem to have put up a much better performance than we had, although to be fair, the Germans were not formally notified of the forthcoming exercise. A member of TRE, Mr D.H. Preist, went on one of the ships taking part in the raid, but was judged to be too well informed to risk capture by going in with the attack.

Reprisals for the Bruneval raid were expected and we had a visit from some infantrymen, who knocked holes in the walls of TRE laboratories for the installation of machine-guns. But shortly after, we were informed of secret plans to move TRE in its entirety to Malvern. Actually, many of us learned this from our Swanage landladies. The officers inspecting possible sites in Malvern and Marlborough were very discreet, but the driver of their car must have said something to his wife who mentioned it in the grocer's shop etc.

Stanley Ratcliffe stayed on at Malvern after the war working on military radar. Since 1964 he has studied Air Traffic Control problems and still works as a consultant to the UK Civil Aviation Authority, to NATO, to the European Space Agency, to the EC and others. He retired from the Civil Service in 1981 as a Senior Principal Scientific Officer. In 1977 he was awarded the Gold Medal of the Royal Institute of Navigation.

Lady Adams

*'We soon found out that we had
come to a unique place.'*

My arrival at Swanage in 1941 along with nineteen other women, all dressed in Air
Force blue and sporting a single narrow white band on our cuffs showing the rank of
Assistant Section Officer was the final stage in a six-month training course on a highly
secret weapon. We had been chosen by Watson-Watt himself from about 200 science
graduates to train as Technical Officers; sent first on an officers' training course to
Loughborough; then on an RDF Operators' course to Cranwell, and then to an
operational CH station.

I had been with a colleague to Ventnor which had recently been bombed, had
suffered damage and casualties but was proud of the fact that radar coverage was soon
restored. Strangely enough, although all the stations on the coast to the east had been
bombed, Worth Matravers, which seemed to be next on the list, had escaped.

We had learned about the Chain of home stations all round the south-east and
southern coasts which had been keeping watch twenty-four hours a day tracking
enemy aircraft. Each operator was directly connected by a telephone headset to the
Filter Room at Stanmore, to which they reported all aircraft within coverage. The
Filter Room received information from several CH stations and evaluated it,
identified it as Hostile or Friendly, and then passed it directly to the Ops Room
where it was plotted on a large map and could be seen by the Chiefs of Staff
conducting operations.

We learned of some of the difficulties that had been experienced by the severe radio
jamming put out by the Germans during the air raids on London and other towns and
cities, and of some of the mistakes in identification of aircraft. We were told that all
these were being counteracted by the boffins – mysterious people, usually civilians, who
appeared from time to time with advice and sometimes extra equipment to help keep
the station on the air. The operators told us of times when aircraft had been plotted
miles off course over the sea because of difficulties of navigating at night. This problem
was overcome later by navaids invented by the research staff at TRE which enabled the
Pathfinder squadrons to direct our bomber force.

Posted to TRE Worth Matravers for a three-month course on electronics, we were at
last to meet some of these boffins who were at the centre of the research on what is
now universally known as radar. Our Commanding Officer was Flt Lt Ratcliffe and we
were taken to our billets at the Grand Hotel in Swanage, and were to have very special
treatment. Soon after we were taken to Forres School, a preparatory school that had
been evacuated and was now a very different kind of school specialising in courses
mostly for operational radar personnel.

We soon found out that we had come to a unique place. Scores of scientists all
working on radar research had been stationed in the town and occupied labs in barracks
up at Worth Matravers or in empty school buildings, wherever they could be found.
Many were billeted with local residents, with whom they soon fraternised. Everything
was hush-hush and nobody would tell you what they were doing.

Lady Adams with her husband, John Adams.

We were kept very busy with lectures on electronics, circuitry, detectors and amplifiers, transmitters and receivers, transmission line theory and antennas. It was quite a difficult course for the non-physicists. The powers that be had been able to find only perhaps half a dozen women with physics degrees but the chemists and botanists worked hard at the exacting course, at the end of which there was to be an exam, after which we would be posted to operational duties.

Being at the Grand Hotel we used to have informal dancing on Saturday nights (called 'hops') and here we often met the young men from TRE. They were very interesting people with a distinctive style of dress: tweed jackets with leather patches on the elbows and brogues on their feet. A few had old cars with long, low bonnets in which we were sometimes driven around when they had the petrol.

It was at one of these hops that I first met John Adams, my future husband. He helped me a little to master transmission theory and I must have done rather well in the exams as I was then posted back to Worth Matravers to lecture at Forres School. Most of the other members of the course went to Wing Headquarters to keep an eye on the operations of a group of CH stations. We were all promoted to the rank of Flight Officer.

I was to help on a course for radar supervisors run by two civilians, John Whitehouse and Johnny Clegg. These were courses for chosen RAF and WAAF radar personnel:

often non-commissioned officers who had been in charge of the operational watches. I soon found out the calibre of these people coming from all walks of civilian life: secretaries, hairdressers, solicitors, clergymen – all working together and keen on their jobs. They spent their time at the school working very hard indeed at aerial theory, counteracting jamming, identification of aircraft, estimation of numbers and enough electronics theory to know when the transmitter or receiver needed attention. Some evenings we had to lock them out of the classrooms to make them take a break from work. They all realised the importance of the work – giving advance warning of air raids to both civilians and RAF flying personnel, and they worked with a remarkable will to succeed. They were usually rewarded for their labour, for if they passed the course after a dreaded interview with Sqn Ldr Scarfe (who decided whether or not they had made the grade) they were commissioned before being sent back to be supervisors at the CH and CHL stations now covering the coast from the Firth of Tay to Land's End.

Forres School continued to grow as more and more courses became necessary. J. Ratcliffe left and Len Huxley became the new Director. Soon there were courses for new entrants to TRE; mechanics' courses; courses for supervisors on CHL stations and for Ground Controlled Interception stations and I took over the supervisors' course.

It is difficult to stress too highly the immense importance of TRE and its immeasurable contribution to the war effort. It was therefore not surprising that our intelligence services received evidence that a raid on TRE and Worth Matravers was imminent. We had already experienced many air-raid warnings. The Army sent in troops to protect the area and then TRE was evacuated to Malvern School. A few days after they left, Swanage was badly bombed. The first billet I had lived in, near the station, received a direct hit.

After the war Lady Adams maintained her interest in science through her husband's appointment as Director General of CERN (Conseil Européen Recherches Nucléaires), Geneva and her work teaching physics and mathematics at an international school.

Geoffrey N. Harding, B.Sc. (Hons) Physics, AMIEE

'Whenever I smell madonna lilies today
I remember that first night at Worth.'

I arrived in Swanage in July 1940 straight after getting my BSc in Birmingham. I had been offered a job as Assistant Grade III with a salary of £250 per annum. I knew a little of RDF, having been on a three-week vacation course at Stoke Holy Cross CH station the previous Easter. I got off the train at Swanage with my bike and found a good bed and breakfast for 5s 6d, then next morning I cycled (and pushed) up the hill to Worth Matravers; I booked in for the night at the Square and Compass pub and reported for duty.

I was interviewed by W.B. Lewis and sent off to the library to read: I suppose there had been an influx of new recruits and nobody knew quite what to do with us. The Battle of Britain was on and the sky full of vapour trails curling and twisting in fantastic patterns. The weather was glorious and outside my bedroom in the summerhouse at the pub was a bed of madonna lilies in full flower. The scent was wonderful and whenever I smell madonna lilies today, I remember that first night at Worth.

Dr W.B. Lewis,
Deputy to A.P. Rowe.

I liked the look of AMRE and Worth and I was very happy to be doing something useful for the war at last. I rented a top floor flat in Swanage at 27s 6d a week and laid in some food. Alas for my plans! The next day I was sent for by Willy Cochrane and packed off to the ACH station at Thrumster[1] (just south of Wick in Caithness) to assist F.E. Jones as a Scientific Observer.[2] So ended my first stay at Worth.

When I returned to Swanage I was under a bit of a cloud, having taken part in a rather noisy party in the Receiver Block at Branscombe. There was no aerial activity at the time but the CO was rather conscientious and wrote to Rowe asking for my recall. I was duly ticked off and told I could no longer be a scientific observer. I was delighted – it was a soul-destroying job.

My next assignment was in Kingston Woods, calibrating the aerials of mobile radar stations to be sent out to the Middle East. The aerials were mounted on 105 ft towers

A 105 ft telescopic portable mast used for mobile CH stations (AMES Type 9) and for numerous other applications including Gee-H mobiles. RAF personnel heading for Europe were trained in erecting these at Renscombe Farm, Worth Matravers, after TRE had moved to Malvern.

---

[1]   90 ft wooden towers; MB1 transmitter. I don't think we saw a single hostile aircraft in the month that I was there.
[2]   Scientific Observers were supposed to find out how well the CH and other stations were actually doing, compared with their theoretical potential, and report back to AMRE.

A Crossley lorry used as a mobile receiver vehicle. Air-conditioning equipment can be seen over the driver's cabin.

designed by Freddie Lutkin. Every time one blew down he said they hadn't been guyed correctly – the guy ropes had to be slackened off if it was going to rain to allow for shrinkage. We used a variety of methods for calibrating; the one I remember most vividly involved a 'squegging' transmitter suspended from a large kite. This was during the winter of 1940–1 and there was plenty of wind, occasionally too much for the kite. We also used balloons filled with hydrogen, but this was abandoned later when a balloon being used to calibrate a receiving aerial in East Anglia broke loose and carried our 'squegger' over in the direction of Germany, with risk of giving away our frequency. My main memory of Kingston Woods is of mud, knee deep at times. We were in Crossley lorries, one of which was permanently listing at about 10 degrees.

At this time I lived in the Anchor Inn in Swanage where the landlady, Mrs Humby, was kindness itself. I also bought a second-hand Austin 12/6 for £15 which served me well on my many trips seeing to aerials. For a short time I joined a madrigal group in Swanage run by Bill Penley.

From 1946–8 Geoffrey Harding worked at the Atomic Energy Research Station at Chalk River, Canada. He was then with UKAEA until 1969 at Harwell and Culham where he was involved with thermonuclear research. He is currently self-employed as a silversmith and goldsmith.

Cyril Banthorpe (dec.)

'I remember a man called Bainbridge-Bell –
a very ingenious man.'

One of the most exciting things for me was meeting these great men who really didn't bother at all about small problems. They just disregarded them as they would be solved by people much lower down the pyramid. And it worked. I remember one particular time when I was told to go to Whitehall and report to Watson-Watt. I set off in the very early hours of the morning from Swanage, motored up to London, went to Whitehall and arrived at his office. He wanted me to go up to Felixstowe and set up some aerials on a barrage balloon cable and listen to enemy signals, the signals which were used by enemy aircraft for bombing targets in Britain. I was interested of course and very proud to be selected to do this job. As I was leaving the office, Watson-Watt said: 'By the way, on the way down there, get a barrage balloon and take one with you.' I was a very young man of course, and a bit staggered by this, so I said: 'Well, where do I get this balloon from?' 'Oh, get one on the way!' he said, and dismissed me.

So I set off for Felixstowe and somewhere between Ilford and Romford I saw a big balloon station. It was late in the evening and I drove up to the gate and the guard stopped me and asked me what I wanted. 'I want a balloon!' I said. 'Well you'd better come in and see the officer in charge.' I went in, and the officer said, 'What's this you want?' 'I want a balloon,' I said. 'What sort of balloon?' 'A barrage balloon. With a crew. And I want to take it to Felixstowe now!' 'Well that's all right,' he said, and got a crew together and off I set to Felixstowe with my balloon and crew. And I don't really remember being particularly staggered by this.

Anyway, when we got to Felixstowe I found to my surprise that it was a balloon centre. Hundreds of balloons they had there, together with their winches to raise them up and down. In fact they had to dig one of these out of the sand with a tank to put mine in its place! The crew were marvellous. A corporal arranged for some stakes to be put up on the beach with some rope around them to keep my balloon roped off and separate from the common people with their balloons. I made some aerials which went up and down with the balloon. Most balloons were a lovely silvery colour, but mine was very dirty. The corporal frightened the life out of me by telling me that a balloon cost £400 and if it was destroyed or damaged, we'd probably have to pay for it.

Well, the aerials were fitted and when the balloon went up, my aerials went up too and I was able to listen to the enemy signals and do what was necessary. Every now and again there was a panic, and I was told that whatever the other balloons did I had to do as well, so when the others suddenly went up, mine had to go up too and that meant some very high-speed action. If my aerials weren't quite on properly, we had to quickly fix them on or else remove them. Similarly, if there was very bad weather coming up, the balloons would suddenly be called down, and to prevent the aerials getting mangled up in the winch, some very messy, high-speed work had to be done to get the aerials off the steel cables.

Quite a lot of the balloons were destroyed by lightning and all sorts of other things, but my dirty old balloon stayed alive. Years after the war I was talking to someone about how long it takes to get things going in the scientific world and he said, 'Yes, that's quite true. I knew a thing for stopping balloons getting struck by lightning.' He had worked in a balloon squad during the war and had had this device fitted to his balloon. He said that in all the storms and all the things that happened this balloon was never damaged when sometimes nearly all the rest of the balloons were wiped out. And he said that although it was nearly one hundred per cent successful, it was never really put to use properly.

Another time I was working on the aerials at the radar station near Felixstowe.[1] I was absolutely petrified climbing the 360 ft towers there. The transmitter that these aerials were connected to was an extremely high-powered one indeed. It was the first of the megawatt transmitters and it practically wiped out radio listening in Felixstowe. So the Post Office were called in by people who were getting severe interference. A young Post Office engineer came round in his little van and said he wanted to look at this machinery that was causing interference. They got hold of me and told me to go and talk to him. I went down to the gate, which was all locked up, and he said: 'I want to come in and see about this interference that's upsetting all the radios.' 'I'm afraid you can't come in,' I said, 'it's all secret.' 'You've got to let me in,' he said, but I said I was sorry, I couldn't do that. Well, he was vexed by this and he pushed into my hand a little suppressor – a little tiny thing. 'Well, all right,' he said, 'you find the bad contact that's causing all this trouble and fit this suppressor will you?' and he got in the van and drove away. Little did he know that the interference was caused by an enormous great radar transmitter.

Another odd thing happened when I was in Scotland, working on a big transmitter and receiver at a station looking out to sea on the east coast. Every Monday, Wednesday and Friday a German seaplane used to come in and drop mines in the water. On Tuesdays, Thursdays and Saturdays the minesweepers used to go out and sweep them up. I'm not quite sure what happened on Sundays. We were very glad of this German aircraft because we used to plot its progress and use it to check our radar. We knew where it was going and someone lower down the pyramid decided to tip off the minesweeping people and tell them where the mines were being seeded, without actually letting them know how we knew. So on the Tuesdays, Thursdays and Saturdays the minesweepers used to go out and they knew exactly where to look for them.

One day somebody with rather lateral thinking said, 'Supposing we don't go out one day and just see what happens.' So on the Wednesday the German seaplane came in, landed in the minefield and was blown to bits. The crew were picked up and they were livid! They didn't think this was at all the right way to run a war. They said, 'But you always come and sweep them on Tuesdays, Thursdays and Saturdays!'

I had to go to Portsmouth and install on a small ship some radar equipment that was designed for an aircraft. I was a civilian driving an RAF lorry. I found the ship, asked to see the skipper and told him I'd come to install this radar and he said yes, he was

[1] Bawdsey.

expecting me. I completed the installation and we went out into the Channel. The radar was up on the bridge with a little canvas screen we'd put up to protect it and me from the sea and the rain. We threw some little metal buoys out and cruised around picking them up with the radar. After a while, I looked out from under the canvas sheet and found that we were steering straight towards a coast. I said to the skipper, 'Where's that then, skipper?' He said: 'That's Cherbourg.' I said, 'But isn't Cherbourg held by the enemy?' 'Oh yes,' he said, 'and we're well into an enemy minefield, but you said "steer such-and-such a course" and that's what we're doing!' So I said, 'Well, could we turn round perhaps, and go back the other way?' and he said 'Right,' and we turned round and headed in the other direction, somehow escaping through the minefield. I said to the skipper later, 'It was only a coincidence that I happened to look out from under the canvas at that time. What would have happened if I hadn't?' And he said, 'We'd have sailed into the harbour.' I said, 'But wouldn't they have fired on us?' and he said, 'Oh, no doubt they would, but we would have fired back. We were all ready to.' And that was one of my experiences with the Royal Navy.

One of my pleasures in working with those great men was to see how ingenious they were in overcoming obstacles – problems that most of them had never had to cope with before, coming as they did from an academic world. They had a genius for solving any problem. I remember one instance in particular, with Bainbridge-Bell (he was one of the original radar boffins with Watson-Watt), a very ingenious man. One bit of equipment had to have a very small bulb shining on a screen giving a nice sharp point of light.[2] Bainbridge-Bell fixed up a light with a child's Mickey Mouse slide torch. It so happened that that bulb had a lens built in – it was made in Germany – and he wanted to use this particular bulb. Well, everybody said 'you can't use that because you won't be able to get these bulbs from Germany!' So Bainbridge-Bell just went out to all the toyshops he could find and bought up all the Mickey Mouse slide torches. He bought dozens of them; took the bulbs out and threw the torches away. He solved the problem as simply as that. In due course, when these parts were made, he was asked what this bulb was called and he said it was called 'Projector Bulb MM' and it went down in the schedules and the parts list as MM and probably only a handful of people ever knew what that stood for!

Philip Woodward, DSC

'The cream of Britain's scientific talent had been thrown together at TRE under single-minded leadership and most were under thirty years of age.'

War service recruitment boards for undergraduates at Oxford were chaired by A.D. Lindsay, Master of Balliol. This classical scholar told me curtly that mathematics was of no practical value and put me down for the Royal Corps of Signals. Fortunately

---

[2]   The 'optical converter' at CH stations that enabled national grid references to be obtained from local ranges and bearings. Bainbridge-Bell worked extensively on this, but it was soon superseded by the Electrical Calculator.

his decision was overruled by Frederick Brundrett who placed me at TRE. In his kindly way Mr Brundrett said that a salary of £214 was the best he could do. From my point of view it was the entrée into the world of science that I craved.

On arrival in Swanage in February 1941, my first problem was to find the whereabouts of the secret laboratory and I decided the safest plan might be to enquire at the town hall. The town clerk seemed a little taken aback, asked if I had a degree, and told me that degrees were 'two a penny up the road there'. Within a day or two I was to discover that there were many more Doctors of Philosophy at TRE than there had been at my college and a first degree was nothing at all.

For one night I stayed at the Ship in Swanage where I met a large and jovial gentleman in the bar wearing carpet slippers and a strange device in the lapel of his jacket – like an inverted horse-shoe of plain brass. He was Mr Bruce of TRE but it wasn't the thing to mention TRE in public. My real acquaintance with him came much later, when he explained how to strike a wooden rod in order to excite its fundamental frequency of vibration. Questions such as this were, of course, food and drink to young scientists at TRE.

Soon I was issued with an Air Ministry pass and a lapel badge of my own with an emblem and the motto 'Per Ardua ad Astra'. However, there were strict instructions to wear this badge back to front, so that its face was kept hidden, as if to conceal its wearer's true occupation. On entry to TRE each morning, members of staff would shiftily invert their lapels towards the warden at the gate. This strange practice was soon to be discontinued; badges were withdrawn and passes used in the usual manner.

TRE was a revelation. Here was real research with a real purpose. The establishment was imbued with a single-mindedness that came straight from the top man – A.P. (Jimmy) Rowe. At that time, February 1941, he would gather the whole of TRE together on Friday afternoons for a meeting at which we were ALL privy to fundamental matters of radar policy. This arrangement had the advantage and purpose of making every member feel privileged and responsible. I particularly recall the quiet learning of Dr W.B. Lewis and the more aggressive interventions of Dr B.V. Bowden (later Lord Bowden). Unfortunately, TRE was soon to grow too big for the practice to continue; more exclusive meetings were held and from that time on, all important decisions were made behind closed doors at one grade higher than my own.

I need not have worried about my capacity to do the work required of me. I was allocated a 'Brunsviga' (a German-built manual calculating machine) and what seemed an immense mathematical formula to compute. The results were to be plotted and presented to Dr Henry Booker who seemed able to detect errors with the same facility that a music teacher has for detecting a wrong note without looking at the music. I believe that a persevering child of twelve could have done my job, but this is where single-mindedness came in. There was a war on. Menial scientific tasks had to be done and graduates could do them without fuss and without having to ask too many questions. The calculation, which nowadays would take a fraction of a second, took exactly two weeks to complete and gave the expected pattern of radio field strength from a coastal radar station.

Difficulties arose from interference between direct rays and rays reflected from the land or sea. The principal reflection at low angles of elevation was that from the sea; but for targets at closer ranges or flying at a great height, the reflection from the land in front of the aerial mast could predominate. The hardest part of the calculation was where the one merged into the other, as this involved the theory of diffraction at a real or imagined cliff edge. When the calculation was complete there was another and another, until the winter months of 1941 gave way to spring. Calculations for aerials at different places on one mast helped in the problem of finding the heights of approaching enemy aircraft whose ranges were known from the velocity of radio waves.

The attention of the mathematicians then switched to the theory of aerials themselves, and especially to the design of multi-element Yagi aerials nowadays common for TV. The theory called for the solution of sets of simultaneous equations too numerous for manual methods. Fortunately there was an electrical machine at the Mathematical Laboratory, Cambridge, for just such problems and I was sent off for two weeks to use it. There I met its inventor, Professor Mallock, who came in, having retired, to see what I was doing. The idea of the machine was good, but the technology was less satisfactory. Given a set of equations known in mathematics as 'ill-conditioned', the machine would reveal all its worst idiosyncrasies. I obtained enough answers to be useful and also had a wonderful time at the other half of Oxbridge.

By 1941 when most young able-bodied men and women had been called up, those in civilian clothes were somewhat conspicuous doing their shopping in the streets of Swanage on Saturdays. Buses to Bournemouth enabled us to see and hear good entertainment at the Pavilion, including classical ballet, Ivor Novello in a musical and pianist Clifford Curzon playing with the Wessex Symphony Orchestra conducted by Reginald Goodall. The composer Percy Whitlock was Borough Organist at the Pavilion and in 1941 he applied for a job at TRE. As I was known to be a keen organist I was consulted as to Mr Whitlock's suitability for a post. I heard no more of him until his untimely death in 1946 at the age of forty-two.

Many members of TRE already had cars and those belonging to the younger set could be entertaining. John Pinkerton, one of my flatmates, had a Lancia tourer of inordinate length. He was later to design and build England's first business computer for J. Lyons. I sat in the back of the Lancia on the only trip we could afford on the petrol ration; we made it as far as Kingston. Pinkerton was a gramophone enthusiast and he started a gramophone society, which met one evening a week at the Grand Hotel. His home-built equipment for playing 78s incorporated 'expansion', which made loud passages of music louder and soft passages softer. I never could believe that this was possible without introducing horrendous non-linear distortion, but the music seemed all right. Evenings of a lighter nature were spent at the Grosvenor Hotel's weekly dance. There we would drink Pimms No. 1 or 2 while smoking Players No. 5.

Some years later I was asked by Dr Reginald Smith-Rose of the National Physical Laboratory how TRE had achieved successes unmatched by anything at the NPL. The answer was clear enough: the cream of Britain's scientific talent had been thrown together at TRE under single-minded leadership, and most were under thirty years of age. Nothing was impossible to people like Martin Ryle (eventually to become Astronomer Royal), whose name I recall because of our contact on a problem which I made the mistake of declaring insoluble. The heyday of this great establishment was its

Martin Ryle (future Astronomer Royal) queueing for his lunch at the Malvern canteen.

time at Swanage, where the pattern of work in electronics was set to bear fruit for many years to come. I was indeed fortunate to have been able to learn my trade from so many famous people in the making.

After the war, Dr Woodward remained at the Royal Radar Establishment (TRE's later name) at Malvern, where he led the mathematical research team. He was also Visiting Lecturer at Harvard University, Honorary Professor at Birmingham and Visiting Professor at Reading. After retirement, he became a Fellow and Silver Medallist of the British Horological Institute.

5

Epilogue: The Radar Memorial at Goodrich

Dr E.H. Putley

The memorial window in the chapel of Goodrich Castle.

On 7 June 1992, a memorial window in the chapel of Goodrich Castle near Ross-on-Wye was dedicated to those airmen and scientists who lost their lives in the development of radar, Britain's secret weapon in the Second World War. Radar was a major scientific achievement which, through the impetus it gave to the development of electronics, has had a profound influence on the shape of the world today – as Sir Stafford Cripps foretold when he revealed the wartime radar story on 14 August 1945:

> It has played a greater part in the war than the atom bomb and holds far more immediate potentialities of service to the human race than the splitting of the atom.

The day of the window dedication ceremony marked the fiftieth anniversary of the worst single disaster: the loss on 7 June 1942, near Goodrich, of a Halifax fitted with TRE's prototype H_2S equipment. H_2S was the first self-contained navigational and bombing aid – developed at Malvern with the greatest urgency under the explicit direction of Churchill and his personal scientific adviser Lord Cherwell. It was a precise navaid, enabling Bomber Command to penetrate to the most distant targets in Germany without the range limitations imposed by earlier radar aids, which depended on ground stations in Britain.

The principal speakers at the dedication ceremony were Sir Bernard Lovell FRS, who had been in charge of the H_2S project in 1942, and Gp Capt Frank Griffiths (RAF retired) who had been a senior officer in the RAF Flying Unit responsible for flight trials of the radar equipments. The Air Force Board was represented by AVM R.J. Honey. The

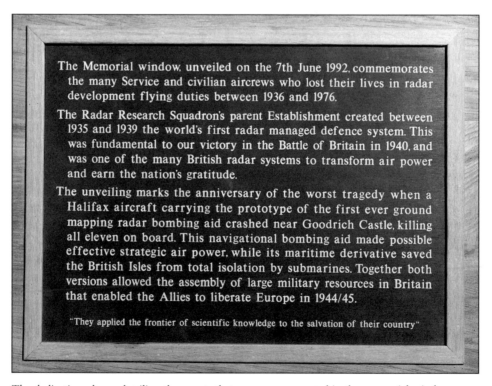

The Memorial window, unveiled on the 7th June 1992, commemorates the many Service and civilian aircrews who lost their lives in radar development flying duties between 1936 and 1976.

The Radar Research Squadron's parent Establishment created between 1935 and 1939 the world's first radar managed defence system. This was fundamental to our victory in the Battle of Britain in 1940, and was one of the many British radar systems to transform air power and earn the nation's gratitude.

The unveiling marks the anniversary of the worst tragedy when a Halifax aircraft carrying the prototype of the first ever ground mapping radar bombing aid crashed near Goodrich Castle, killing all eleven on board. This navigational bombing aid made possible effective strategic air power, while its maritime derivative saved the British Isles from total isolation by submarines. Together both versions allowed the assembly of large military resources in Britain that enabled the Allies to liberate Europe in 1944/45.

"They applied the frontier of scientific knowledge to the salvation of their country"

The dedication plaque detailing the events that are commemorated in the memorial window.

RAF provided a chaplain, a trumpeter, an ATC guard of honour and a fly-past by a Nimrod.

A bronze plaque explaining the significance of the window has been installed beneath it by English Heritage, responsible for Goodrich Castle, who had accepted the memorial window for safe keeping on behalf of the nation. A register containing the names of the seventy-one known casualties in TRE was accepted for safe keeping at Hendon by Dr M.A. Fopp, Director of the RAF Museum.

The design of the window incorporates a number of significant motifs. The flower symbols represented the countries of the United Kingdom; the badges of the RAF units involved in radar research flying, and the coat of arms of the Royal Signals and Radar Establishment (RSRE – the postwar successor to TRE) are self-explanatory. But the three motifs representing radar research require a brief explanation.

These motifs represent the magnetron; the Home Chain (of radar stations begun in 1935 that provided vital defence during the Battle of Britain and for the remainder of the war); and finally the H_2S system, which was the peak of wartime airborne radar development and played a major role in Bomber Command's offensive and – in its ASV (Air to Surface Vessel) mode – the Battle of the Atlantic.

The memorial window was erected through a fund set up by a group of friends who invited donations from ex-colleagues of the Civil Service, the RAF, and industrial companies associated with wartime radar development.

Goodrich Castle is some 3 miles SSW of Ross-on-Wye, Herefordshire.

'The British scientists who did so much to win
the Second World War have recorded almost
nothing of their efforts and indeed seem
unwilling to use either radio or TV to tell of
how much was achieved.'

Sir Samuel Curran in the Glasgow Herald, *10 August 1995*

By the end of the Second World War there were hundreds of scientists working at
TRE yet only a few of them wrote comprehensive accounts of their wartime
achievements. Most were probably too busy pursuing careers or too reticent. We
hope this book will fill part of the huge gap left after fifty years and that it would
have pleased Sir Samuel.

C.L., A.S.

Appendix

The foregoing reminiscences are limited in number by the availability of contributors and by the constraints of a single volume. Regrettably, of the many more who worked with TRE and whose contribution to the war effort was great, little or no mention is made. Some giants of science appear only fleetingly within the pages while others are mentioned more or less incidentally; and some who did so much do not appear at all.

We are sorry for these omissions. Yet we hope that from what we have been able to include the reader may be encouraged to seek more; the Bibliography and CHiDE's growing archives should provide a great deal of fascinating information.

The following are some of the characters whose names appear merely in passing.

AIREY, J.E. (Joe). The Site Engineer at Swanage and Malvern having been in charge of general essential services to scientists throughout the evolution of radar. He had worked with Watson-Watt from 1927 at Slough, was widely respected and awarded the MBE.

BLUMLEIN, A.D. An outstanding electronics engineer at EMI, he made a major contribution to the pre-war development of high-definition television and to airborne radar in wartime, until he was killed with others in the tragic Halifax air accident on 7 June 1942.

BURCHAM, Professor W.E. From Cavendish Laboratory, Cambridge, he went to RAE until he was transferred to AMRE Worth Matravers in May 1940. He made a major contribution to the development of centimetric airborne radar.

DEE, Professor D.I. A distinguished physicist from the Cavendish Laboratory. E.G. Bowen said of him, 'From sheer strength of personality, Dee rapidly became a powerful force.'

DIPPY, R.J. (Bob). Bob joined the Bawdsey Research Station early in 1937 from the television research labs of A.C. Cossor. He had long been interested in navigation and on becoming a member of TRE he set his ideas down in a paper which he handed to Watson-Watt in 1937. But Watson-Watt had the CH chain at the top of his priorities and Dippy's paper lay forgotten until 1940 when an urgent need arose for Bomber Command to have a reliable system of navigation. Dippy's Gee became operational early in 1942. After the war he was deservedly given a substantial award as the inventor of Gee, the principles of which found application in the field of civil aviation and shipping.

JONES, Dr F.E., MBE. Of the famous duo who invented Oboe, A.H. Reeves was the thinker and F.E. Jones the 'doer' – the man who could harness Reeves's flights of fancy and translate them into realistic projects. The perfect partnership to create that outstandingly successful instrument of war, Oboe.

LEWIS, Dr W.B., CBE, FRS. An ex-Cavendish Laboratory specialist in radio technology. Deputy to the Chief Superintendent of TRE, he is credited with encouraging A.P. Rowe to support centimetric research at a time when its future application was unsure – a bold strategy that was to bring enormous benefits in radar performance during wartime.

RATCLIFFE, J.A. He joined TRE from Cambridge University to become a senior staff member responsible for the essential post design services division as well as setting up training schools for both TRE and the Army. Best known and most highly respected as an outstanding lecturer, he was said to be 'accurate and precise' and 'oozed efficiency'. After the war he returned to Cambridge and subsequently became Director of the Radio Research Laboratories near Slough, the appointment once held by Dr Watson-Watt.

REEVES, A.H., OBE, CBE. The inventor of Oboe worked before the war for Standard Telephones and Cables, and in the early 1930s he pioneered pulse modulation for VHF communications, effectively laying the foundations for modern digital communications. After the war he returned to STC where he continued his flare for consistently making ahead-of-the-field inventions. He was awarded many honours on both sides of the Atlantic.

SKINNER, Professor H.W.B. He joined AMRE from Bristol University. His significant contributions to microwave radar development included hand-made prototypes of crystal diodes for use as low-noise mixers in receivers.

TIZARD, Sir Henry Thomas, GCB, FRS. Scientist, airman and administrator, he was universally acknowledged as one of outstanding ability and influence whose perception in the 1930s of Britain's coming air defence needs – especially an effective early warning system – was a major factor in the salvation of the country. He led the Scientific Mission to the USA in 1940.

WILLIAMS, Sir Frederic C., OBE, CBE, FRS. Many contributors to this book refer to the genius of F.C. Williams who masterminded some of the most complex circuits used in radar and navigational aids. The following note is based on parts of a tribute written by one of his colleagues:

> In 1939 Professor Williams moved from his position as Assistant Lecturer at Manchester University to assist with the further development of RDF (radar) at Bawdsey Research Station, where he became recognised for his expertise in electrical circuit analysis.
>
> He redeveloped and formulated an IFF system which was introduced to the RAF in 1941 as IFF MkIII which was used by all the Allied Air Forces. This system led to the Secondary Surveillance Radar (SSR) used for Air Traffic Control throughout the world today. For this work Dr Williams was given a 'Pioneer Award' from the IEEE, USA. He returned to Manchester after the war and led the development of the world's first electronic digital computer.

Glossary

ADEE	Air Defence Experimental Establishment, Biggin Hill.
ADRDE	Air Defence Research and Development Establishment – the revised title for ADEE, following the move to Christchurch.
AEO	Assistant Experimental Officer (Civil Service).
AI	Air Interception. (Marks I–IV, 1.5 m wavelength; later marks on centimetric wavelengths.)
AIF	'Lock-follow' version of AI.
AIH	Centimetre wavelength AI with helical scanning.
AIS	Centimetre wavelength AI with spiral scanning.
AMES	Air Ministry Experimental Station. This title, as well as a type number, was given to early radar stations, to conceal their true function, starting with CH = AMES Type 1.
AMRE	Air Ministry Research Establishment.
AOC	Air Officer Commanding: an RAF appointment.
ASV	Air to Surface Vessel (radar). (Marks I–III, 1.5 m wavelength; later Marks on centimetric wavelengths.)
ASVS	A project for 10 cm ASV, but abandoned in 1942 in favour of an adaptation of H2S which became ASV MkIII.
BABS	Blind Approach Beacon System.
Breadboard	General term for an experimental electronic circuit or system from the early days of radio when hastily wired-up components might be mounted on any handy piece of board.
BRS	Bawdsey Research Station.
BTH	British Thomson–Houston Company, Rugby. A leading electrical company with its own research laboratories. It played a significant part in developing microwave radars and associated specialised components.

CAS	Chief of the Air Staff.
Cavendish	Famed physics laboratory, Cambridge University.
CD	Coastal Defence (early 1.5 m radar, led on to CHL.)
CH	Chain, Home (AMES Type 1).
CHEL	Chain, Home Extra Low (10 cm radars, various AMES types).
CHL	Chain, Home, Low (1.5 m radars, AMES Type 2).
Cossor, A.C. Ltd, London	Pre-war manufacturers of radio/television receivers, advanced test gear and cathode ray tubes. Defence equipment included CH receivers and Army gun-laying radars.
DCAS	Deputy Chief of the Air Staff.
DCD	Director of Communications Development.
Dipole	The simplest single element of a transmitting or receiving aerial (antenna). Often a wire or rod of linear dimension approximating to a half-wavelength at the radio frequency in use.
DME	Distance Measuring Equipment.
EMI	Electrical & Musical Industries Ltd, a complex grouping of pre-war radio and television companies including The Gramophone Company (His Master's Voice) centred at Hayes, Middlesex. Powerful research capability in fields of sound recording, television and airborne radar.
EO	Experimental Officer (Civil Service).
EW	Early Warning.
GCI	Ground Controlled Interception.
GEC	General Electric Co., whose Wembley Research Laboratories contributed to numerous aspects of radar development.
GEE	Widely employed wartime navigational system using accurately phased pulses from ground-based transmitters.
GL	Gun-laying radar.
Goniometer	Generally used in this book as an abbreviation of radiogoniometer, a device for measuring the angle of arrival of radio signals. Used for finding bearings and heights of radar targets.
Gramophone Company	See EMI.
Ham	A radio amateur licensed to transmit signals.
Happidrome	Operations block of fixed 'Final' GCI station (AMES Type 7) housing all equipment for control of interceptions including multiple radar displays, plotting tables ground-to-air radio links etc.
Hz	The unit of frequency named after Heinrich Hertz,

	1857–94. 1 Hz = 1 cycle per second. Also kHz and MHz for multiples of thousands and millions respectively.
IEE	The Institution of Electrical Engineers. Prefixes M, F, J indicate Member, Fellow and Journal of the respectively.
IFF	Identification, Friend or Foe.
Jostle	Airborne jammer against German communications.
JSO	Junior Scientific Officer (Civil Service).
Leigh Light	A powerful searchlight mounted beneath Coastal Command aircraft to permit visual identification of U-boats detected by ASV. Brainchild of Wg Cdr H. de V. Leigh.
£ s d	The symbol for pounds, shillings and pence, the British currency used before decimalisation. 20 shillings = £1; 12 pence = 1s. E.g. 10 pounds, 8 shillings and 2 pence written as £10 8s 2d.
LW	Light Warning. Highly mobile 1.5 m ground radar (AMES Type 6).
Mandrel	Airborne jammer (several versions) against German EW radars.
MAP	Ministry of Aircraft Production.
METOX	German receiver enabling U-boats to detect approach of aircraft carrying 1.5 m ASV.
MGB	Motor Gun Boat.
MIT	Massachusetts Institute of Technology, Boston, USA. The seat of wartime radar design in America.
Modulator	In radar, the unit or circuit that causes a transmitter to produce pulses of radio energy.
MTB	Motor Torpedo Boat.
M-V; METROVICK; METVIC	Metropolitan-Vickers Electrical Co. Ltd. Vast factory with research laboratories at Trafford Park, Manchester made a wide range of defence equipment including almost all ground radar transmitters (e.g. CH, CHL, GCI, GEE, etc.).
NAXOS	German successor to Metox, but at cm wavelengths.
NPL	National Physical Laboratory.
PEO	Principal Experimental Officer (Civil Service).
PPI	Plan Position Indicator. A radar display – now the form commonly used – which as its name implies presents a plan view of a given area with echoes shown in relation to the radar at the centre of the screen.
PPS	Pulses per second.
PRF; prf	Pulse Recurrence Frequency. The number of pulses per second transmitted by a radar, e.g. 25 pps for

	CH, but generally several hundred pps for typical EW radars and higher still for airborne radars.
PSO	Principal Scientific Officer (Civil Service).
PTO	Principal Technical Officer (Civil Service).
RAE	Royal Aircraft Establishment, Farnborough, which had become well established between the wars. In addition to its famous airfield, it possessed technical departments and workshops for the design and testing of aircraft and associated equipments. Some laboratories were evacuated in wartime, e.g. to Crowthorne and Exeter.
R&D	Research and Development
RDF	Radio Direction Finding. A deliberately misleading term used for radiolocation in the early days before 'radar' had been coined. Other interpretations of the R have been suggested (e.g. 'Range and' in Army parlance) but that given here is believed to be original and correct.
R/T	Radio Telephone.
RX; Rx	Receiver.
SCR	Service Command Radio: American prefix for type numbers of certain radar equipments.
SEO	Senior Experimental Officer (Civil Service).
SLC	Searchlight Control Radar ('Elsie').
SO	Scientific Officer (Civil Service).
SOE	Special Operations Executive.
SSO	Senior Scientific Officer (Civil Service).
STO	Senior Technical Officer (Civil Service). (May also indicate an appointment – not a rank - in the RAF.)
TFU	Telecommunications Flying Unit (formerly SDF, Special Duties Flight)
TO	Technical Officer – remarks for STO apply.
TX; Tx	Transmitter.
VCAS	Vice Chief of Air Staff.
VCCE	Vice Controller of Communications Equipment.
VEB	Variable Elevation Beam.
White noise	Noise having no predominant frequency but consisting of many frequencies spread evenly across the receivable spectrum. (Analogous to white light formed from all the colours of the rainbow.)
WIDU	Wireless Intelligence Development Unit.
Yagi	A directional aerial (antenna) of the 'fishbone' form, consisting of a half-wave dipole with a reflector behind it and multiple directors in front (usually at least 4 or 5 but maybe up to about 20 where very high gain is required). Commonly used for domestic television reception.

Bibliography

The following selection of published books is recommended for further reading, although some of the older ones may be obtainable only through libraries or specialist dealers. An increasingly useful source of material is provided by the periodical *Transmission Lines* available to Friends of CHiDE.

Batt, Reg. *The Radar Army*, Robert Hale, London, 1991

Bauer, M. and Duggan, J. *LZ130 Graf Zeppelin and the End of Commercial Airship Travel*, Zeppelin Museum, Friedsrichshafen, 1996 (available in German or English editions)

Bowen, E.G. *Radar Days*, Adam Hilger, Bristol, 1987

Buderi, R. *The Invention that Changed the World*, Little Brown, London, 1997

Clarke, R.W. *Tizard*, Methuen, London, 1965

Hanbury Brown, R. *Boffin*, Adam Hilger, Bristol, 1991

Hartcup, Guy. *The Challenge of War*, David & Charles, Newton Abbott, 1970

Hodgkin, Alan. *Chance and Design*, Cambridge University Press, 1992

Jones, R.V. *Most Secret War*, Coronet Books, London, 6th Impression, 1987

Kinsey, Gordon. *Bawdsey – Birth of the Beam*, Terence Dalton, Lavenham, 1983

——. *Orfordness – Secret Site*, Terence Dalton, London, 1993

Latham, Colin and Stobbs, Anne. *Radar: A Wartime Miracle*, Sutton Publishing, Stroud, 1996

Lovell, Bernard. *Astronomer by Chance*, Macmillan, London, 1991

——. *Echoes of War*, Adam Hilger, Bristol, 1991

Miller, George. *The Bruneval Raid*, The Bodley Head, London, 1974

Price, Alfred. *Instruments of Darkness*, MacDonald & Jane's, London, 1967

Rowe, A.P. *One Story of Radar*, Cambridge University Press, 1946

Watson-Watt, Robert. *Three Steps to Victory*, Odham's Press, London, 1958

Zimmermann, D. *Top Secret Exchange*, Sutton Publishing, Stroud, 1996

Index